AN **INCONVENIENT** SEQUEL

TRUTH TO POWER

Earth, as seen by the DSCOVR
satellite, positioned about 1 million
miles away.

———

Lagrange Point 1, Outer Space
December 8, 2015

AN **INCONVENIENT** SEQUEL

TRUTH TO POWER

Your action handbook to learn the science, find your voice,
and help solve the climate crisis

AL GORE

Printed in the United States of America

Rodale Inc. makes every effort to use acid-free, mixed content recycled paper.

MIX
Paper from
responsible sources
FSC® C132124

Library of Congress Cataloging-in-Publication Data is on file with publisher.

ISBN 978-1-63565-185-0 limited signed edition

Distributed to the trade by Macmillan

2 4 6 8 10 9 7 5 3 1 paperback

Published by

 RODALE.

We inspire health, healing, happiness,
and love in the world. Starting with you.

733 Third Avenue
New York, NY 10017
rodalebooks.com

Produced by

 MELCHER
MEDIA

124 West 13th Street
New York, NY 10011
melcher.com

This book is dedicated to my children:
Karenna Gore, Kristin Gore, Sarah Gore Maiani,
and Albert Gore III—and to my grandchildren,
Wyatt Schiff, Anna Schiff, Oscar Shiff, and Aria Maiani

At this point in the fight
to solve the climate crisis,
there are only three
questions remaining:

Must we change?

Can we change?

Will we change?

Having spent the better part of my life for the past several decades trying to learn from experts on the climate crisis and working with technology and policy innovators to develop solutions for the unprecedented challenge humanity faces, I have never been more hopeful.

At this point in the fight to solve the climate crisis, there are only three questions remaining:

Must we change?
Can we change?
Will we change?

In the pages that follow, you will find the best available evidence supporting the overwhelming conclusion that the answer to the first two of these three questions is a resounding "Yes."

I am convinced that the answer to the third question—"Will we change?"—is also "Yes," but that conclusion, unlike the answer to the first two questions, is in the nature of a prediction. And in order for that prediction to come true, there must be a continued strengthening of the global consensus embodied in the Paris Agreement of December 2015, in which virtually every nation on Earth agreed to take concerted action to reduce net greenhouse gas emissions to zero as early in the second half of this century as possible.

That strengthened consensus depends in turn upon the continuing growth of a global grassroots movement to encourage political leaders in every nation to take even bolder steps than the ones agreed to in Paris. Luckily, that grassroots movement is already growing rapidly, not only among activists and leaders of civil society but also among business leaders, investors, mayors, and other elected officials who recognize that the stakes have never been higher. As more and more people come to the same realization that we really *must* change, the movement continues to gain momentum.

In other words, all three of these questions are intimately interrelated. In order to accelerate and complete the historic transformation of global civilization that is already under way, it is first necessary to come to grips with the unprecedented threat to humanity

A young woman holds a symbolic tulip at a climate change demonstration.

Paris, France
December 12, 2015

I have never been more hopeful.

Action is needed to prevent catastrophic harm.

posed by our continued reliance on fossil fuels, our unsustainable industrial transportation, agriculture, forestry, and ocean management practices—and our habit of short-term thinking that blinds too many of us to the unimaginable damage we are causing. And in order to summon the will to act with the requisite boldness, we have to have confidence that once we commit ourselves, we *can* succeed.

So let's begin with the first question: must we change?

In some ways, it is easy to understand one of the main reasons it has taken so much time to fully recognize the self-destructive nature of our current pattern. After all, humanity has gained immeasurable benefits from the burning of fossil fuels—higher standards of living, longer lifespans, historic reductions in poverty, and all of the blessings of the elaborate global civilization that has been developed over the past 150 years.

Moreover, because we still depend on fossil fuels for more than 80 percent of the energy that powers our civilization,

Arctic meltwater gushes from an ice cap.

—

Nordaustlandet, Norway
August 7, 2014

we are naturally daunted by the prospect of a rapid transition to renewable sources of energy and the speedy development of much higher levels of efficiency in all human activities.

Nevertheless, the obvious and overwhelming evidence of the damage we are causing is now increasingly impossible for reasonable people to ignore. It is widely known by now that there is a nearly unanimous view among all scientists authoring peer-reviewed articles related to the climate crisis that it threatens our future, that human activities are largely if not entirely responsible, and that action is needed urgently to prevent the catastrophic harm it is already starting to bring.

More importantly, Mother Nature is reminding us almost daily that the impacts of the climate crisis are growing steadily more severe, with more frequent and powerful climate-related extreme weather events. Every night, the TV news is like a nature hike through the Book of Revelation.

But before diving further into examples of the unprecedented harm we are causing, please remember how important it is to guard against feelings of despair. Despair, after all, is simply another form of denial, and can serve to paralyze the will we need to fight our way out of this crisis. And bear in mind that the hopeful news about the availability

Every night, the TV news is like a nature hike through the Book of Revelation.

of solutions is a powerful antidote to the feelings that can be aroused by the disconcerting news about the self-harm we are presently inflicting upon humanity.

High temperature records are being routinely broken on every continent—even Antarctica, where, in 2015, scientists confirmed one measurement of 17.5°C (63.5°F). Because of the physics of global warming, nighttime temperatures are rising even faster than daytime temperatures, and heat waves are becoming far more common.

Air temperatures are predicted to steadily increase all around the world because of the continuing accumulation of man-made global warming pollution in the atmosphere, the thin shell of air that surrounds our planet. The cumulative amount of this gaseous pollution exceeded 400 parts per million for the entire year for the first time in human history in 2016 (43 percent higher than preindustrial levels).

The combination of higher ocean temperatures and the growing acidification of ocean water (approximately one-third of the CO_2 we release into the atmosphere settles into the ocean, where it has already increased acidity by 30 percent) are leading to the death of coral reefs throughout the world. It is also disrupting the process by which coral polyps—and all sea creatures with shells—scavenge calcium carbonate from seawater and transform it into the hard structures necessary for their survival.

Warmer ocean temperatures are also causing the mass migration of fish populations, many of which are simultaneously being depleted by overfishing, the runoff of pollution from coastal areas, and a sharp decline of oxygen in the growing number of "dead zones" in the ocean. The decline of fish populations in the tropics and subtropics is especially threatening because of the heavy reliance on seafood in those regions.

The climate crisis is resulting in more

Day 21 after Hurricane Katrina.

Plaquemines Parish, Louisiana
September 19, 2005

frequent downpours around the world, but the geographic distribution and the periodicity of rainfall have also been altered. As the water cycle is disrupted, some areas are receiving big increases in precipitation, while others are receiving much less. While much more precipitation falls in big storm events, the period of time between rainfalls has also been increasing in many regions. And during the intervals between rainfalls

the higher air temperatures suck more moisture from the first several centimeters of the soil, leading to deeper and longer droughts.

Driven by these droughts and warmer temperatures, there has been a dramatic increase in fires and a radical extension of the "fire season" (in the western United States, for example, the annual fire season has already increased by 105 days). Firefighters are now having

Firefighters are now having to deal with a new phenomenon they call "mega-fires."

to deal with a new phenomenon they call "mega-fires." These extremely large fires are particularly severe in the northern boreal forests of Alaska, Canada, and Siberia. The higher temperatures have also greatly increased the damage to forests from pine beetles and bark beetles, which survive milder winters in greater numbers and reproduce more generations during the longer summers.

When they attack trees weakened by drought, they end up devastating millions of acres of forestland, turning them into kindling for the larger fires.

The seasonal timing of rainfall patterns has become more erratic and less predictable, which has had a harsh impact on subsistence farmers who depend on rain-fed agriculture. Especially in the tropics and subtropics, many farmers report that they can no longer rely on the age-old rainy season/dry season pattern that previous generations counted on to decide when to plant and when to harvest.

Because the larger downpours rush off the surface of the land, carrying larger amounts of topsoil with them, the underground aquifers beneath are not being replenished as efficiently as they are by more regular, gentler rains. And because higher temperatures increase the need for water—by plants and animals, in agriculture and energy production, and for human consumption—growing populations in many regions have begun to rely more heavily on underground aquifers, depleting those sources more rapidly than they are replenished.

Increasing temperatures are also accelerating the melting and breakup of land-based ice—in mountain glaciers, and more significantly, in Greenland and Antarctica—thus accelerating sea level rise and threatening the inundation of low-lying coastal areas where hundreds of millions of people live.

Food supplies are also being threatened by the climate crisis. Higher temperatures are already decreasing crop yields of corn, wheat, rice, and other staples.

Diseases affecting humans have become more threatening because of the climate crisis. The so-called "vectors" that carry many infectious diseases—such as mosquitoes, ticks, snails, algae, and others—are extending their range in a warmer and wetter world. Viruses such as Zika, dengue fever, and West Nile virus, among others, incubate faster.

Climate has always mediated the relationship between human beings and microbes. Indeed, some historians have suggested that civilizations in higher latitudes have more readily flourished because they are relatively freer from the overburden of microbial diseases that are much more prevalent in the hotter and wetter regions of the lower latitudes of the tropics and subtropics. According to Princeton's Andrew Dobson, "Climate change is disrupting natural ecosystems in a way that is making life better for infectious diseases."

One of the most startling examples of the new threat from tropical diseases is the recent outbreak of a mutated form of the Zika virus that causes microcephaly and other serious birth defects. Zika is also the first mosquito-borne disease known to be sexually transmitted by humans. Although air travel has played a large role in the spread of tropical diseases, the changing climate conditions have given them a chance to take root in regions where they never thrived previously.

For all of these reasons, and more, the answer to the question "Must we change?" is abundantly clear: "Yes!" Indeed, some scientists have warned that if we do not change, the future of human civilization itself is at dire risk.

But here is the good news: the answer to the second question—"Can we change?"—is also a resounding "Yes!" In just the past 10 years the cost of clean, renewable solar energy and wind energy has fallen so quickly that in a growing number of regions throughout the world, it is now cheaper than electricity made from the burning of fossil fuels—and the cost continues to decline year by year.

Some areas of technology—such as computer chips, flat screen televisions, and mobile telephones—respond to research and development spending in an almost magical manner. Not only does the cost go down much faster than anyone expected, the quality goes up at the same time.

Consider, for example, what has happened with cell phones: in 1980, AT&T took note of the new technology that led to the first bulky mobile telephones and asked one of the world's leading market research companies, McKinsey, to predict for them how many such mobile phones they might be able to sell by the year 2000. They were excited to get the answer that they could probably count on selling 900,000 such phones. When the year 1999 arrived, the telephone industry did sell 900,000 mobile phones—in the first three days of the year! By the end of the year, 109 million phones had been sold—120 times more than predicted.

Smoke rises from a factory in Chiba province, a hub for Japanese industry.

—

Soga City, Japan
February 14, 2008

So the answer to the question "Must we change?" is abundantly clear: "Yes!"

The cost had come down far more quickly than anyone anticipated, even as the quality of the phones increased dramatically, with many more features packed into a much smaller form factor. Moreover, these cell phones proved especially popular in developing countries, where landline telephone grids had never been built in the first place. The people in those regions simply leapfrogged the technology on which the wealthy countries were still dependent.

The same thing is now happening with renewable energy, especially solar. Panels are being installed on the roofs of grass huts in Africa and South Asia—and on rooftops throughout the world.

And here is the good news: the answer to the question "Can we change?" is also a resounding "Yes!"

Utility-scale "solar farms" are producing electricity at even lower rates. In fact, some of the new contracts for large solar farms signed in 2016 provide electricity at rates less than half the cost of the cheapest electricity generated from the burning of coal or natural gas. And the price continues to decline rapidly.

As a result, just as the early predictions of growth in the number of cell phones were badly wrong, so were the best predictions made 15 years ago on the spread of solar and wind energy.

For the year 2016 in the United States, 70 percent of all new electricity-generating capacity came from solar and wind. Less than two-tenths of 1 percent came from coal. And in a growing number of areas, solar electricity is now beating proposals to generate electricity from the most efficient forms of gas turbines.

To brighten the renewable energy story still further, the cost of battery storage is also now beginning to rapidly decline. This is particularly important, because more efficient, cheaper batteries can solve the so-called "intermittency" disadvantage of renewable sources—that is, they can continue providing electricity at nighttime when the sun doesn't shine and during periods of the day when the wind is slack. As Noah Smith, a *Bloomberg View* columnist, wrote, "Solar-plus-batteries is set to begin a dramatic transformation of human civilization."

Non-polluting electric vehicles are also beginning to make inroads in the transportation sector of the economy. While their percentage of the vehicle fleet is still small, demand is growing rapidly and competition is driving virtually every major vehicle manufacturer to introduce more affordable models in the next 12 months. The leading electric vehicle manufacturer in the United States, Tesla, has just surpassed General Motors and Ford to become the most valuable car company in the nation. Homeowners with solar panels on their rooftops and an electric car in their garages are already paying less than the equivalent of $1 per gallon in gasoline costs. Electric buses are predicted to take over from diesel buses in major cities over the next decade.

Moreover, by using the powerful new digital tools now available in our civilization—including the fast-growing "Internet of Things"—industrial

This Japanese solar power plant will supply energy to approximately 22,000 homes.

——

Kagoshima, Japan
August 13, 2015

The fossil fuel industry is engaged in a losing battle to confuse people into thinking that the climate crisis isn't real, and that the renewable energy revolution is trivial and meaningless.

Smoke billows from a coal plant at sunset.

Portugal

and business managers are achieving much higher levels of efficiency in the use of energy and natural materials. Thousands of new technology solutions are spreading rapidly through the global economy. LED lighting is displacing incandescent bulbs and compact fluorescent light bulbs at an unprecedented rate in what is now being called perhaps the fastest technology transformation in any market sector in the history of the world.

In fact, taken together, the spread of renewable energy, battery storage, electric vehicles, LEDs, and the thousands of new hyper-efficiency solutions all make up what many are now referring to as "The Sustainability Revolution." It combines the *scale* of the Industrial Revolution with the *speed* of the Digital Revolution.

The fossil fuel industry, which is already engaged in a losing, rearguard battle to confuse people into thinking that the climate crisis isn't real, is also engaging in what some have described as "a strange new form of denial"—an effort to convince people that the renewable energy revolution is trivial and meaningless. In their failing efforts to both persuade people the crisis isn't real and that solar and wind energy are not cost-effective solutions to it, they bring to mind the famous scene in the Marx Brothers movie *Duck Soup*, in which

Workers walk past the vast cluster of solar panels at the Gujarat Solar Park.

—

Gujarat, India
April 14, 2012

Chico asked, "Who you gonna believe, me or your own eyes?"

Importantly, investors around the world are ignoring the fossil fuel industry's arguments and are now shifting resources massively into renewable energy and are financing the highly profitable Sustainability Revolution. As the renewable energy industry has flourished, the market capitalization of the global coal industry has fallen almost *90 percent* in the past seven years.

And with the International Energy Agency warning that two-thirds of the proven reserves held by oil and gas companies can never be burned—lest human civilization be destroyed—investors are beginning to realize that they are in danger of the kind of financial catastrophe that was caused in 2007–2008, when the value of subprime mortgages was suddenly discovered to be worthless. In the same way, "subprime carbon assets" now pose a serious threat to the stability of the global economy. And smart investors are moving quickly to minimize their exposure to this historic risk.

TRUTH TO POWER

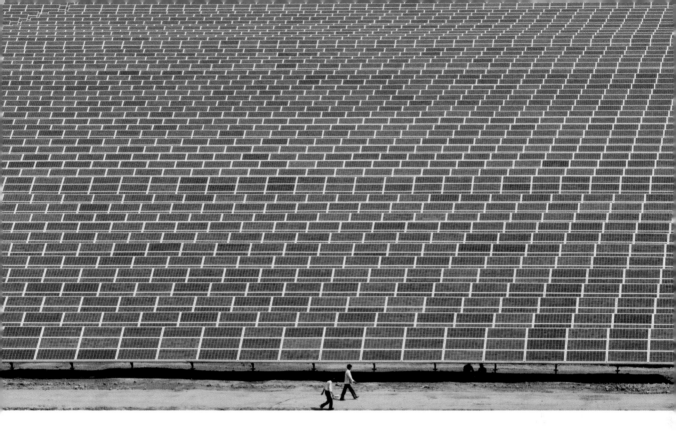

The Sustainability Revolution combines the *scale* of the Industrial Revolution with the *speed* of the Digital Revolution.

It is also important to note that the conventional air pollutants from the burning of coal and other fossil fuels that accompany CO_2 emissions—including particulates and sulfur dioxide—have now reached intolerable levels in many cities around the world—especially in China and India—where people are becoming desperate to reduce the levels of pollution. The health problems associated with air pollution are driving political unrest in some areas as people become more aware of the dangers they face.

So the answer to the second question—"Can we change?"—is clearly "Yes."

But that leaves the third and final

I have heard over and over again a hunger to engage in this struggle for the future. That gives me hope every day.

question: "Will we change?"

I am convinced that the answer to this question is also "Yes." The global agreement reached in Paris at the end of 2015 is encouraging not only because of the universal commitment from governments but also because it amplified the signal to investors, industries, businesses, and institutions that the entire world is poised to move quickly to a sustainable and renewable future. This transformation has already begun and is picking up speed. The Paris Agreement also calls for regular five-year reviews of the commitments made by the nations that are party to the agreement to encourage them to increase their commitments to emission reductions as the new technologies become ever cheaper and as opposition to the pollution from fossil fuels grows ever stronger.

Many state, provincial, regional, and local governments are already moving faster than national governments. A growing number of cities in the United States have succeeded in obtaining 100 percent of their electricity from renewable sources, and many regions around the world are making similar progress.

While the answer to "Will we change?" is almost certainly "Yes," it is not yet clear that we will change rapidly enough to avoid the catastrophic damage we *must* avoid. Yet it is abundantly clear that we *can* avoid it if we accelerate the pace of transformation.

And that is why, starting on page 176, you will find an action handbook for anyone who wants to be a part of the answer to the biggest question our civilization has ever confronted.

Because many governments in the world—especially the United States government in 2017—are still controlled by fossil fuel interests, the growing citizen activist movement pushing for more rapid change is actually the most important movement in world history.

As I have traveled the world, including during the filming of *An Inconvenient Sequel: Truth to Power*, the companion film to this book, I have heard over and over again a hunger on the part of everyday citizens to engage in this struggle for the future of our civilization. And that gives me hope every day.

If you want to be a part of this historic change, you will find in the following pages not only a more detailed description of the crisis and its solutions but also a list of actions that you can take to join the climate movement and ensure that we *will* change—and that we will change in time. ◉

If we were to fail, the next generation would be well justified in looking back at us and asking:

What were you thinking?

Couldn't you hear what the scientists were saying?

Couldn't you hear what Mother Nature was screaming at you?

The original Rapa Nui people of Easter Island, who created these statues, nearly disappeared due to the exhaustion of natural resources in the area.

—

Easter Island, Chile
January 1998

TRUTH T

There's a hunger for information about *what's* happening, *why* it's happening, and *how* we can fix it. **Ten years ago, I launched a training program, the Climate Reality Project, for anyone who wanted to learn how to communicate to others the threat of and solutions to the climate crisis. What follows are selections from that training program.**

O POWER

I always start my trainings by showing this photo, *Earthrise.* This was the first picture that humans saw of the Earth taken from space. It had a profound impact on the consciousness of humanity. This was the first time that human beings left near-Earth orbit and went far enough into space to see the planet whole, floating in the void.

Earth, with the lunar landscape in the foreground.

———

Apollo 8 mission
December 24, 1968

Our perspective on the ground looking up at the sky can mislead us. We see the atmosphere as a vast and limitless expanse. But scientists have long known what this picture from the International Space Station shows: the sky is actually an extremely thin shell surrounding our planet. That is what makes it so vulnerable to human activities.

If you could drive straight up in a car at highway speeds, you'd be in outer space in under an hour.

We put 110 million tons of global warming pollution into this very thin space every day.

Earth's atmosphere, from the International Space Station.

—

June 2014

One reason we've failed to recognize the damage we're doing is that we've assumed it's fine to use our atmosphere as an open sewer.

The basic science of global warming is straightforward, but it is important to understand it fully.

Energy from the sun enters the Earth's atmosphere as light. The wavelength of light is very short, so it cuts right through the atmosphere and it warms the planet. Then, that heat energy is radiated back into space in the form of infrared radiation, which has a longer wavelength. Some of that outgoing infrared radiation is trapped by the natural layer of greenhouse gases, which has long been just the right thickness for supporting life. It keeps the temperatures on Earth within a comfortable range: not too hot like Venus, and not too cold like Mars.

The Earth's natural greenhouse gas layer is now being transformed, mainly by the burning of fossil fuels.

This pollution makes the layer thicker, which traps more outgoing infrared radiation, also known as heat.

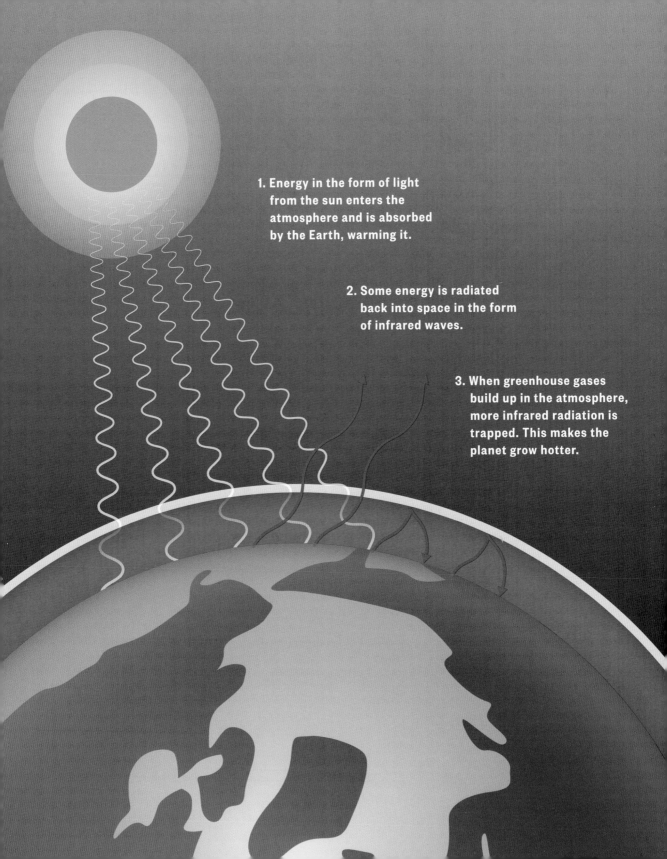

1. Energy in the form of light from the sun enters the atmosphere and is absorbed by the Earth, warming it.

2. Some energy is radiated back into space in the form of infrared waves.

3. When greenhouse gases build up in the atmosphere, more infrared radiation is trapped. This makes the planet grow hotter.

In 2006, when *An Inconvenient Truth* was released, the concentration of CO_2 in the atmosphere had reached 382 parts per million—up from a preindustrial level of 280 ppm.

In March 2017, the level reached an all-time high of 409.5 ppm.

Many scientists believe that a "safe" level for humanity is 350 ppm.

CARBON DIOXIDE CONCENTRATION MEASURED AT MAUNA LOA OBSERVATORY, HAWAII

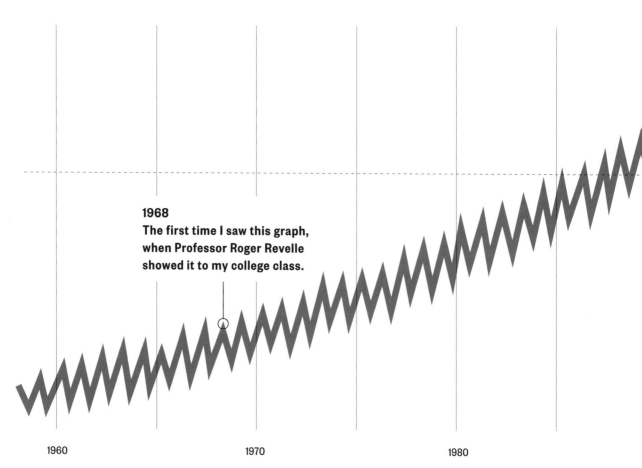

1968
The first time I saw this graph, when Professor Roger Revelle showed it to my college class.

1960   1970   1980

SOURCE: SCRIPPS INSTITUTION OF OCEANOGRAPHY

TRUTH TO POWER

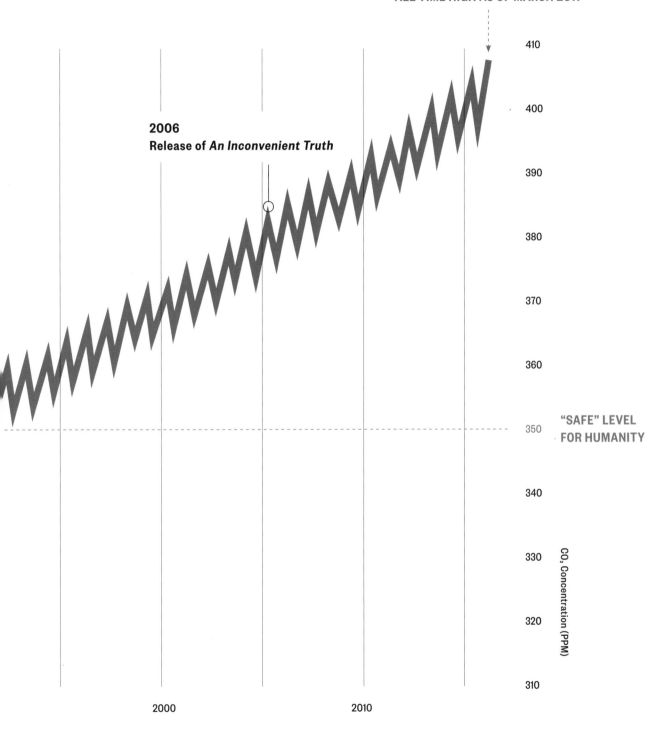

ALL-TIME HIGH AS OF MARCH 2017

410

400

390

2006
Release of *An Inconvenient Truth*

380

370

360

"SAFE" LEVEL
FOR HUMANITY

350

340

330

320

310

2000

2010

CO$_2$ Concentration (PPM)

Common sources of greenhouse gases include agriculture, mining, and the burning of forests. But the principal source is the burning of carbon-based fuels. After World War II, the use of fossil fuels began to increase dramatically. In recent years, it has accelerated even more.

This is the heart of the problem. If we solve this, it will be much easier to address the other sources.

THAWING PERMAFROST

COAL BURNING

COAL MINING

INDUSTRIAL PROCESSES

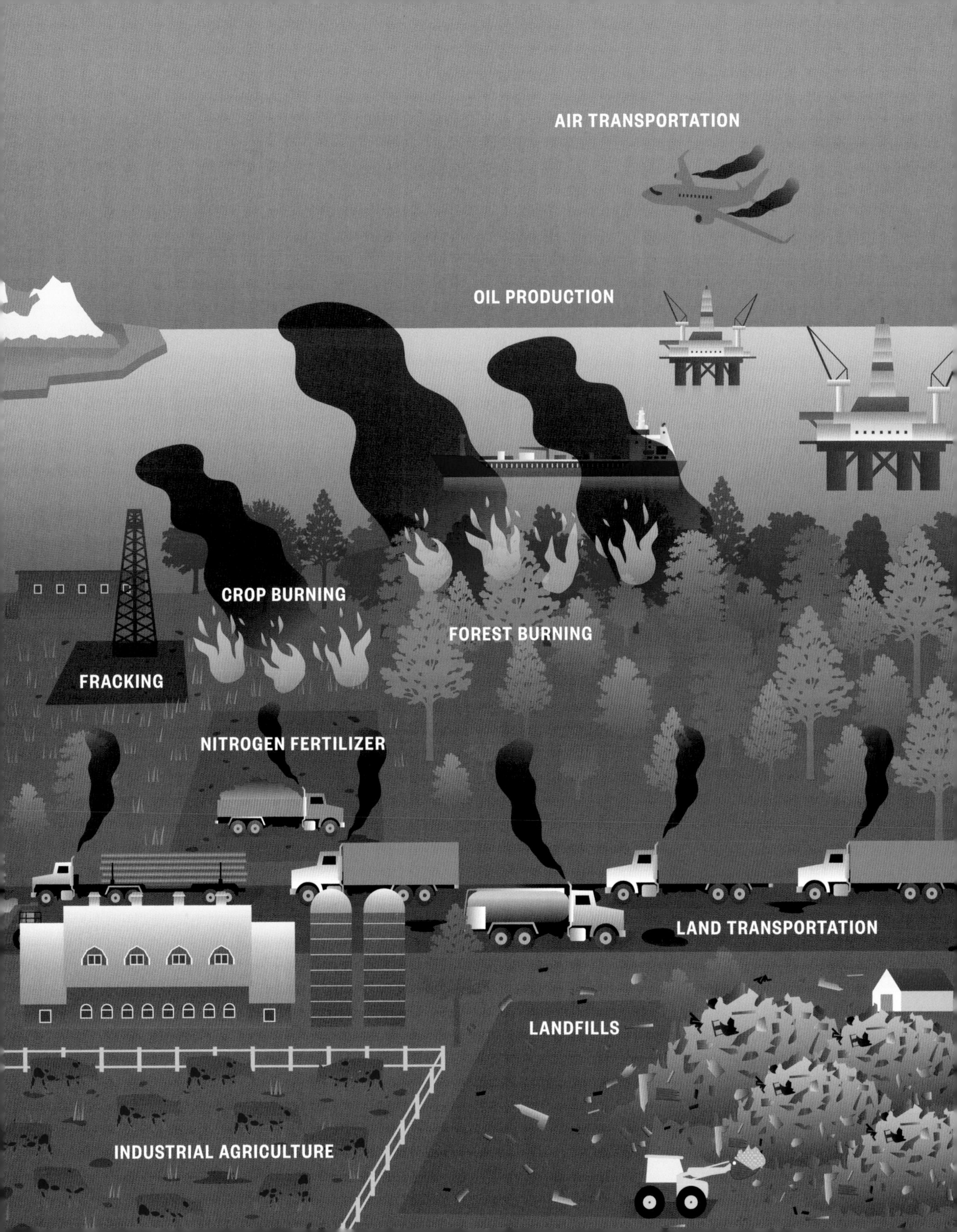

AIR TRANSPORTATION

OIL PRODUCTION

CROP BURNING

FOREST BURNING

FRACKING

NITROGEN FERTILIZER

LAND TRANSPORTATION

LANDFILLS

INDUSTRIAL AGRICULTURE

Why Do the Scientists Feel So Strongly?

AS THE CLIMATE CHANGES, so do a variety of wind and ocean patterns, along with the distribution of plant and animal life. That's why the U.S. Environmental Protection Agency (EPA) has tracked 37 different indicators of climate change on land and over water, including surface temperature, bird wintering ranges, and coastal flooding. Taken together, the data collected paints a picture of our climate and its changing impact on all of Earth's systems. But where does this data come from? What instruments are used? In short, how do we really know what's happening to the climate now—and what happened to it in the past?

Ice cores are a good place to start. These long cylinders of ice are drilled out of the glaciers and ice caps covering Greenland and Antarctica. The lowest layers of them date back thousands of years. In fact, the oldest ice core records, from Antarctica, extend back 800,000 years. The U.S. National Ice Core Laboratory is home to more than 17,000 meters of ice from all over the world that can be used to understand the planet's climate history. These layers of ice store tiny bubbles of air that were trapped by the snow when it fell. By measuring the ratio of different isotopes of oxygen in these air bubbles, scientists can re-create both the CO_2 content of the air year by year and the temperature of the air that was trapped.

While ice cores enable scientists to build the record of past millennia, sophisticated, modern tools also allow them to better understand present and future climate patterns. NASA operates a fleet of satellites that collect a broad range of climate information. For example, the GRACE (Gravity Recovery and Climate Experiment) missions record the steady retreat of ice sheets in astonishing detail, while the Jason-3, OSTM/Jason-2, and Jason-1 missions track sea level rise, which has increased by an average of three inches since 1992. You can read about another satellite, DSCOVR, on page 164. The National Oceanic and Atmospheric Administration operates sophisticated data collection instruments, including underwater drones, buoys, and shipborne instruments, to measure the oceans' carbon levels and temperatures in order to better predict the impacts of climate change. Other devices used by scientists include weather balloons, ships, and radar, each of which contribute their own unique types of data to create a big picture of our climate at any given time. ◉

Scientists use ice cores to measure levels of atmospheric carbon and other gases trapped in layers of ice. Ross Sea, Antarctica, November 16, 2011

Katharine Hayhoe

Codirector of Texas Tech University's
Climate Science Center

LUBBOCK, TEXAS

KATHARINE HAYHOE HAD BEEN married for six months before she realized that her husband didn't think climate change was a scientific fact.

"I had no idea that there were people who didn't agree with the science," said Hayhoe, who is the codirector of Texas Tech University's Climate Science Center.

The realization led the couple to embark on a grueling debate that would last years. It was ironic, in retrospect, because Hayhoe was already a rising star in climate modeling, working at the University of Illinois Urbana-Champaign under famed researcher Donald Wuebbles in the emerging field of statistical downscaling.

Statistical downscaling combines historical weather observations with computer models to predict how climate change will affect a particular geographic region. It's a field of study that offers intimate portraits of the climate impacts on particular communities, which has led Hayhoe to approach her work with great empathy.

"If you discover that your patient has a new, very serious disorder, you don't just write a paper about it," she said. "You try to help them. You can't say, 'Oh, that's not really my job.'"

Hayhoe has used her computer models to consult on the effects of climate change for the cities of Washington, D.C., Boulder, Colorado, and Chicago, as well as for the Department of Defense and the United States Fish and Wildlife Service. Her recommendations can cover topics ranging from urban planning considerations like managing sewers to how storms and droughts will affect agricultural infrastructure.

But the worlds of academia and policy aren't enough for Hayhoe, who also goes out of her way to connect with climate change deniers, often on their home turf. In those ad-hoc debates, which have played out at symposiums and city council meetings across the nation, Hayhoe remains unflappable, and never misses a chance to build bridges to those she speaks with.

And in the end, Hayhoe won the debate with her husband, who now teaches linguistics at Texas Tech and serves as the pastor of a small church. In fact, the two ended up coauthoring a book titled *A Climate for Change: Global Warming Facts for Faith-Based Decisions*.

"We were highly motivated to work it out," Hayhoe said dryly. "We were married, and we wanted to stay that way." ◉

See page 226 for more information about talking with climate deniers.

We are now trapping as
much extra heat energy
in the atmosphere as
would be released by

400,000 Hiroshima-class atomic bombs exploding on the Earth's surface every day.

We live on a big planet,
but that is an unimaginable
amount of heat energy.

The mushroom cloud from a
Hiroshima-class explosion in
Operation Upshot-Knothole.

Nye County, Nevada
May 25, 1953

It's getting much warmer very quickly. This classic bell curve shows the distribution of summer air temperatures. Scientists use the 30 years between 1951 and 1980 as a so-called normal period, when there were roughly equal number of days with average temperatures, cooler than average temperatures, and warmer than average temperatures. In the 1980s, the entire curve shifted toward the warm side. And for the first time there were a statistically high number of extremely hot days, showing at the lower right in red. Then

SHIFT IN SUMMER TEMPERATURES, 1951–2015

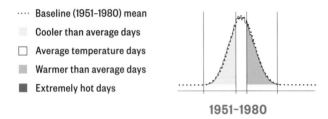

···· Baseline (1951–1980) mean
☐ Cooler than average days
☐ Average temperature days
☐ Warmer than average days
■ Extremely hot days

1951–1980

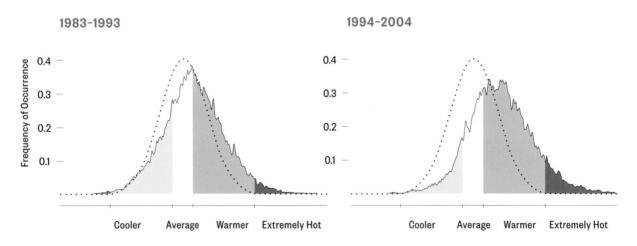

1983–1993

1994–2004

SOURCE: HANSEN, ET AL., 2016

in the 1990s, the curve shifted farther to the warm side and a combination of warmer and extremely hot days began to dominate. Over the past 10 years, the extremely hot days have become more numerous than the cooler than average days. In fact, the extremely hot days are now almost 150 times more common than they were just 30 years ago.

There are still cold days, but they are far less frequent.

Extremely hot days used to cover 0.1 percent of the Earth. They now cover 14.5 percent.

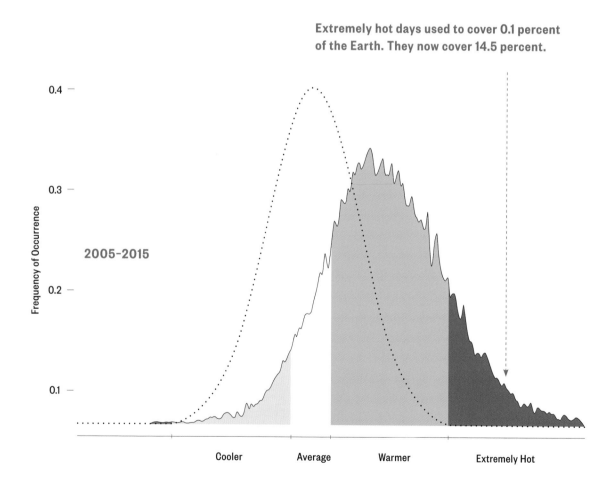

2005–2015

Frequency of Occurrence

0.4

0.3

0.2

0.1

Cooler   Average   Warmer   Extremely Hot

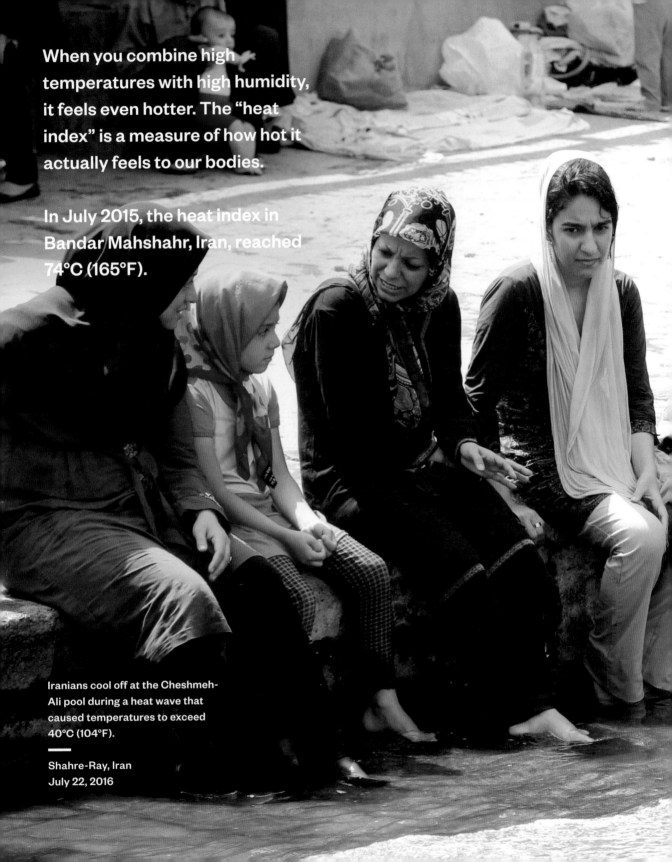

When you combine high temperatures with high humidity, it feels even hotter. The "heat index" is a measure of how hot it actually feels to our bodies.

In July 2015, the heat index in Bandar Mahshahr, Iran, reached 74°C (165°F).

Iranians cool off at the Cheshmeh-Ali pool during a heat wave that caused temperatures to exceed 40°C (104°F).

———

Shahre-Ray, Iran
July 22, 2016

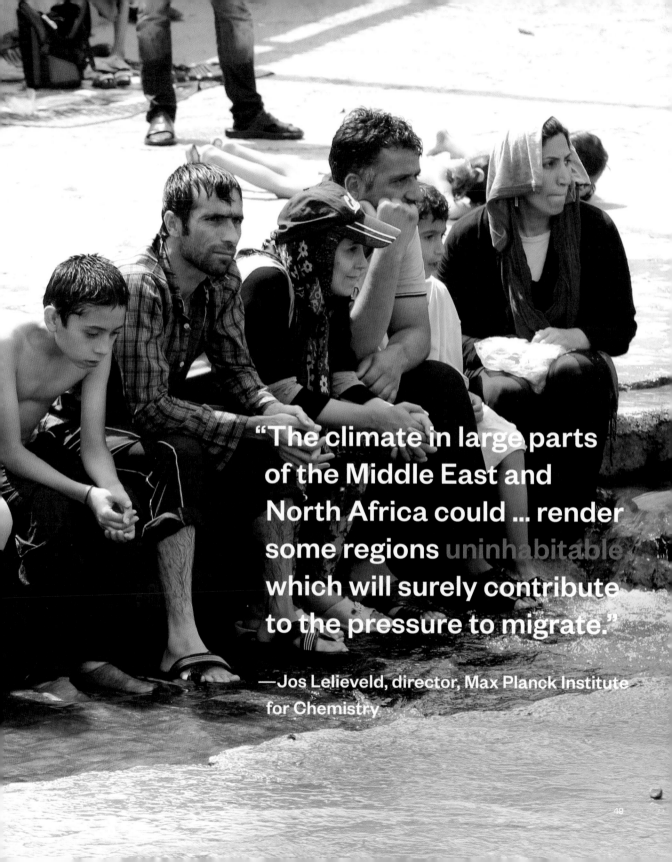

"The climate in large parts of the Middle East and North Africa could ... render some regions uninhabitable which will surely contribute to the pressure to migrate."

—Jos Lelieveld, director, Max Planck Institute for Chemistry

On his late night show, Jimmy Kimmel said, "You know how you know climate change is real? When the hottest year on record is whatever year it currently is."

In fact, 16 of the 17 hottest years ever measured with instruments (a practice that dates back to 1880) have occurred in the past 17 years. And the hottest year of all was 2016. The second hottest was the year before, and the third hottest was the year before that.

GLOBAL LAND AND OCEAN TEMPERATURE ANOMALIES, 1880–2016

Compared to average temperature 1901–2000

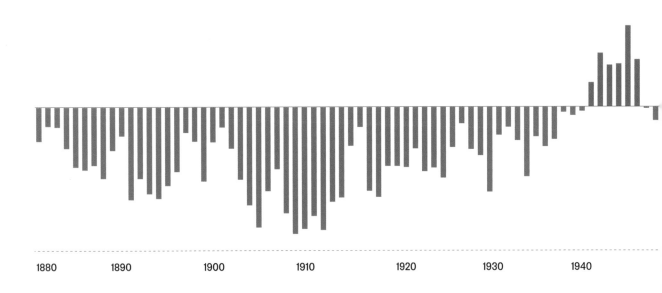

1880 　 1890 　 1900 　 1910 　 1920 　 1930 　 1940

SOURCE: NOAA

　 TRUTH TO POWER

1880 1881 1882 1883 1884 1885 1886 1887 1888 1889 1890 1891 1892 1893

1894 1895 1896 1897 1898 1899 1900 1901 1902 1903 1904 1905 1906 1907

1908 1909 1910 1911 1912 1913 1914 1915 1916 1917 1918 1919 1920 1921

1922 1923 1924 1925 1926 1927 1928 1929 1930 1931 1932 1933 1934 1935

1936 1937 1938 1939 1940 1941 1942 1943 1944 1945 1946 1947 1948 1949

1950 1951 1952 1953 1954 1955 1956 1957 1958 1959 1960 1961 1962 1963

1964 1965 1966 1967 1968 1969 1970 1971 1972 1973 1974 1975 1976 1977

1978 1979 1980 1981 1982 1983 1984 1985 1986 1987 1988 1989 1990 1991

1992 1993 1994 1995 1996 1997 **1998** 1999 **2000 2001 2002 2003 2004 2005**

2006 2007 2008 2009 2010 2011 2012 2013 2014 2015 **2016**

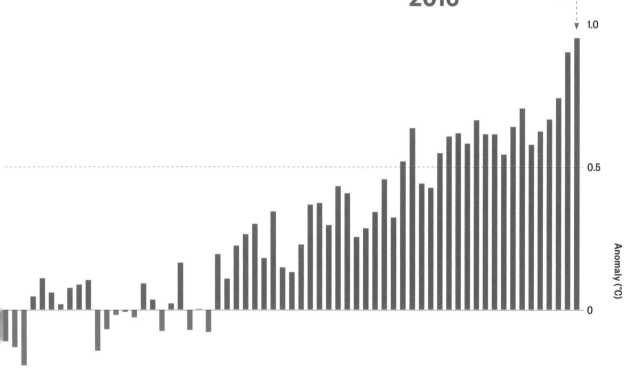

The streets are melting. We have built a civilization for conditions that we are now in the process of radically changing.

A road melt caused by temperatures exceeding 45°C (113°F).

New Delhi, India
May 24, 2015

In 2003, a European heat wave centered in France killed 70,000 people.

In 2015, a heat wave in Pakistan killed more than 2,000 people.

In the same summer, a heat wave in India killed at least 2,500 people.

ایدهی سرد خانه

A Pakistani man waits while volunteers search for the body of a deceased relative at the Edhi Foundation morgue.

Karachi, Pakistan
June 22, 2015

More than 90 percent of all the heat energy trapped by man-made global warming pollution goes into the ocean.

As a result, the buildup of ocean heat content has increased dramatically—especially in the past 25 years—and it is accelerating.

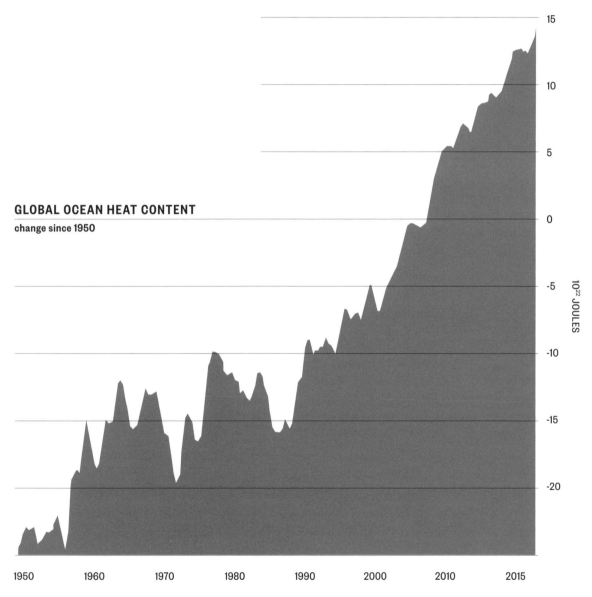

GLOBAL OCEAN HEAT CONTENT
change since 1950

10^{22} JOULES

SOURCE: L. CHENG, K.E. TRENBERTH, ET AL., 2017

TRUTH TO POWER

A direct consequence is that when ocean-based storms cross warmer ocean waters, they pick up more convection energy. The storms get stronger and more destructive.

Super Typhoon Haiyan (known as Yolanda in the Philippines) crossed areas of the Pacific 3°C (5.4°F) warmer than normal. When it struck the city of Tacloban in the Philippines, it had become the strongest ocean-based storm to ever make landfall.

PATH OF TYPHOON HAIYAN

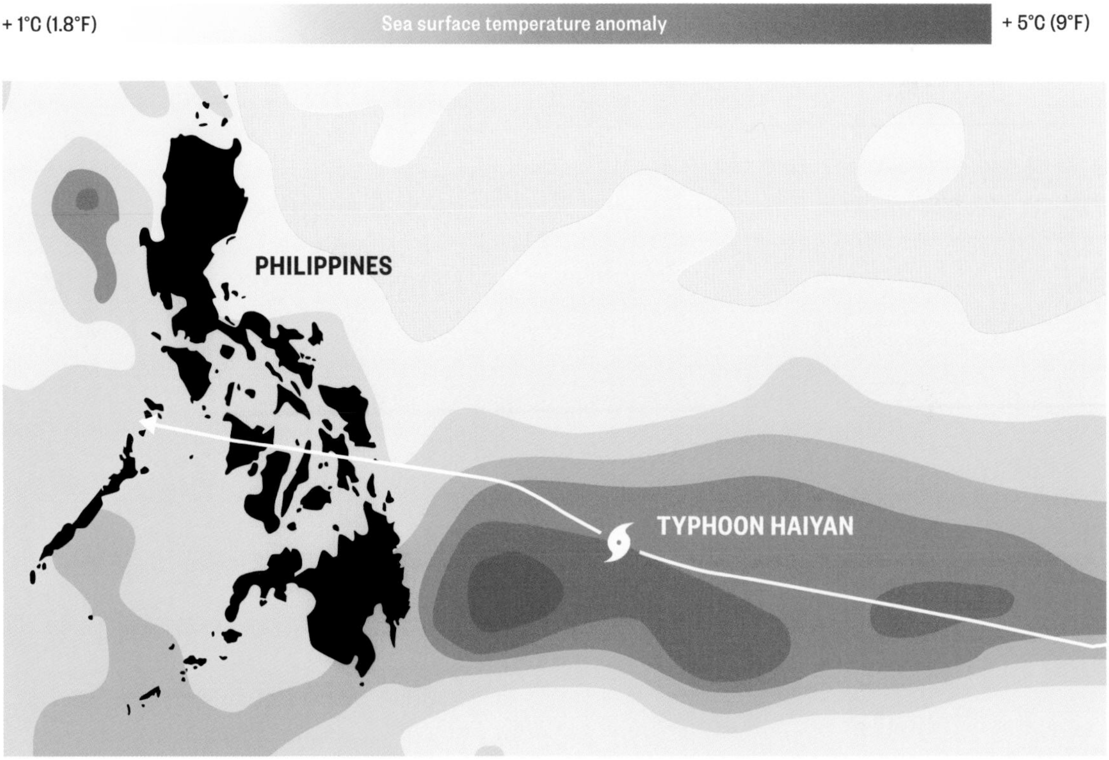

+ 1°C (1.8°F) Sea surface temperature anomaly + 5°C (9°F)

PHILIPPINES

TYPHOON HAIYAN

SOURCE: JAPAN METEOROLOGICAL AGENCY VIA WEATHER UNDERGROUND

A survivor stands among the wreckage left behind by Super Typhoon Haiyan.

Tacloban City, Philippines
November 10, 2013

Super Typhoon Haiyan caused 4.1 million refugees, some of whom are still not back in their homes. I traveled to Tacloban and visited some of the graves of the thousands of victims. Families were invited to pick one of these graves and inscribe the name of their loved one on it.

Visiting the Holy Cross cemetery, which houses the remains of thousands of Typhoon Haiyan victims.

—

Tacloban City, Philippines
March 11, 2016

John Leonard Chan

Climate Reality Leader

TACLOBAN CITY, PHILIPPINES

JOHN LEONARD CHAN recalled the morning when the typhoon began. The winds started to tear at his family's single-story dwelling in Tacloban, a small city on the Philippine island of Leyte.

By midmorning, floodwaters were rushing into the home. But transportation and communication systems had broken down during Typhoon Haiyan, so the family stayed put for two terrifying days before setting off on foot for Chan's grandparents' house. The journey took three hours of climbing over debris, and Chan remembers seeing dead bodies in the street.

"People were crying, people were screaming," said Chan, now 22, of the chaos after the 2013 typhoon. "Nobody knew what to do."

The family eventually secured enough food to survive for five days until they were evacuated to Manila, where they have lived ever since.

As his family adjusted to life in Manila, Chan became increasingly concerned with how climate change might have given rise to Haiyan, one of the most powerful cyclones in the history of the world.

"That's what made me interested in giving voice that climate change is real," he said. "I'm a first-hand survivor of an effect of climate change. I think my voice will be interesting to others."

In 2016, I met Chan at the Climate Reality Project's three-day training session in Manila, where he became a climate leader. Since then, he has also joined the Philippine Youth Climate Movement, a student group that raises awareness about climate change at home and abroad, and has given seminars about the science of global warming at high schools in Manila.

Chan is also leveraging his education into opportunities to more deeply study the effects of climate change. He's currently enrolled in a microbiology program at the University of the Philippines Los Baños, and last year he returned to the Tacloban area to study how the typhoon has impacted ocean life in the region.

Chan isn't sure yet what he intends to do after graduate school. But he's sure of one thing: he's going to continue to do everything in his power to give voice to the victims of climate change.

"There are people suffering because of climate change," he said. "People around the world need to hear from people from Tacloban, so they can understand that climate change is real." ◉

Turn the page to learn more about the Climate Reality Project.

What Is The Climate Reality Project?

Climate Reality: How It Began

When *An Inconvenient Truth* was released back in 2006, no one knew what to expect. I hoped it would spark a conversation but certainly didn't expect the incredible response and enthusiasm from people across the globe wanting to take action to solve the climate crisis.

These were people who'd probably never thought of themselves as activists, but now that they understood what the climate crisis meant for the planet and the people they loved, they wanted to make a difference.

So I invited 50 people to come to my farm in Tennessee and trained them—in the barn—to use the slideshow in the movie and talk to others about the crisis and how to solve it.

Climate Reality: Its Work Today

What began on that day in the barn has grown to become The Climate Reality Project, an international nonprofit with headquarters in the U.S. and branches in Australia, Brazil, Canada, China, Europe, India, Indonesia, Mexico, the Philippines, and Africa.

Our mission is daunting but simple: catalyze a global solution to the climate crisis by making urgent action a necessity across every level of society.

We've grown and changed a lot since those early days. But what hasn't changed is our commitment to training and empowering regular people to change the world. One conversation at a time.

Now we train thousands each year in multiday events, not in barns but in cities from Denver to Delhi. The people who come as concerned citizens leave as world changers we call Climate Reality Leaders. Today, this global network of more than 12,000 activists (and counting) is out there spreading the word and organizing friends, neighbors, and communities for climate solutions in 136 countries.

Of course, today, the conversation online is also important. With social media a critical battlefield in the fight not just for hearts and minds, but for the very idea of truth—upon which democracy is founded—we give people the digital tools to combat climate denial, share good news about solutions, and put real pressure on policy makers.

The story doesn't end there. Our 100% Committed campaign enlists citizens to help cities, colleges, and businesses switch to 100 percent renewable electricity. We hold Days of Action where people take over the streets to build public support for key policies that accelerate the switch to clean energy and protect our climate.

And because we approach our work as I've always done—speaking to people where they're at and speaking truth to power—we're building a

The Climate Reality Project logo, which includes the iconic *Blue Marble* photo.

movement of activists capable of incredible things and winning against the odds around the world.

We saw it in Florida in 2016, when the fossil fuel industry tried to kill solar with a misleading ballot initiative. Along with others, we shared the truth about how solar could cut costs and create jobs. Voters responded, defeating the initiative and winning a resounding victory for Florida and our planet.

We're seeing it on college campuses around the world, where young student activists are pushing their schools to choose a clean energy future and shift to 100 percent renewable electricity through our 100% Committed campaign. Colorado State University, Plymouth State University, Hampshire College, and the University of Wisconsin-Stevens Point have already made the commitment and more are on the way.

This is only part of our story and it's only beginning. You can be a part of the next chapter. So if you're ready to make a difference, visit *climaterealityproject.org* to join Climate Reality and we'll show you how. ◉

Climate Reality Leadership Corps

WHAT: Trains citizens to become powerful change agents.

MAKING A DIFFERENCE: Climate Reality Leaders led successful campaigns to push Brazil to ratify the Paris Agreement and protect clean energy in Florida.

GET INVOLVED: climaterealityproject.org/training

Climate Speakers Network

WHAT: Trains community leaders as climate storytellers.

MAKING A DIFFERENCE: Thousands of faith, business, health, Latino, and African-American leaders become trusted messengers.

GET INVOLVED: climatespeakers.org

24 Hours of Reality

WHAT: 24-hour global broadcast highlighting the crisis and how we solve it for millions.

MAKING A DIFFERENCE: 30 million live views online in 187 nations (2016).

GET INVOLVED: 24hoursofreality.org

100% Committed

WHAT: Organizes cities, college campuses, businesses, ski resorts, and institutions to switch to 100 percent renewable electricity.

MAKING A DIFFERENCE: Salt Lake City, Park City, and Moab in Utah have committed to 100 percent renewable electricity.

GET INVOLVED: climaterealityproject.org/content /roadmap-100

Digital Action

WHAT: Digital tools to raise awareness of climate solutions and pressure lawmakers to act.

MAKING A DIFFERENCE: United over 2.2 million people in calling for action at COP 21, helping create overwhelming public pressure leading to the historic Paris Agreement.

GET INVOLVED: climaterealityproject.org/joinreality; facebook.com/climatereality; twitter.com/ climatereality

When *An Inconvenient Truth*
came out, the most criticized
scene was an animation showing that the combination of
sea level rise and storm surge
would put ocean water into
the 9/11 Memorial site, which
was then under construction.
Some climate deniers said that
was ridiculous, an exaggeration.

Superstorm Sandy crossed
areas of the Atlantic 5°C (9°F)
warmer than normal and
became a monstrous storm.

BOTTOM: Projected flooding of
the 9/11 Memorial site from *An
Inconvenient Truth* (2006).

TOP: Actual flooding of the
Memorial site from Superstorm
Sandy (2012).

○ World Trade Center site
■ Actual Flooding

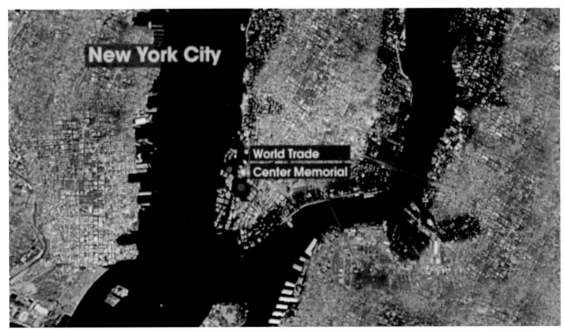

A satellite image of Superstorm Sandy off the east coast of the United States.

——

Atlantic Ocean
October 29, 2015

On the night of October 29th, 2012, seawater flooded the 9/11 Memorial site.

Seawater floods the 9/11 Memorial construction site in New York during Superstorm Sandy.

———

New York, New York
October 29, 2012

Months after Superstorm Sandy, a roller coaster still sits in the ocean.

Seaside Heights, New Jersey
February 25, 2013

A second-order consequence of the oceans heating up is the disruption of the global water cycle.

A storm brews above the
Atlantic Ocean.
—
Cape San Blas, Florida
August 2, 2012

When ocean temperatures go up, the water vapor rising from the ocean increases significantly. Moreover, warmer air can hold a lot more water vapor. For each additional 1°C (1.8°F) of temperature, the atmosphere's capacity to hold water vapor increases by 7 percent. There is already 4 percent more water vapor over the oceans than there was just 30 years ago.

THE HYDROLOGICAL CYCLE

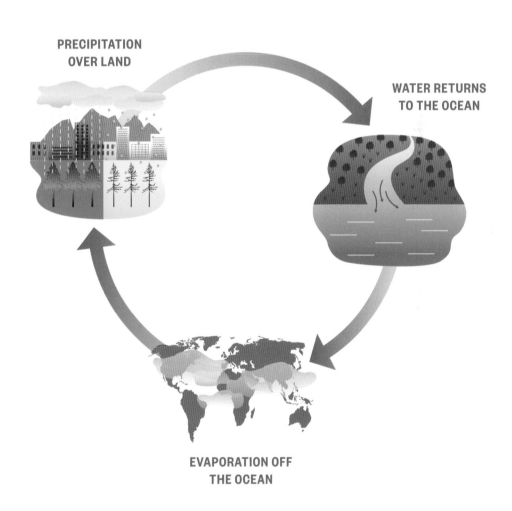

PRECIPITATION
OVER LAND

WATER RETURNS
TO THE OCEAN

EVAPORATION OFF
THE OCEAN

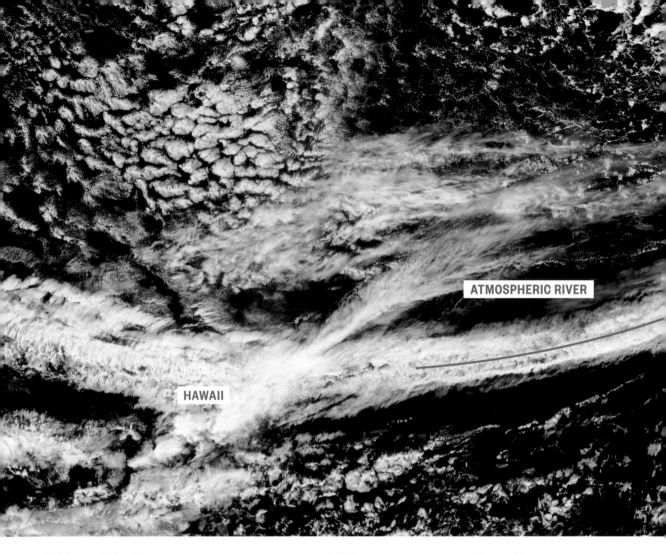

ATMOSPHERIC RIVER

HAWAII

This added water vapor can strengthen what are called atmospheric rivers (or "flying rivers")—flows of water vapor hundreds of miles wide that can carry 15 times as much water as the Mississippi River.

When atmospheric rivers reach the continents, they often release record-breaking downpours.

CALIFORNIA

When a complex system has many consequences and you change the system, *all* of the consequences change. That means every storm is different now because it takes place in a warmer and wetter world.

An atmospheric river drenching the western United States—seen from the NOAA/NASA Suomi NPP satellite.

Pacific Ocean
February 20, 2017

Water vapor is often funneled thousands of miles from the oceans over land. Then, much more of it falls all at once.

They are calling these events rain bombs.

An intense downpour drenches the American southwest.

—

Phoenix, Arizona
July 18, 2016

Extreme weather events are happening with much greater frequency. In a single year, Houston, Texas, was hit by two 1-in-500-year floods and a 1-in-1,000-year downpour. What used to be a 500-year flood is not that anymore.

Nayelo Cervantes helps her friend's daughter, Sophia Aviles, through the floodwaters after a huge downpour.

—

Houston, Texas
May 26, 2015

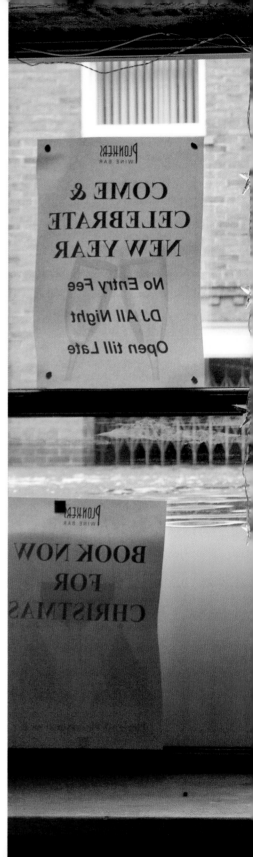

A woman cleans the inside windows of her bar after the Foss and Ouse Rivers burst their banks, causing the city to flood.

York, United Kingdom
December 28, 2015

Catherine Flowers

Founder of the Alabama
Center for Rural Enterprise

MONTGOMERY, ALABAMA

CATHERINE FLOWERS WAS a young girl in Birmingham during the Civil Rights Movement, and she vividly remembers when terrorists bombed the 16th Street Baptist Church. Her family later moved to nearby Lowndes County, in Alabama's Black Belt, where they embraced the tight-knit rural community.

"My parents had their own vegetable garden," Flowers said. "When you went to their home, it was customary to give you something from their garden."

Flowers soon noticed something unsettling about the local cotton industry, which dated back to the days of slave plantations. When the farmers sprayed their crops with DDT, she would soon see dead birds and snakes in the road nearby.

The images of these dead animals stayed with her, even after she left Lowndes County to serve in the Air Force. Years later, when she was working as a social studies teacher, she came across a map predicting how the United States would be reshaped if the polar ice caps melted. Eventually, she started to take note of devastating storms, invasive species, and summers that seemed to go on and on. She became a committed environmentalist.

"As a grandparent, I'm concerned," said Flowers, who has come to see deep connections between race, poverty, spirituality, and the environment. "That's one part of why I'm in this movement. I don't want my grandchild to wake up and realize the apocalypse was man-made."

In 2000, when she returned to Lowndes after decades away, she was horrified to discover how little the area's legacy of inequality had changed. Poverty was widespread, public health was poor, and the infrastructure was crumbling. Lowndes was particularly troubled by substandard wastewater sanitization treatment resources, which she came to suspect were related to outbreaks of hookworm and other parasitic diseases.

Flowers started going door-to-door to survey the community about sewage and sanitation. What she found shocked her: raw sewage that bubbled up into residents' bathtubs and yards when it rained, poor access to the municipal sewer, and a sewage sprayfield that overflowed into a local creek. These findings were bolstered by a 2011 United Nations report about sanitation and water quality in the United Stations that highlighted dire conditions in the Black Belt. She also noticed that the heavier rainstorms caused by the climate crisis were making the sewage overflow problems much worse.

"We found that there was no wastewater infrastructure," Flowers said. "We also found that people were being arrested because they could not afford on-site septic tanks."

Flowers founded a nonprofit, the Alabama Center for Rural Enterprise, which advocates for better

Poor wastewater infrastructure causes sewage to overflow into a creek and contaminate the local water supply.

—

Uniontown, Alabama
May 21, 2015

basic infrastructure in the area. In 2012, she read an op-ed in the *New York Times* by Peter Hotez, a tropical disease researcher at Baylor College, who decried domestic outbreaks of dengue fever, cysticercosis, toxocariasis, and other illnesses specific to the developing world. The two are now working together to test for tropical disease in Alabama.

"One of the most extreme examples of inequality in this country is finding tropical parasites in one of the wealthiest nations in the world," Flowers explained. "Wherever you see this in the world, you find poverty."

Flowers has also had a long-standing interest in the ways that spirituality can inform discussions of racial justice, poverty, and environmentalism. Since 2015, she's augmented her community work in Alabama with a position at Union Theological Seminary's Center for Earth Ethics, where she works with my daughter, Karenna Gore, to encourage religious communities to engage with climate issues and to create partnerships between secular and faith-based environmental leaders.

"The Center for Earth Ethics is about helping religious and spiritual leaders understand and articulate to their congregations the science of climate change," Flowers said. "I think it's been very powerful."

Last year, Flowers visited the camp at Standing Rock, where people were demonstrating against the Dakota Access Pipeline. She observed a series of ceremonies honoring water and the Earth that made a lasting impact on her. She recalled how struck she was by activists from such diverse backgrounds all coming together to celebrate the universal importance of clean and safe water. The Standing Rock Sioux captured this powerful truth with their saying "Water Is Life."

"I'm very hopeful," she said. "I'm very hopeful because we have people talking about these things now. It has brought us together in a way that's never happened before." ◉

Scientists say that the United States could see a 400 percent increase in extreme downpours by the end of this century. The same pattern is true globally.

Predictions of our future can no longer be based on our past.

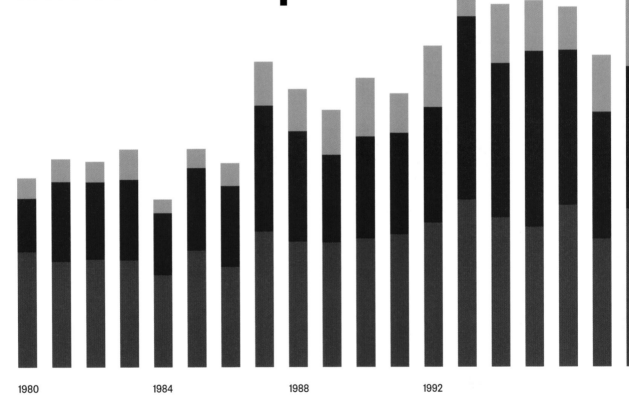

1980   1984   1988   1992

SOURCE: INSURANCE INFORMATION INSTITUTE

TRUTH TO POWER

WORLDWIDE EXTREME WEATHER CATASTROPHES, 1980–2016

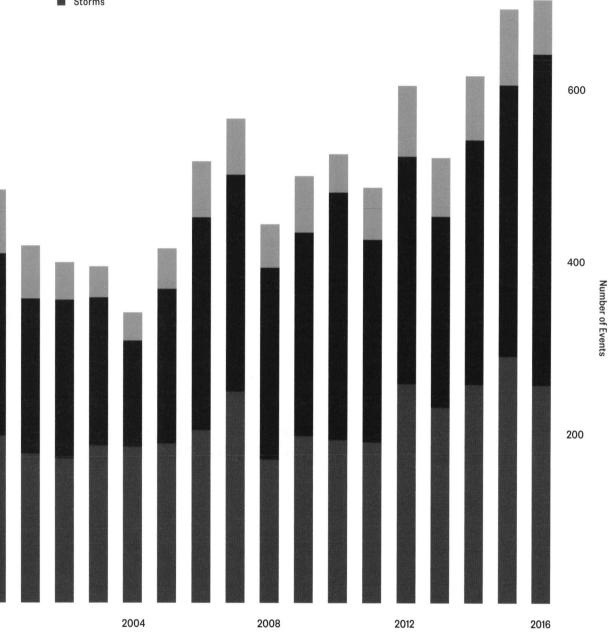

 Extreme temperatures, droughts, fires

■ Floods, mudslides

■ Storms

800

600

400

200

Number of Events

2004   2008   2012   2016

The same extra heat that is evaporating water off the oceans is also sucking moisture out of the soil, causing more droughts, deeper droughts, and longer droughts.

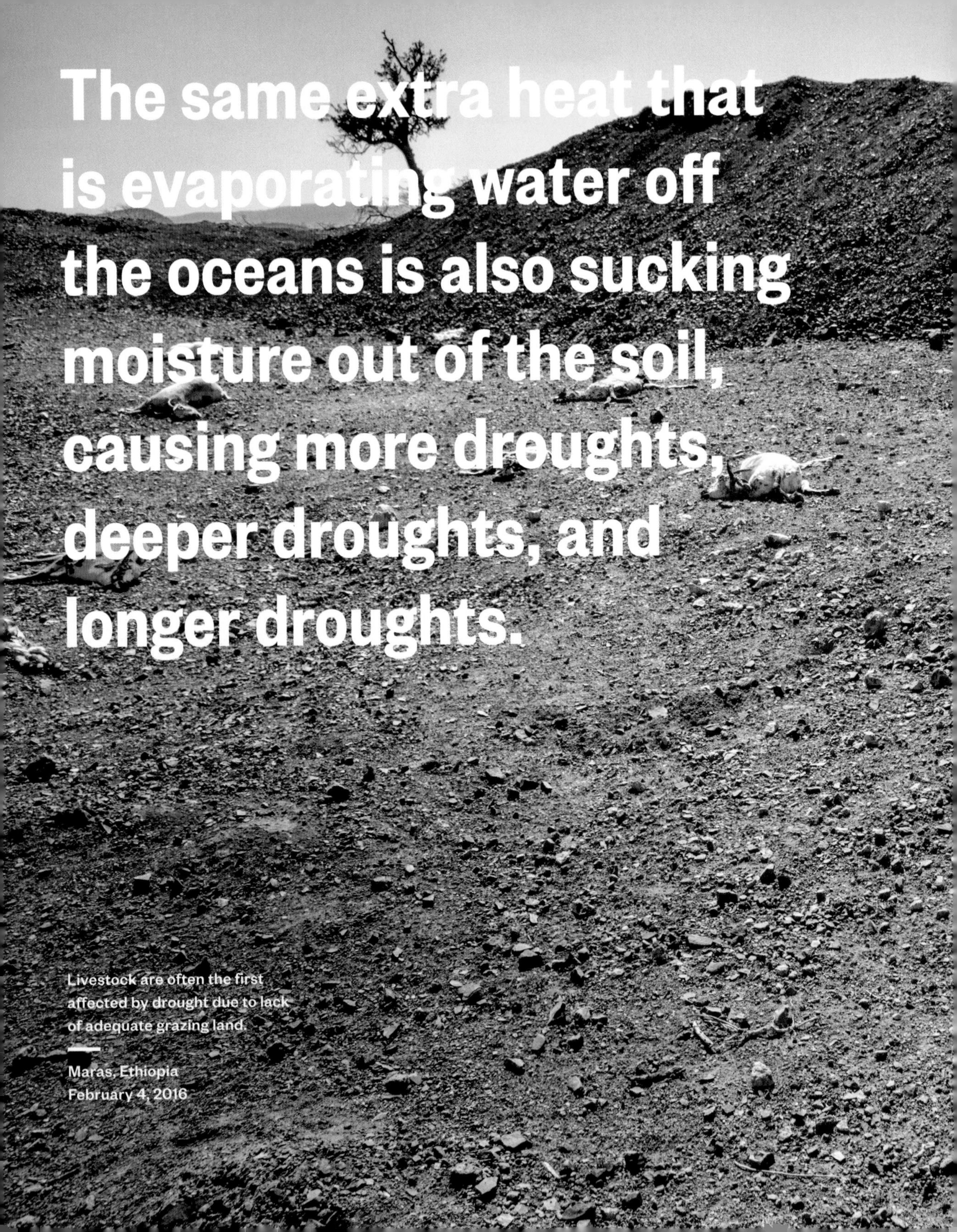

Livestock are often the first affected by drought due to lack of adequate grazing land.

Maras, Ethiopia
February 4, 2016

Historic droughts in eastern and southern Africa are contributing to a region-wide famine, putting 20 million people at risk. The United Nations has called this emerging tragedy the worst humanitarian disaster since 1945.

More than 400 Indian farmers committed suicide in the first four months of 2016, due mainly to pressures from the region's ongoing drought.

The dry bed of the Manjara Dam reservoir, which is supposed to supply water to several towns and villages.

——

Near Kaij, India
May 10, 2016

Where there's drought, the vegetation dries out and fires increase. Fires are becoming much larger and occurring much more frequently.

It is unprecedented.

Aggravated by drought and high temperatures, wildfires burn in the Angeles National Forest.

Los Angeles, California
June 20, 2016

A wildfire threatens Highway 63, causing drivers to abandon their vehicles.

—

Fort McMurray, Canada
May 7, 2016

In Fort McMurray, the heart of Canadian tar sands production, 100,000 people had to be evacuated from their homes because of a 1.5 million acre wildfire in 2016. The temperature in the area was 22.2°C (40°F) above normal, and most of the trees had been killed by bark beetles. All production from the tar sands came to a halt.

The amount of forestland burned in Canada has doubled since the 1970s. It's expected to double again, or even quadruple, because of climate change.

The linkage between high temperatures, drought, and fire is extremely well established.

NUMBER OF LARGE FIRES IN THE WESTERN U.S.

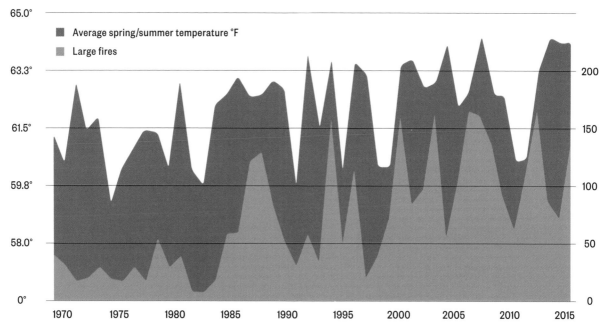

SOURCE: NOAA, US FORESTRY SERVICE, CLIMATE CENTRAL

Following a historic drought in 2010, wildfires and a record heatwave killed 55,000 people in Russia. After these fires, Russia took all of its grain off world markets and Ukraine restricted its grain exports.

World food prices hit an all-time record level for the second time in three years. These two price spikes caused food riots or civil unrest in 60 countries.

FOOD PRICE INDEX

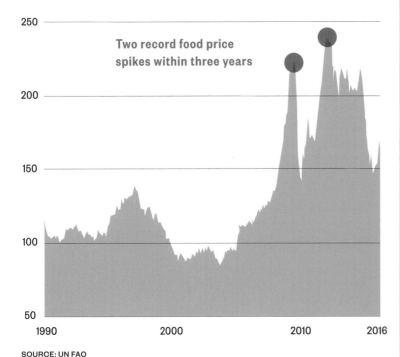

Two record food price spikes within three years

SOURCE: UN FAO

A woman flees one of a wave
of forest fires that devastated
central Russia.

Near Vyksa, Russia
July 29, 2010

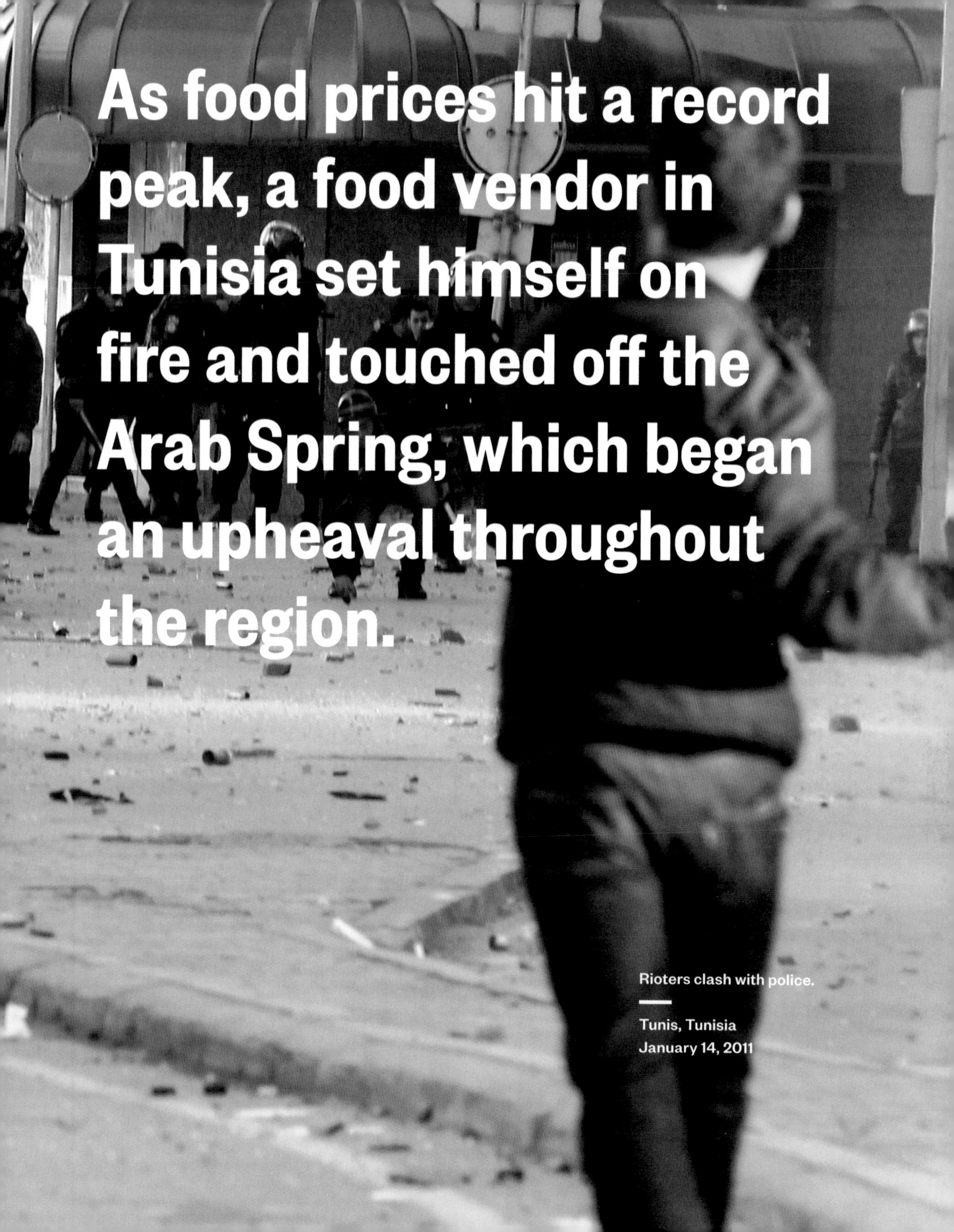

As food prices hit a record peak, a food vendor in Tunisia set himself on fire and touched off the Arab Spring, which began an upheaval throughout the region.

Rioters clash with police.

Tunis, Tunisia
January 14, 2011

Look at what has happened in Syria. From 2006 to 2010, the country had a record-breaking drought. Sixty percent of all the farms in Syria were destroyed. Eighty percent of all the livestock were killed. The drought drove 1.5 million people into Syria's already crowded cities.

Syrian officials said that the effects of the drought were "beyond our capacity as a country to deal with."

The gates of hell opened in Syria. There are multiple causes for the civil war there, but the principal underlying cause was the climate-related drought (the worst in 900 years) that devastated that country.

Syrian farmer Ahmed Abdullah looks out onto a landscape that is turning barren due to drought.
—
Al Raqqa, Syria
September 23, 2010

"I had 400 acres of wheat,
and now it's all desert."

—Ahmed Abdullah, Syrian farmer

The climate-related drought throughout the Middle East and North African region is contributing to a tremendous flow of refugees.

Migrants try to board a train traveling west from the Croatian border with Serbia.

—

Tovarnik, Croatia
September 20, 2015

"Climate change will likely lead to food and water shortages, pandemic disease, disputes over refugees and resources, and destruction by natural disasters in regions across the globe."

—U.S. Department of Defense, 2014

Migrants off the coast of Libya, hoping to be rescued by members of the NGO Proactiva Open Arms.

Mediterranean Sea
October 4, 2016

Nana Firman

Climate Reality Leader

RIVERSIDE, CALIFORNIA

WHEN NANA FIRMAN AND her husband moved to California in 2012, they attended the Islamic Center of San Diego, California, a local mosque. But in the evenings during Ramadan, Firman noticed that the congregation was using disposable dishware and throwing out a lot of food.

It bothered Firman, who has been a committed environmentalist since her days as a city planner helping rebuild her native Indonesia after the tsunami that devastated the Aceh region in 2004.

So she arranged a meeting with the mosque leadership to discuss how they could reduce waste and take climate change seriously. But since she was new to the community, she decided to prepare by poring over the Quran for verses advocating a sustainable lifestyle.

"I'm a Muslim, so I went back to my own faith to study what Islamic teachings said about protecting the environment," she said. "I used that language as a narrative."

The pitch was successful: the board of directors committed to celebrating a "Green Ramadan" the following year, and eventually ended up installing solar panels on the mosque's roof. The Imam was so impressed that he suggested Firman hold a talk about sustainability for the congregation.

The talk went over well, and Firman ended up holding similar presentations about the connections between her faith and environmentalism at five other mosques in the area. Picking up momentum, she started writing about the topic for Muslim publications and delivered a TEDx talk in France.

She also became a fellow at GreenFaith, an interfaith nonprofit that advocates for environmental leadership in religious communities.

"In a lot of ways, we have the same problems," she said of her interfaith colleagues at GreenFaith. "Everybody wants to have more efficiency in their house of worship."

The thought she has put into the connections between Islam and conservation, Firman says, has deepened both her commitment to climate progress and her understanding of her own religion.

"The prophet taught people to plant trees," she said. "If tomorrow is the end of the world, and you have a seedling in your hand, you should plant it. You should always have hope." ◉

These solar panels offset 100 percent of the mosque's annual electric use.

San Diego, California
October 2016

When any great moral challenge is ultimately resolved into a binary choice between what is right and what is wrong, the outcome is foreordained because of who we are as human beings.

When we upset the balance of nature, we must understand that the consequences can be more severe than simply higher temperatures. Many interrelationships are profoundly affected.

An example is our globally integrated food system. The crops we eat today were patiently selected over hundreds of generations during the Stone Age. These food crops thrive in the natural conditions in which they evolved. Now that we are changing those conditions, many of these crops are becoming stressed, especially by higher temperatures. And they are not giving us the same yields or nutrient quality.

THE IMPACT OF THE CLIMATE CRISIS ON FOOD

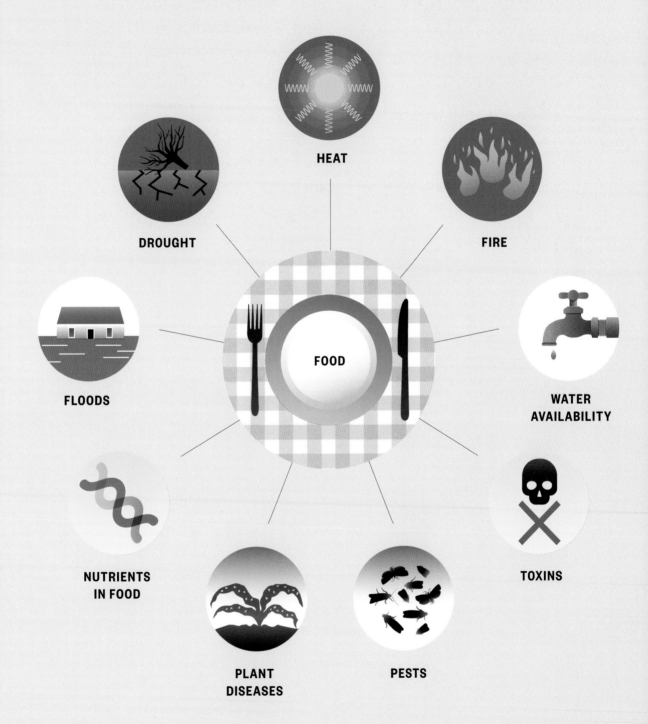

Research shows that when temperatures go above a certain level, it causes significant drops in food crop yields. In China, we have already seen a decline in wheat and corn yields of 5 percent in the past three decades. In the U.S., the yields for corn could drop by one-third from heat stress alone. Wheat yields could drop by more than one-fifth.

A Mexican farmer shows corn that has died due to lack of rain.

Pocoboch, Yucatan

GLOBAL WATER USE

70% AGRICULTURE

11% DOMESTIC

19% INDUSTRIAL

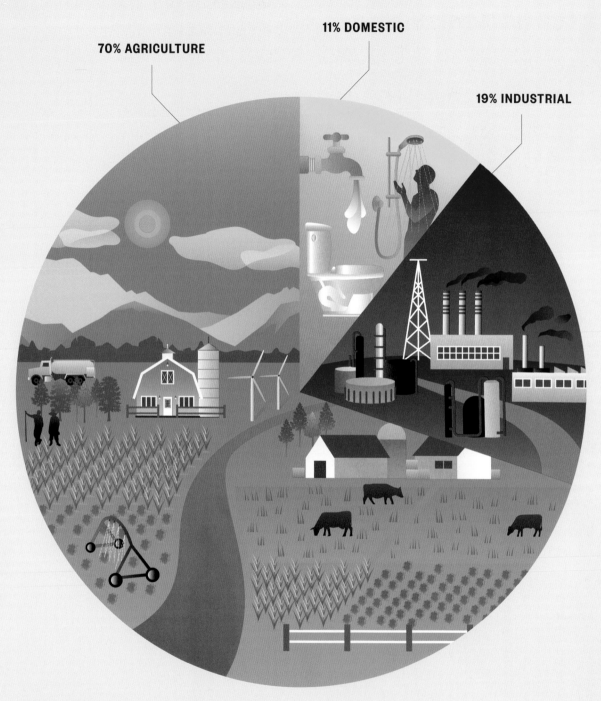

SOURCE: AQUASTAT

Everything—people, crops, energy production, industry, and animals—requires more water when the temperature goes up.

In many areas of the world, water scarcity is one of the single most serious aspects of the climate crisis.

Higher temperatures increase the demand for water. About 11 percent of consumption of the world's freshwater is used in our homes, about 19 percent by industry, and 70 percent by agriculture.

Cows roam a drought-ridden landscape at a cattle range in California's Central Valley.

—

Delano, California
February 3, 2014

The even more complex systems of human and public health are also being stressed by climate change, which has been declared a global health emergency by the prestigious medical journal *The Lancet*. We have recently seen some of the dangers scientists have predicted beginning to get more severe.

"The effects of climate change are being felt today, and future projections represent an unacceptably high and potentially catastrophic risk to human health."

—*The Lancet Commission on Health and Climate Change,* April 2015

THE IMPACT OF THE CLIMATE CRISIS ON HUMAN HEALTH

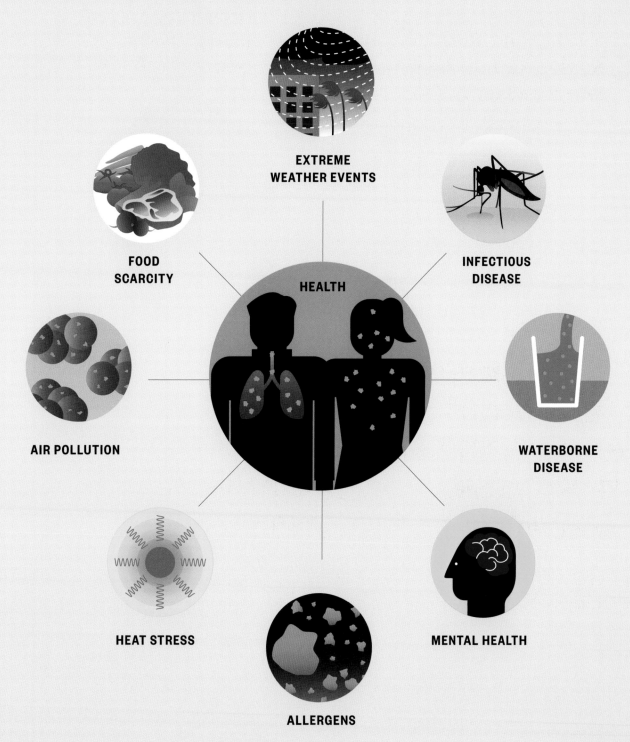

EXTREME
WEATHER EVENTS

FOOD
SCARCITY

INFECTIOUS
DISEASE

HEALTH

AIR POLLUTION

WATERBORNE
DISEASE

HEAT STRESS

MENTAL HEALTH

ALLERGENS

Susan Pacheco

Pediatrician and Climate Reality Leader

HOUSTON, TEXAS

DRAWING ON HER DECADES of experience as a pediatrician, Susan Pacheco has a simple message for doctors everywhere: the health of the environment affects the health of their patients.

She points to research associating heat waves with elevated numbers of emergency room visits, air pollution with developmental problems in children, and natural disasters with population-wide spikes in depression, anxiety, and post-traumatic stress disorder. And those ailments, she worries, could be just the tip of the iceberg.

"There's heart disease, there's lung disease, there's kidney disease," said Pacheco, a professor of pediatrics at the University of Texas McGovern Medical School. "Every organ system can be affected by climate change. When I say that, I get goosebumps."

Pacheco, who was born and raised in Puerto Rico, didn't become concerned with climate science until 2006. Her eldest son was learning about climate change in school, so she took the family to see *An Inconvenient Truth*.

This trip to the theater proved to be a wake-up call. She had never paid much attention to climate science, but after seeing the movie she found herself preoccupied by it. As time passed, she decided she needed to take action, and applied to take part in the second-ever Climate Reality Leadership Corps, a training program I led in Nashville in 2006.

It wasn't until she returned home to Houston and started giving her own presentations that Pacheco found her niche. She began to familiarize herself with the body of research on how the climate affects health, and she was startled by the gravity of what she learned.

Beyond the obvious concerns about extreme heat and pollution, researchers worry that extended allergy seasons could disrupt the functioning of our immune systems, and higher temperatures allow mosquitoes and ticks to spread diseases for a longer period than ever before. High carbon dioxide levels can even affect the nutritional value of crops.

Pacheco became convinced she could see the effects in her own clinic's waiting room, in the Texas children she saw suffering from asthma, heat sensitivity, and allergies. Children and the elderly, she discovered, tend to be the most vulnerable. And while many adults have lived for years in an environment less affected by climate change, today's youth will grow up with an entire lifetime of exposure. The potential for damage and illness, she suspects, is much higher.

She decided that those vulnerable populations needed an advocate inside the health care system, and she started to adapt her presentation for the task of educating other physicians about the health implications of the changing climate. "The

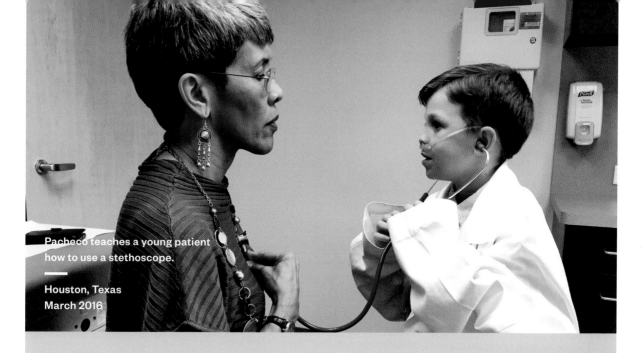

Pacheco teaches a young patient how to use a stethoscope.

Houston, Texas
March 2016

knowledge about climate change in the health community was almost nonexistent," she said. "So that's what I've been doing since that time: working to educate and build awareness in the health sector."

In the years since, she has spoken in dozens of professional settings, to ethnic and religious organizations, to family groups, and, above all, to health care practitioners. At first, some fellow doctors resisted her message. Her own father suggested, pointedly, that she spend more time focusing on her medical career and less on the environment.

But as time went on and the national conversation around the climate shifted, Pacheco found the medical community to be more and more receptive. A key victory has been that medical schools have started to integrate the health effects of climate change into their curricula, starting with her own students at McGovern.

Pacheco also founded the Texas Coalition for Climate Change Awareness, a network dedicated to educating communities across the state about the threats of climate change, and penned newspaper editorials in both English and Spanish about the importance of EPA regulations. She worked with the American Academy of Pediatrics' Council on Environmental Health to publish a policy statement about the importance of considering the environment in pediatric health.

Some authorities have started to take notice of Pacheco's efforts. Last year, 13 federal agencies collaborated on a report concluding that climate change is a "significant threat" to the health of Americans.

"The changes are happening right now," said former U.S. surgeon general Vivek Murthy. "Climate change is going to impact health, and it's not a pretty picture."

In 2013, the White House bestowed Pacheco with the illustrious "Champions of Change" award in recognition of her efforts. "I want to educate," she said. "I will talk to as many people as I can." And she doesn't intend to rest until the entire medical establishment has taken note. ◉

See page 302 for advice on adapting the Climate Reality presentation for your own passions.

One major consequence of the climate crisis is that the balance between human beings and microbes is being upended. Climate change means the "vectors" that carry diseases, including mosquitoes and ticks, have a wider range. In central China, the reemergence of malaria is directly related to increased temperatures and disruptive rainfalls.

In the United States, the range of the *Aedes aegypti* mosquito is extending northward. This is the principal mosquito that carries the Zika virus.

In addition, the life cycles of both *Aedes aegypti* and the Zika virus have been acceler-ated by warmer temperatures, increasing the time available for transmission of the virus.

AEDES AEGYPTI LIFE CYCLE

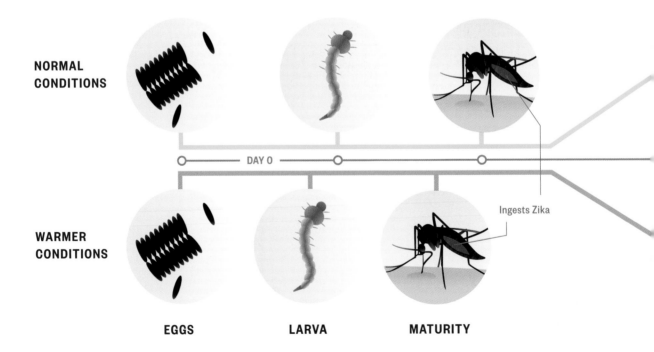

NORMAL CONDITIONS

WARMER CONDITIONS

DAY 0

Ingests Zika

EGGS

LARVA

MATURITY

TRUTH TO POWER

CURRENT RANGE OF *AEDES AEGYPTI* IN THE CONTINENTAL UNITED STATES

■ *Aedes aegypti* range

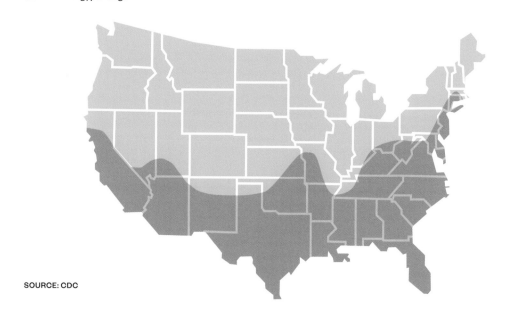

SOURCE: CDC

Zika incubates more slowly

The mosquito often dies
before it becomes infectious

DAY 14–16

Zika incubates
much faster

The mosquito is infectious
for a longer period

In several countries in South America and Central America affected by Zika, doctors advised women not to get pregnant for two years. Telling women that they should not get pregnant until we have this under control—that is a message that is new in the history of the human race.

¿Enfermo con CHIKUNGUNYA, DENGUE, or ZIKA?

At 37 weeks pregnant, this mother is at risk of her baby having birth defects due to the Zika virus.

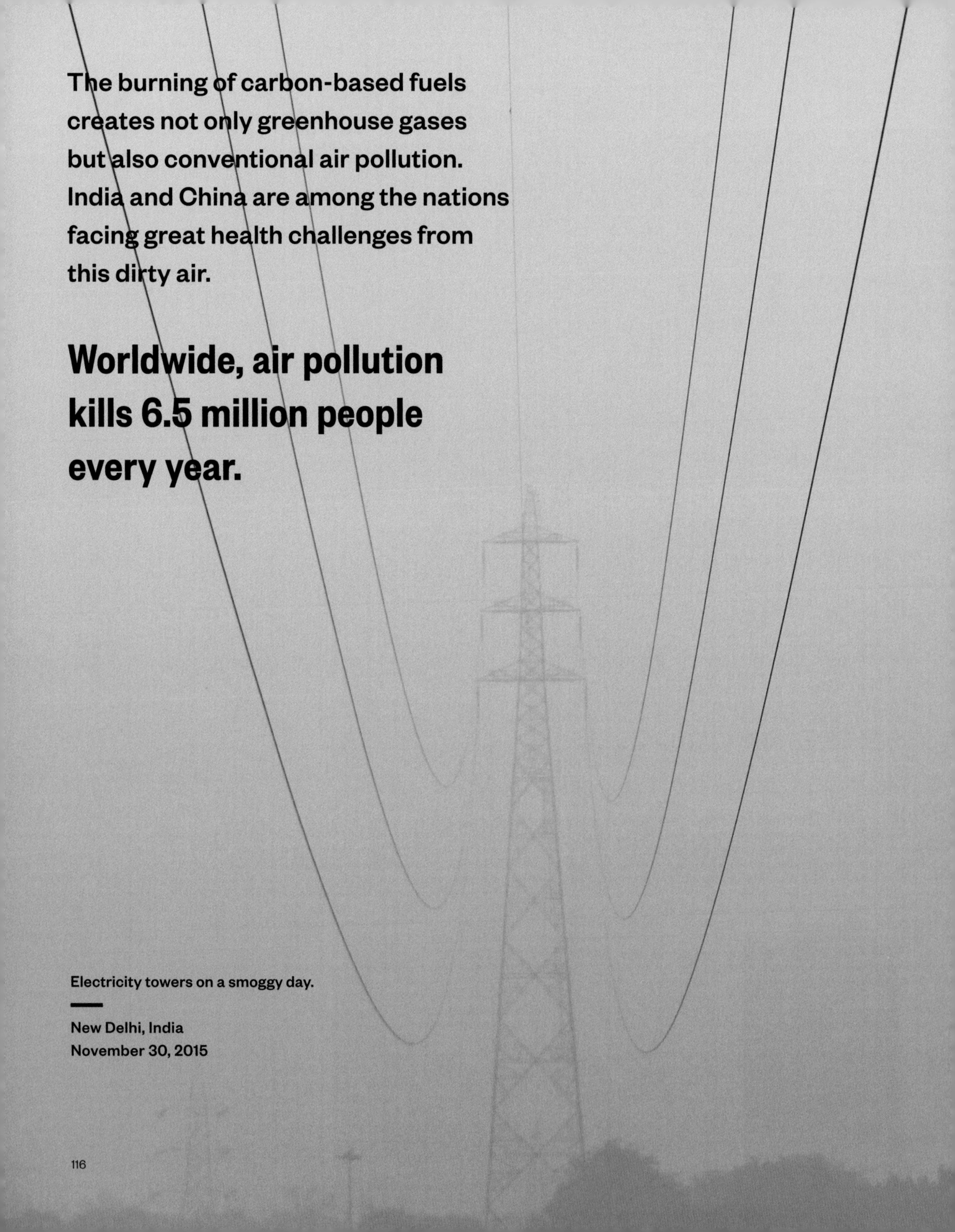

The burning of carbon-based fuels creates not only greenhouse gases but also conventional air pollution. India and China are among the nations facing great health challenges from this dirty air.

Worldwide, air pollution kills 6.5 million people every year.

Electricity towers on a smoggy day.

—

New Delhi, India
November 30, 2015

Ivy Chipasha

Climate Reality Leader

LUSAKA, ZAMBIA

IVY CHIPASHA WAS BORN in Zambia's Copperbelt region, where mineral and emerald mines dot the landscape. She later moved to the country's Central Province, where swamplands surround the mouths of the Lukanga and Kafue Rivers, and finally to the relatively cosmopolitan Lusaka area, where she raises four children. In each place, she has witnessed climate change ravage her homeland.

She has seen deforestation menace the country's woodlands, which are among the most prolific in Africa. Droughts now alternate unpredictably with heavy rainfall and flash floods, and the irregular weather has wreaked havoc on the nation's hydropower infrastructure, causing outages and power shedding.

"We've been hit hard by climate change," she said ruefully.

Chipasha originally came to environmentalism by way of her work in the financial sector, where she became convinced that Africa's energy future lay in renewables. In 2014, she attended the Climate Reality Leadership training I led in Johannesburg, South Africa, and in the years since, she has given many presentations, often to students in the Lusaka area.

She is also a steering committee member of the African Renewable Energy Alliance, an organization that helps policy makers, business leaders, and academics make plans for the continent's energy future.

"If leeway is given to climate change activists, a lot will change," she said. "Climate change affects everyone."

Because the Zambian government has limited financial resources, Chipasha is also interested in ways that education and outreach can help individual families conserve. In rural parts of Zambia, families often still cook using firewood and charcoal, and the growing demand is putting a strain on the country's lush forests.

To promote renewable energy in Zambian households, she founded an organization called the Green Environment Foundation, which advocates for clean water, conservation, and lower-impact cooking technologies in Zambian households. Chipasha was a peer reviewer of "Beyond Fire," a report by the World Future Council that was presented at the United Nations Framework Convention on Climate Change in Morocco last year.

One day, Chipasha believes her work will lead to a brighter environmental future for her children and her country.

"I believe that we will win this fight," she said. "Nothing is impossible." ◉

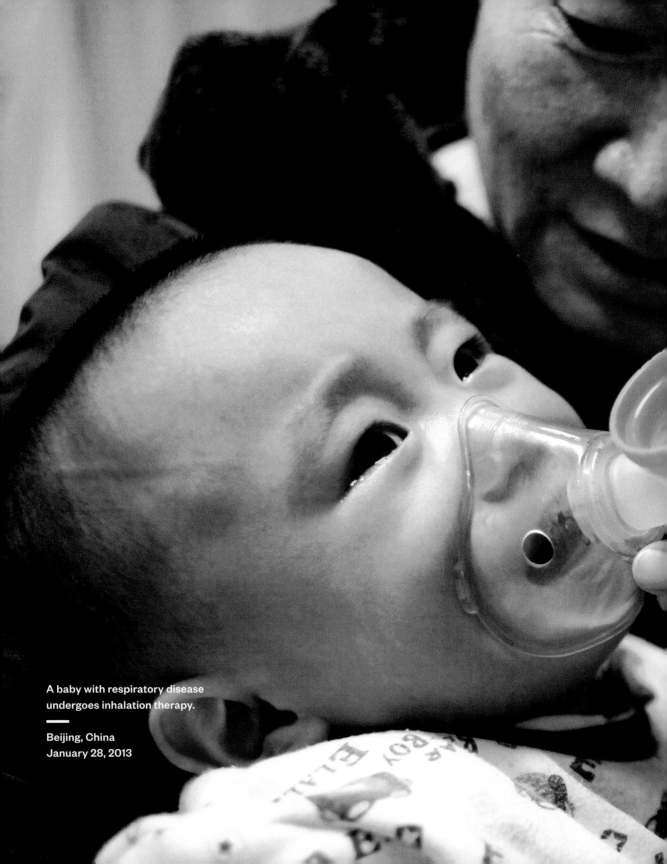

A baby with respiratory disease undergoes inhalation therapy.

Beijing, China
January 28, 2013

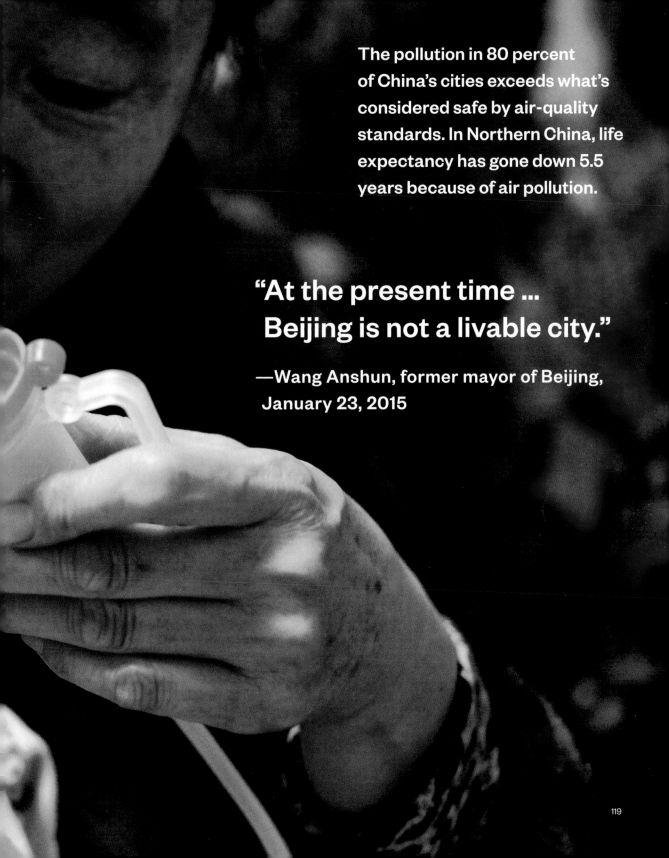

The pollution in 80 percent of China's cities exceeds what's considered safe by air-quality standards. In Northern China, life expectancy has gone down 5.5 years because of air pollution.

"At the present time ... Beijing is not a livable city."

—Wang Anshun, former mayor of Beijing, January 23, 2015

Pollution Monitoring

IN JULY 2008, THE U.S. EMBASSY in Beijing connected its rooftop pollutant monitor to a new Twitter account and began automatically tweeting its data. Using the Twitter handle @BeijingAir, the hourly tweets followed a simple and uniform format: date, time, pollutant type, concentration, and air quality index (AQI).

Beijing's air quality was already notoriously poor. However, despite residents' frequent inability to see the full city skyline due to smog, official government pronouncements listed the city's air pollution as "light." The discrepancy between official government pronouncements and Beijing residents' day-to-day reality was due to the type of air particles the government monitored.

The most dangerous type of air pollutants are PM2.5—tiny particles that measure less than 2.5 microns in diameter, or about the width of spider silk. These particles are small enough to enter the lungs and even the blood, where they can wreak havoc and potentially cause serious heart and lung problems. The Chinese government monitored PM10 pollutants, which are much larger and much less dangerous. Because of the choice of particle size, Beijing's obvious air pollution problem was not reflected in the official measurements by the Chinese government.

In November 2010, the U.S. Embassy sent out a tweet describing Beijing's air quality as "crazy bad."

The AQI measures particle pollution on a scale of 1–500, with 301–500 being "hazardous." That day, the score was quite literally off the charts, at 562. The tweet went viral, and although Twitter is blocked for most users in China, screenshots of it circulated on other platforms, sparking an uproar in Beijing.

The brilliance of the tweets was their simplicity. The account was only tweeting out data. Aside from the "crazy bad" categorization, @BeijingAir was not tweeting analysis or declarations. The account left its tweets to be interpreted by the reader, therefore it was able to avoid being declared subversive. The embassy was allowed to continue its pollution monitoring and tweeting, notwithstanding the fact that their data directly contradicted the official government story.

Local environmental advocates seized upon this new information. Using the momentum of the viral tweet, they mobilized Beijing residents to monitor air quality themselves and to advocate for changes. The Green Beagle Environment Institute began distributing PM2.5 monitors to local residents. These monitors were about the size of a transistor radio, and much less expensive than the embassy's, but they produced the same data.

By 2013, environmental advocates had succeeded in convincing China to set up hundreds of PM2.5 monitoring stations in over 70 cities.

BeijingAir @BeijingAir
01-12-2013 17:00; PM2.5; 810.0; 704; Beyond Index
Expand

U.S. Embassy air quality tweet. Twitter, January 12, 2013

Additionally, China earmarked hundreds of billions of dollars for air cleaning and began implementing policies for air pollution reduction targets in major cities, most importantly adopting the PM2.5 measurement for data.

Today, Beijing's AQI rating hovers around the "unhealthy" score, 151–200. While there is clearly more work to be done, it's a huge change from the "hazardous" and off-the-charts ratings.

Additionally, the increased access to daily data from the monitoring stations helps residents make important decisions about everyday activities, like how long their kids can play outside, or if it's safe to let elders go out for walks. In an age when any news source can be branded "fake," providing the public with raw, objective data can be a subversive act. ◉

The Dongbianmen Gate before and after the smog sets in. Beijing, China, January 12, 2013 (before) and January 16, 2013 (after).

Wang Shi

Founder and Chairman of China Vanke

SHENZHEN, CHINA

WHEN WANG SHI WAS YOUNG, he was drawn to stories of adventure, particularly Jack London's *The Call of the Wild* and Ernest Hemingway's *The Snows of Kilimanjaro.*

And it was on Kilimanjaro, years after he became one of the most successful real estate entrepreneurs in China, that Wang experienced a wake-up call about climate change. In 2002, when his climbing party reached the peak, he was struck by the lack of snow. When he returned home and researched the topic, he discovered that in 20 years the mountain's snows could be gone entirely.

"I began to notice more signs of climate change, as I carried on my adventure journeys in other parts of the world," said Wang, who, in addition to climbing the highest peaks on every continent, also serves as the chairman of Vanke, the largest residential real estate developer in China.

Wang began reading more about climate science. He found that China produces the most carbon emissions of any country in the world, and that the nation's construction industry, where he'd built his career, was responsible for more carbon emissions than Russia and India combined.

After a time, Wang came to believe that he bore a responsibility, as a prosperous businessperson, to advocate for environmentalism at home and abroad. "Although China is growing quickly into the second largest economy, the industrialization process is taking on big environmental and social prices," he said. "I think the current growth model cannot continue in the long term. Chinese companies and entrepreneurs are at a crossroads and need enlightenment for a more sustainable and healthy model."

The first step was to take strides to make Vanke's work more sustainable. Wang was drawn to prefabrication, a construction technique that assembles as many components of a structure as possible in a centralized manufacturing location. While often more costly, prefabrication uses far less timber, water, and energy than conventional methods.

At first, Wang had little support within either the industry or the government. Some at Vanke were unconvinced. But as it became clear that the tide in the construction sector was turning toward prefabrication, Vanke found itself in an auspicious position.

"When the government later announced standards and incentives for implementing new techniques, we were already taking the lead in the industry and did not have difficulty in adjustments," he said. "Our early move was rewarding."

Wang went on to found a group of Chinese entrepreneurs called the C Team, with whom he is working to network business leaders in the country to fight climate change. The group has attended the United Nations' climate conferences almost

The prefabrication lab at Vanke's national R&D center.

Dongguan, China

every year since, and last year brought more than 100 Chinese business leaders to the summit in Marrakech, Morocco.

Wang has also advocated for the health of mountains. In 2010, in conjunction with his second trip to the summit of Mount Everest, the Vanke Foundation organized a campaign called Kilometer Zero that called on Chinese mountaineers to bring trash down from mountainsides. The effort collected some two tons of garbage, including 200 abandoned oxygen tanks.

In recent years, much of Wang's work has been in the realm of higher education. He has taught at the Hong Kong University of Science and Technology and Peking University, and in 2011 he joined the Harvard University Asia Center to study connections between business ethics and Judaism. While at Harvard, he visited Walden Pond and read the works of Henry David Thoreau to reflect on the importance of the natural world.

"It is not the question of *how*, but the question of *why* we should ask ourselves," Wang explained. "The purpose of my study is to bring back inspirations to China from the foundation of Western industrialization."

Last year, Wang took part in the Climate Reality Project's second-ever training in China. He spoke about the ways climate change could impact China's nearly 1.4 billion citizens and the ways that the country can act as a global leader for climate progress.

"I am a cautious optimist," Wang said, not just for the future of the mountaintops he loves, but also because of the growing commitment to environmentalism he sees in China's public and business spheres. ◉

The balance of nature is also visibly upset in the Arctic. Here, during the long polar winter night, the sun doesn't hit the North Pole for six months of the year. Normally, it's extremely cold.

But these are not normal times. Right in the middle of that polar winter night, on February 10, 2017, temperatures were about 27.7°C (50°F) above normal. The North Pole started thawing at night in the middle of winter. A similar temperature spike occurred in December 2015. This is a pattern.

**TEMPERATURE DEPARTURE FROM AVERAGE
FEBRUARY 10, 2017**

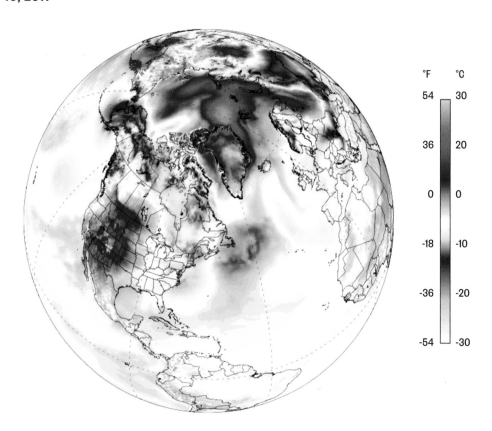

SOURCE: CCI, UNIVERSITY OF MAINE

The Arctic is already undergoing dramatic changes.

As underwater ice melts, methane trapped beneath bubbles up and is released into the atmosphere.

Cook Inlet, Alaska
January 2010

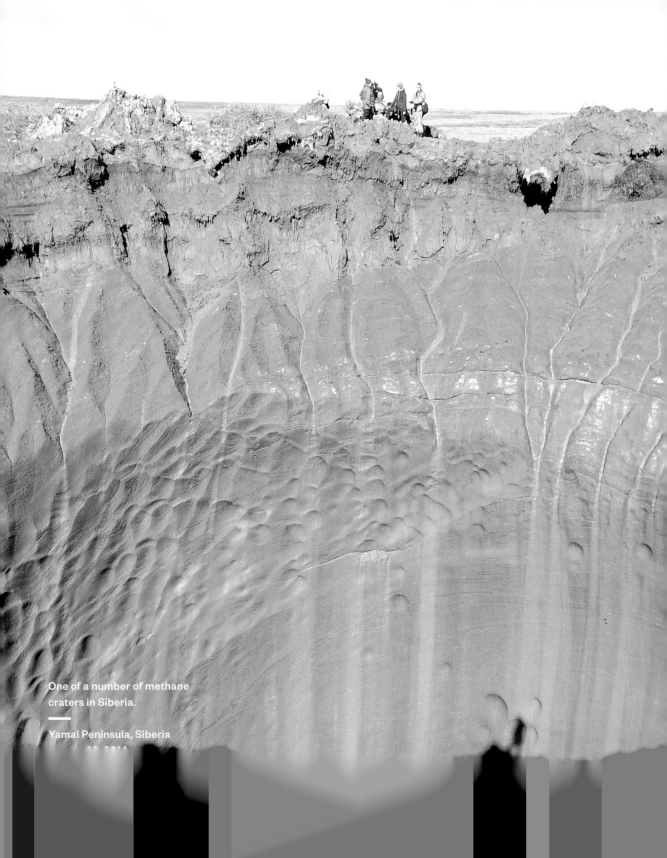

One of a number of methane craters in Siberia.

Yamal Peninsula, Siberia

This is not where a meteor has hit.

It is an outburst crater in Siberia caused by a methane explosion after the tundra thawed and gas built up until it blew out this massive hole.

Throughout the Arctic tundra, huge amounts of plant matter lie frozen in the soil. When it thaws, the decomposition produces some CO_2, and more worryingly, enormous amounts of methane, which is a far more potent greenhouse gas.

We don't yet know how dangerous the release of methane in the warming Arctic will be, or when we might cross a tipping point when there will be a much larger release of methane.

Konrad Steffen

Climate Scientist and Climate Reality Leader

EGG, SWITZERLAND

IN THE YEAR 2000, when my friend Koni Steffen looked at the latest temperature readings from the system of weather stations he'd built in Greenland, he thought something must have gone wrong with the sensors. The temperatures seemed far too high. As a good scientist, he immediately set out to corroborate the new readings.

"I went through it all night without sleeping," he recalled. "And I realized that the data was real."

Further confirmation came later after one of the stations collapsed when the ice supporting it melted rapidly in the Arctic's rising temperatures.

Steffen, whom I've known now for nearly two decades, never set out to study climate change. He was born in Zurich, Switzerland, and originally studied electrical engineering before discovering a passion for earth science.

His most long-standing project has been to monitor the weather patterns and temperatures of the Arctic using a network of solar-powered weather stations he constructed starting in 1976. He has visited Greenland to maintain and expand the network every year since, even during a lengthy period teaching at the University of Colorado during the 1980s and 1990s. This past season marked his 40th trip.

Steffen wears a stately beard, and though his hair is greying, he speaks with the ardor of a much

younger man. He sometimes quips that when he started his academic career in the 1970s, scientists knew more about conditions on nearby planets than they did about Greenland.

Though he's too modest to say it, his work has been instrumental in changing that. Looking back, he's grateful for the opportunity to track climate change in the Arctic since an era when the climate was far more stable—and to have helped inform the international conversation about global warming almost since its inception.

In the years since the weather station collapsed, Steffen's research has convinced him that climate change poses a grave risk to the citizens of the world. In particular, his work has demonstrated that even small changes to the environment can have momentous climatological effects. He has shown that Greenland's ice sheet, long thought to melt more slowly than glaciers, are disappearing far more rapidly than expected, in part because of fissures that drain water down into the bedrock.

In spite of it all, Steffen has been heartened by the growing awareness about climate change over the past decade.

"We are all in it together," he said. "It is a global climate. I am a scientist, and science has no border." ◉

Antarctica Is Warming Too

MOST OF THE ICE ON PLANET EARTH is found on Antarctica. While the Arctic is ocean surrounded by land, Antarctica is land surround by ocean. In the middle of Antarctica, the surface of the ice extends 10,000 feet above sea level. When I visited the South Pole, I got altitude sickness.

The ice of Antarctica has begun to melt and flow toward the ocean at a faster pace, contributing to global sea level rise. The most vulnerable part of the ice cap is in West Antarctica, a region that is roughly the size of Greenland.

A major portion of West Antarctica has now crossed a tipping point, according to scientists, and will eventually break up, flow into the ocean, and melt. Most scientists believe that humankind still has the opportunity to prevent the breakup and melting of the bulk of ice in Antarctica, but they warn us that we must start sharply reducing global warming pollution as quickly as possible. ◉

A penguin navigates a crack in the ice. Rilser-larsen Ice Shelf, Antarctica.

The Arctic is warming faster than any other place on Earth. The melting of its glaciers and the Greenland ice cap is now raising sea levels worldwide.

BELOW: Konrad Steffen's research base on May 22, 2012.

RIGHT: The same research station 4 years later on July 11, 2016.

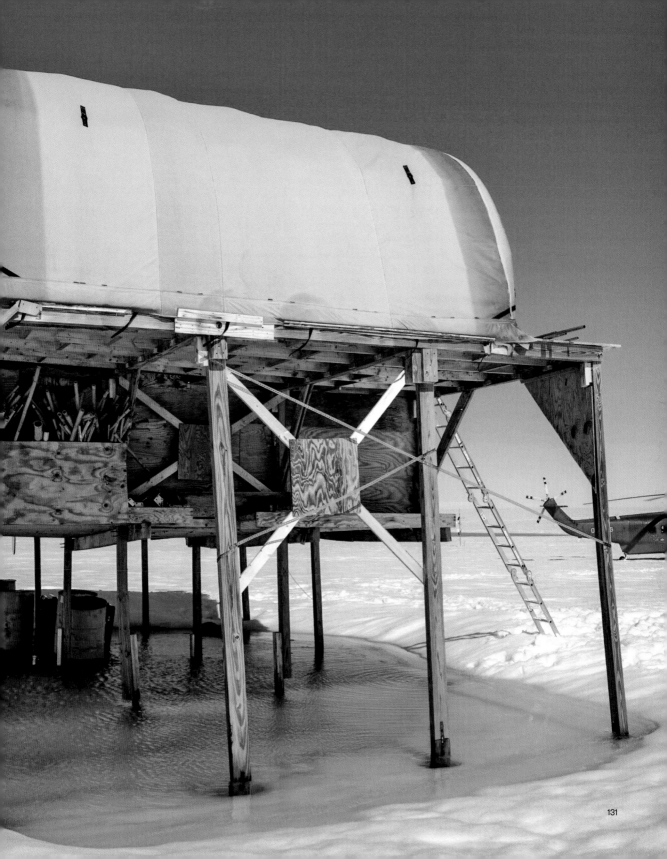

At a Climate Reality training in Miami, I saw fish from the ocean swimming in some of the streets in nearby Miami Beach. It was an example of "sunny day flooding." There was no rainfall, the sea was simply coming up through the storm sewers during high tides. This is happening on a regular basis.

PROJECTED SEA LEVEL RISE IN SOUTH FLORIDA

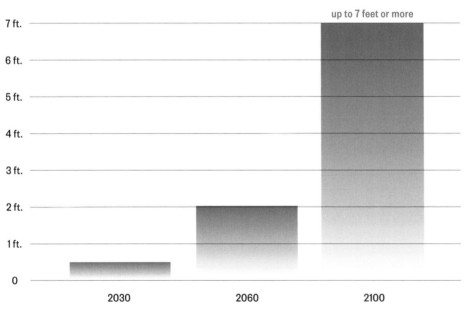

up to 7 feet or more

2030	2060	2100

SOURCE: SOUTHEAST FLORIDA REGIONAL CLIMATE CHANGE COMPACT

Miami is now the number one city in the world in terms of assets at risk due to sea level rise.

Here's something you don't see everyday: an octopus in a parking garage.

—

Miami Beach, Florida
November 14, 2016

Sea level rise is an extremely grave threat, both for economies and for the people who will have to relocate.

TOP 10 CITIES AT RISK FROM SEA LEVEL RISE BY 2070

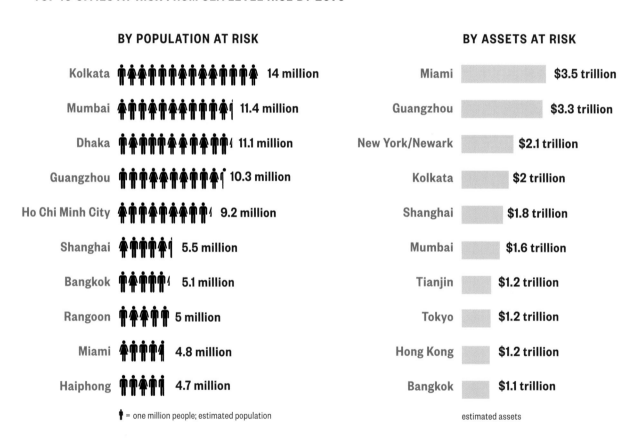

BY POPULATION AT RISK

Kolkata	14 million
Mumbai	11.4 million
Dhaka	11.1 million
Guangzhou	10.3 million
Ho Chi Minh City	9.2 million
Shanghai	5.5 million
Bangkok	5.1 million
Rangoon	5 million
Miami	4.8 million
Haiphong	4.7 million

= one million people; estimated population

BY ASSETS AT RISK

City	Assets
Miami	$3.5 trillion
Guangzhou	$3.3 trillion
New York/Newark	$2.1 trillion
Kolkata	$2 trillion
Shanghai	$1.8 trillion
Mumbai	$1.6 trillion
Tianjin	$1.2 trillion
Tokyo	$1.2 trillion
Hong Kong	$1.2 trillion
Bangkok	$1.1 trillion

estimated assets

SOURCE: NICHOLS, ET AL., 2007, OECD

TRUTH TO POWER

Itzel Morales

Climate Scientist and Climate Reality Leader

DAVIS, CALIFORNIA

ITZEL MORALES'S FAMILY has lived on the Mexican island of Carmen for generations. In 2010, for the first time, they had to buy air-conditioning units because a window and fan were no longer enough to keep cool during the sweltering summer months.

"The nights were suffocating," Morales said. "That fear was what got me involved in climate change."

Spurred to action, Morales enrolled in a master's program at Scotland's Heriot-Watt University, where she studied the impacts and mitigation of climate change. Then she applied to the Climate Reality Project's 2013 training in Chicago, where she participated in an intensive three-day session of climate researchers and communications experts.

After the training, Morales returned to Mexico and flung herself into climate advocacy. "I knew I

Morales and the Colectivo Ambiental Isla Verde distribute recycled notebooks to students.

could do presentations," she said. "I started sending emails to everybody I knew."

The community responded. Morales spoke in living rooms, in every elementary school in her district, and at her alma mater in Yucatán, where she had studied chemical engineering. She even presented in front of a crowd of more than a thousand at an event organized by the Fundación Pablo García, a Mexican scholarship program. In her first year, all told, she gave 25 presentations to thousands of people.

She also became more involved with local issues. Carmen Island sits on the Laguna de Términos, a tidal lagoon on the Gulf Coast where the mangroves shelter a rich ecosystem. Morales is quick to rattle off statistics about the area's abundant biodiversity—and about the looming threats of the petroleum industry. To protect the area, she became a campaign organizer for the Green Island Environmental Group, which advocates for the protection of the lagoon.

Now, she has left the region again, this time for a position as a Hubert H. Humphrey Fellow at UC Davis, where she is studying natural resource conservation and how community empowerment can push back against climate change.

She often thinks about the scorching nights back home on Carmen, but in spite of it all, she remains hopeful. The fight, she believes, is just beginning.

"We definitely have political will," she said. ◉

Our global civilization is now at a point of decision.

But there is good news.

We have all the solutions that we need right before us.

One day in August 2016, Scotland got 100 percent of its electricity from wind. In Portugal, they had four days straight in May 2016 on renewable energy alone.

The transition to renewable energy represents the largest business opportunity in the history of the world. The projections for the future are quite stunning.

The windy hills north of Lisbon are an ideal spot for a wind farm.

——

Sobral de Monte Agraço, Portugal
August 13, 2015

The best projections 15 years ago were that global wind energy would increase by 30 gigawatts by 2010.

WIND POWER PROJECTED VS. ACTUAL

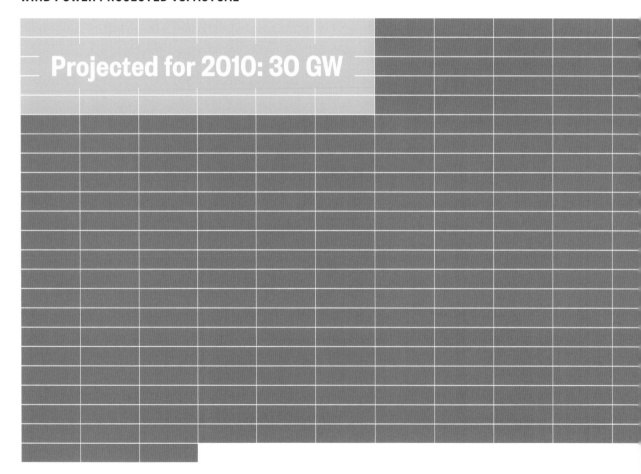

Projected for 2010: 30 GW

TRUTH TO POWER

By 2016, we beat that goal 16 times over.

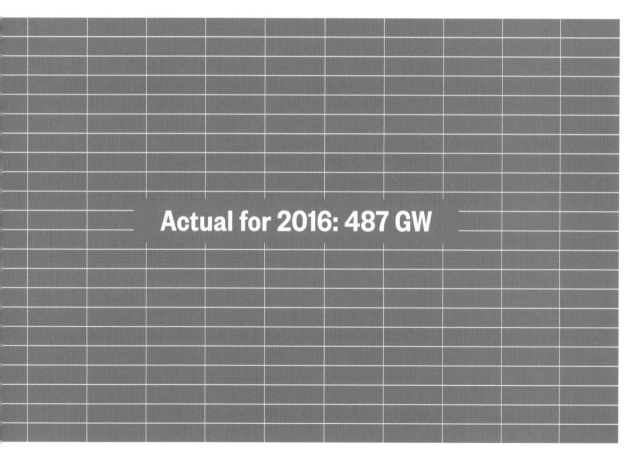

Actual for 2016: 487 GW

SOURCE: IEA, GWEC

The Middelgrunden offshore
wind farm.

Copenhagen, Denmark
March 11, 2015

For 24 hours on April 17th, 2016, wind power met 103.6 percent of Denmark's needs.

Dale Ross

Mayor

GEORGETOWN, TEXAS

JUST NORTH OF AUSTIN, Texas lies Georgetown, a city of about 50,000 known for its Victorian architecture and serene natural landscape. In many ways, it's a conventionally run municipality that tends to attract retirees—except that it's powered entirely by wind and solar energy.

More surprising, perhaps, is that Georgetown mayor Dale Ross doesn't see that incredible accomplishment as an environmental issue. To him, it's just dollars and cents.

"I think people make decisions that are in their own best interest," said Ross, who has lived in Georgetown since the fourth grade. "If you can get things so that people want sustainable green energy, I think you'll get buy-in from across the United States."

There are a handful of other U.S. cities that have made similar decisions, including Burlington, Vermont, and Aspen, Colorado, but Georgetown stands out for the overtly pragmatic language its leaders have used to justify the transition.

"There are a lot of cities that just go with the next budget cycle," Ross said, "but we plan for 25 years in advance."

We could probably all learn a lot from Ross, who spoke with an understated Texas accent as he outlined the thought process behind the transition. Ross worked for decades as an accountant, and he sees his role in government as an extension of that bookkeeping experience.

Georgetown, he explains, has run its own municipal electric utility since the early 20th century. With its wholesale power contract set to end in 2012, Ross realized the city was faced with a historic opportunity. Wind farms had been cropping up in Texas for years, and he was intrigued by the possibility of negotiating renewable rates that wouldn't rise over time.

So he crunched the numbers, examining the wind profile and solar radiance of the region, and what he found surprised him. The combination of falling photovoltaic prices and growing wind infrastructure meant that the wind and sun could not only provide all the community's electricity, but that the town could sell the extra power back to the grid. Unlike coal and oil, which are subject to price fluctuations, the city knows exactly what the costs are going to be in perpetuity.

Furthermore, he found that because fossil fuel power plants use steam, moving toward wind and solar would also reduce strain on the state's water usage during punishing droughts, while improving air quality. Sourcing the entirety of Georgetown's energy needs from renewable resources wasn't just possible, Ross realized—it also made sound financial sense. ◉

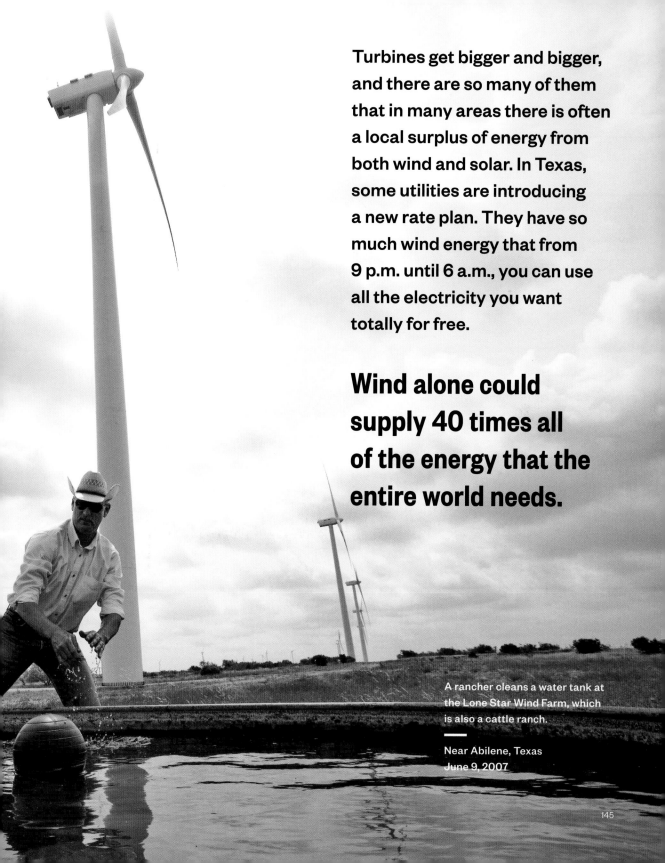

Turbines get bigger and bigger, and there are so many of them that in many areas there is often a local surplus of energy from both wind and solar. In Texas, some utilities are introducing a new rate plan. They have so much wind energy that from 9 p.m. until 6 a.m., you can use all the electricity you want totally for free.

Wind alone could supply 40 times all of the energy that the entire world needs.

A rancher cleans a water tank at the Lone Star Wind Farm, which is also a cattle ranch.

Near Abilene, Texas
June 9, 2007

145

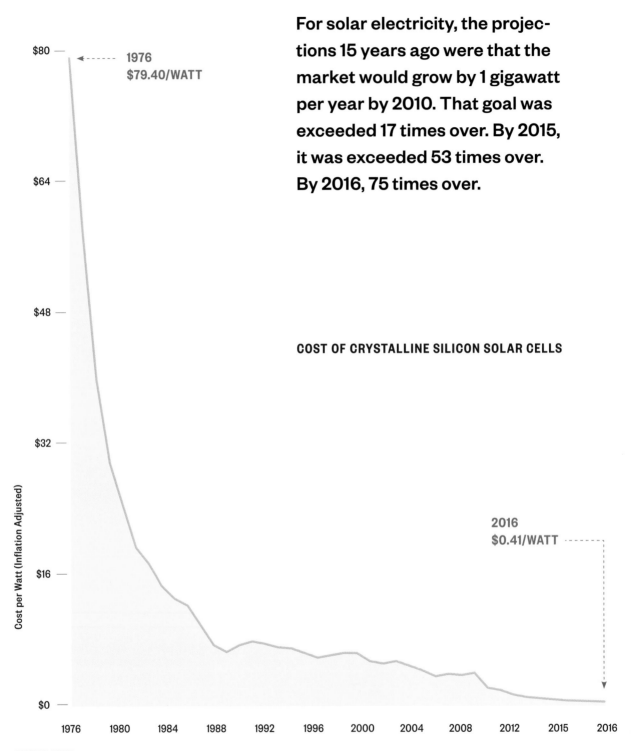

For solar electricity, the projections 15 years ago were that the market would grow by 1 gigawatt per year by 2010. That goal was exceeded 17 times over. By 2015, it was exceeded 53 times over. By 2016, 75 times over.

1976
$79.40/WATT

COST OF CRYSTALLINE SILICON SOLAR CELLS

2016
$0.41/WATT

Cost per Watt (Inflation Adjusted)

$80
$64
$48
$32
$16
$0

1976 1980 1984 1988 1992 1996 2000 2004 2008 2012 2015 2016

SOURCE: BNEF

TRUTH TO POWER

This is an exponential curve, and it continues to go up at a steeper rate because the cost of silicon solar cells continues to go down.

WORLD SOLAR PV INSTALLATIONS

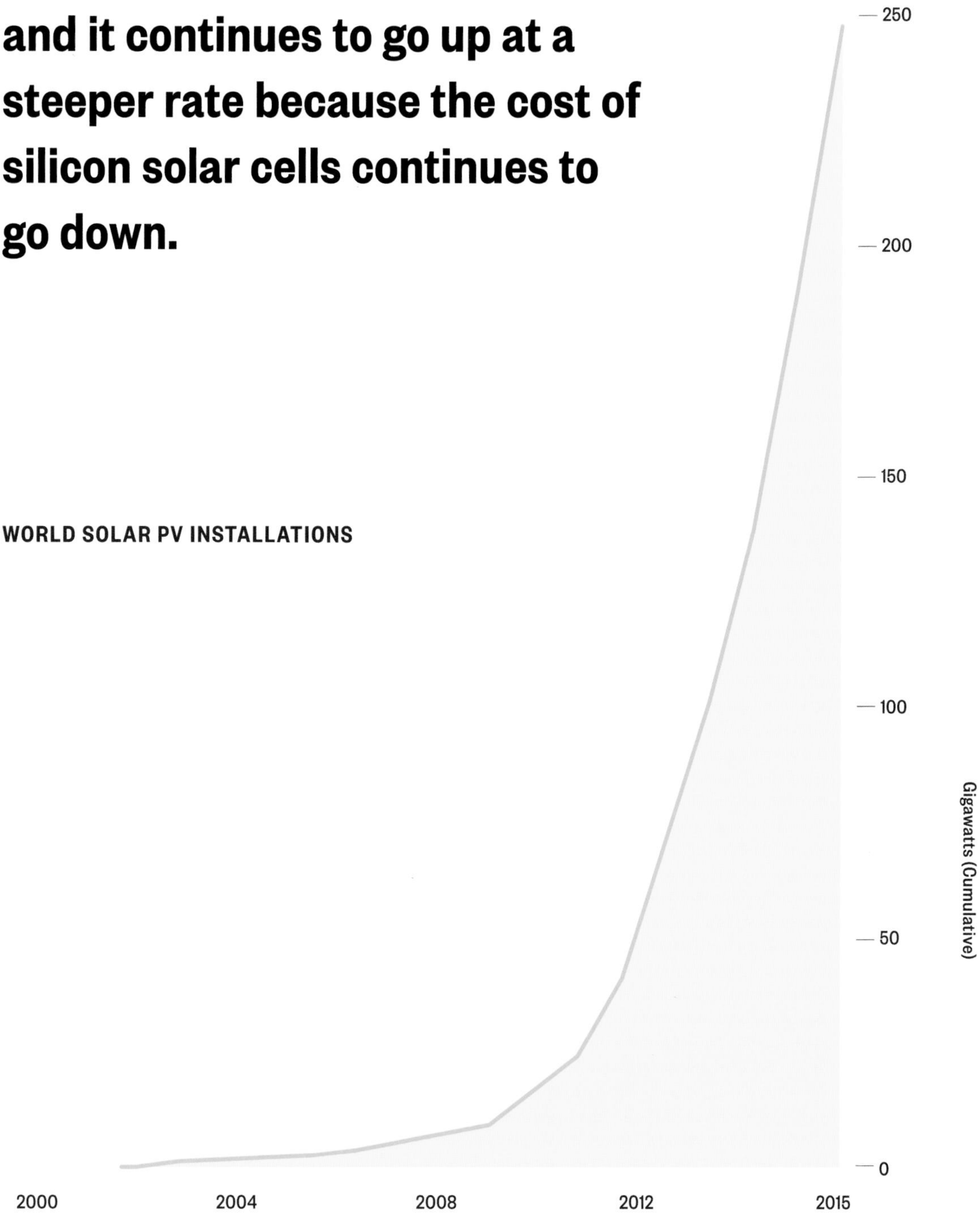

Gigawatts (Cumulative)

250

200

150

100

50

0

2000   2004   2008   2012   2015

SOURCE: EARTH POLICY INSTITUTE/BP

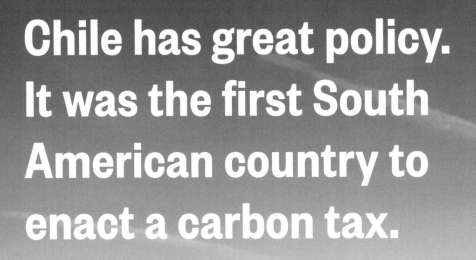

Chile has great policy. It was the first South American country to enact a carbon tax.

This 100 MW solar farm is one of the largest in Latin America.

Copiapó, Chile
June 2014

At the end of 2013, Chile had 11 megawatts of solar capacity. By the end of 2014, more than 400 megawatts. By the end of 2015, more than 800 megawatts. So look at what they had under construction as of 2016, and under contract to soon begin construction. You might have to turn the page.

CHILEAN SOLAR MARKET

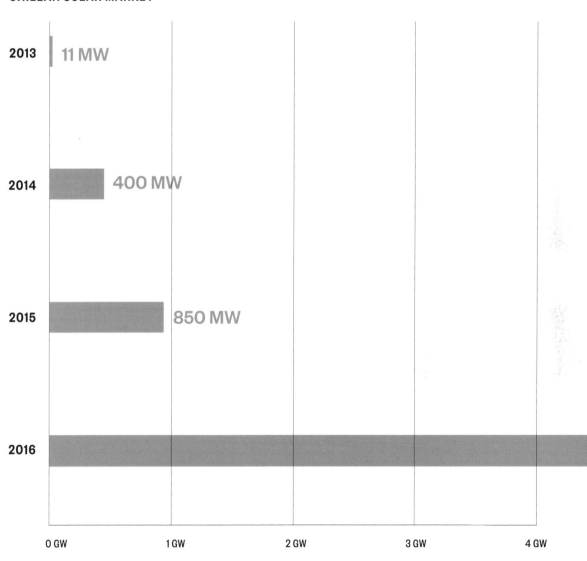

SOURCE: GREENTECH MEDIA, CLEANTECHNICA

You talk about excitement; this story gets me excited.

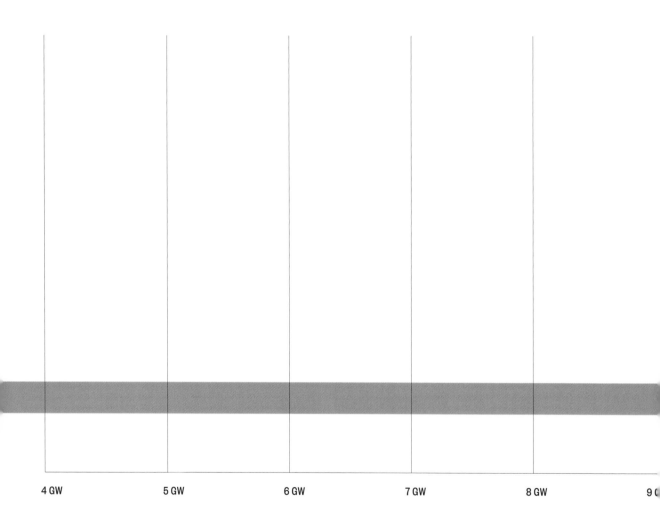

4 GW   5 GW   6 GW   7 GW   8 GW   9 G

Charging stations like this one
power electric vehicles that do
not emit CO_2.

Mountain View, California
August 24, 2016

We have an obligation to accelerate the movement toward meaningful changes in policies in

every nation on the face of this Earth to stop the destruction **of the global ecological system.**

These are all of the coal plants that were proposed in the past 10 years and have been defeated, all the existing coal plants that were retired, and all the coal plants where retirement has been announced. All of these coal plants have been canceled.

We are getting off of coal.

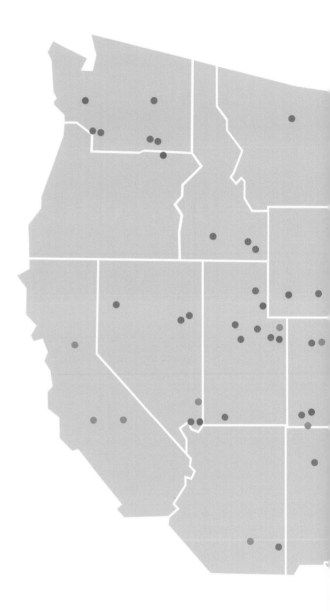

THE U.S. IS MOVING AWAY FROM COAL

● Retired

● Retirement proposed

● Proposed and canceled

SOURCE: THE SIERRA CLUB

TRUTH TO POWER

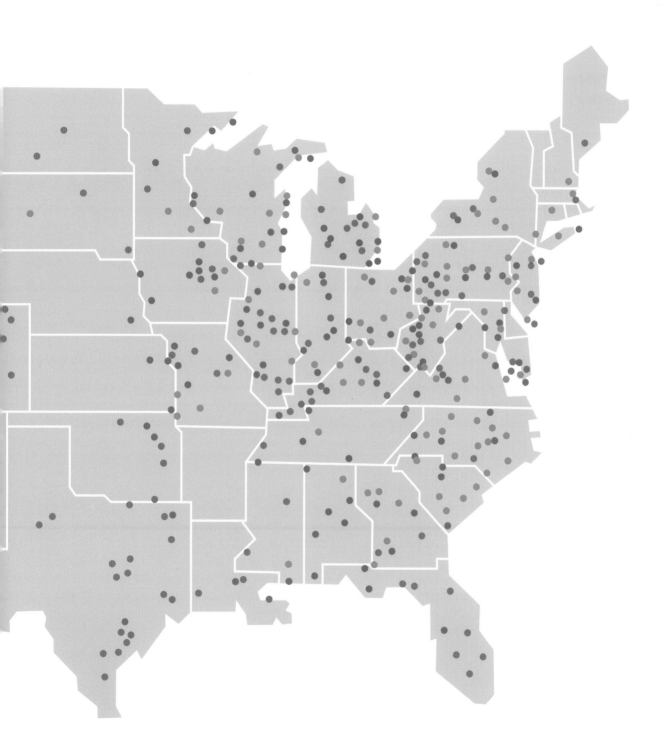

Bjarke Ingels

Architect and Founder of Bjarke Ingels Group (BIG)

COPENHAGEN, DENMARK

WHEN BIG SET OUT TO DESIGN a new waste-to-energy plant in Copenhagen, the company saw it as an opportunity to change public perception of what a utility building could be. Copenhagen is a flat city, so the group decided to embrace the structure's 85-meter height by giving it a sloped roof, complete with trees and trail markers. It would double as a ski slope during Denmark's snowy winters.

Bjarke Ingels, who heads the renowned Bjarke Ingels Group, also devised a "chimney" for the low-emission plant in collaboration with German architecture firm Realities:United that, instead of producing smoke, will puff out gigantic rings of steam each time the plant emits a metric ton of CO_2.

"There are people who imagine that the world is going down the drain," Ingels said, "and there are people who are optimistic about growth, that technology will provide new tools that will save us from problems."

Ingels belongs to the latter category. It's a design philosophy he calls " 'hedonistic sustainability,' which is the idea that sustainability is not a moral burden or sacrifice but a way to improve the quality of life and human enjoyment."

Ingels has made his career transforming cityscapes, but he was born and raised on a lakefront north of Copenhagen. That natural setting made a permanent impression on him, and since he was a young student, he has been drawn to questions of environmental policy and sustainability.

In what might be one of his most innovative projects to date, Ingels, together with the London-based Heatherwick Studio, designed a new headquarters for tech giant Google that features a canopy of photovoltaic panels that can be adjusted to let the perfect amount of sunlight shine down into the offices below while using the rest to generate electricity.

"We harvest every single photon," said Ingels, who often sports messy hair and a boyish grin. The idea behind the Google project, he said, was to use "existing technologies in ways that take advantage of all available resources."

Ingels believes that innovation is an inexhaustible resource—and that's what gives him hope for the future of the planet.

"There have been a handful of revolutions where, when humanity has a vision and a goal and a consensus about it, we can deliver striking results incredibly fast," he said. "All it takes is the resolve and the sense of urgency." ◉

An artist's rendering of the
Amager Bakke waste-to-energy
plant.

Copenhagen, Denmark

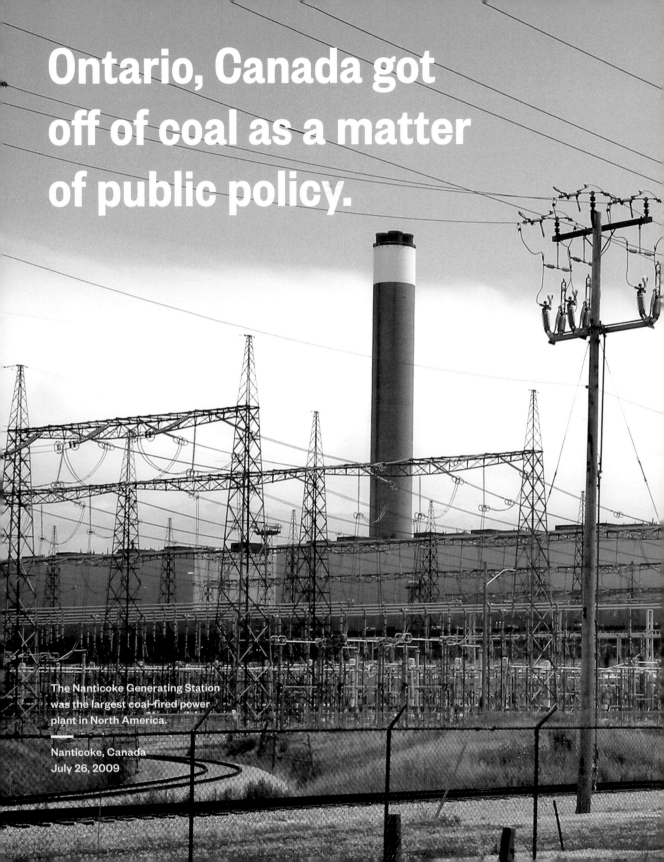

Ontario, Canada got off of coal as a matter of public policy.

The Nanticoke Generating Station was the largest coal-fired power plant in North America.

Nanticoke, Canada
July 26, 2009

The province was the first in North America to shut down its entire coal operation. Its last coal power plant closed down in 2014; a decade earlier, 25 percent of Ontario's power came from coal. One of the worst polluters in Canada, the Nanticoke plant site, is being repurposed as a solar farm.

Why Are Satellites Vital to Fight Climate Change?

WHEN THE CREW OF APOLLO 17 sent back a photo of the entire Earth in one shot in 1972, it was the first time we had seen the *Blue Marble* of our planet in all its majesty.

Today, satellites are one of the only ways to see Earth from afar, where we can observe climatic, weather, and energy patterns. However, even satellites can be limited in their scope.

When I saw that photograph of our planet, I was in awe. I thought, what if we could have these images on a daily basis? What if these images could be more comprehensive and detailed? Could they help build commitment to solving the climate crisis?

As I soon learned, there was nothing at the time capable of delivering what I had hoped for.

During my time as vice president, and inspired by the *Blue Marble* photograph, I called up NASA and proposed we send out a satellite that could get a broader view of Earth, and could stream the view in real time. I hoped that a fresh look at the entirety of our planet could inspire a new generation of environmental activists.

The result of the subsequent work was the Deep Space Climate Observatory satellite (DSCOVR), which to this day provides a full-sphere view of the Earth—and also constantly monitors the sun for potentially dangerous solar activity and solar storms that could threaten electric utility grids and pipelines.

In 2000, DSCOVR, which at that time was named Triana, after the first crew member on Columbus' ships to sight the New World, was approved by Congress despite some opposition. I was about to run for president, and that may have had something to do with the pushback.

In 2001, the satellite was built and ready to go when the new Bush-Cheney administration canceled its launch. At that time, DSCOVR's mission had become even more important as the older satellite that monitored solar activity was aging and carried dead instruments.

When the new administration canceled DSCOVR's launch, it didn't realize it was also cancelling the important solar-storm-monitoring warning system. Excessive energy released during solar storms on the sun can disrupt power grids, telecommunications, and GPS here on Earth. The warning system gives a 15- to 60-minute alert, allowing industries that depend on these technologies to prepare themselves for any disruptions.

Industries that could be negatively affected without the solar-storm warning system began to speak out against the decision to cancel DSCOVR, prompting the Bush-Cheney administration to agree to launch DSCOVR. But the administration proposed removing all of the climate-monitoring instruments, as well as the camera, and replacing them with the equivalent of sandbags. *Wow*, I thought, *that is extremism*.

DSCOVR gathered dust in storage for the remainder of Bush and Cheney's time in office.

Under the Obama administration, the satellite was retrieved from storage, tested, and found to be ready. DSCOVR was launched in February 2015. It now sits a million miles away from Earth at the L1 Lagrange Point, a spot between the Earth and the sun where gravitational and centrifugal forces are in balance and a satellite can remain in equilibrium,

The DSCOVR satellite sometimes captures an image of the
Moon passing between itself
and the Earth.

orbiting the sun in tandem with the Earth.

Onboard the satellite are three instruments, that work with information from other satellites to provide the full-sphere view of Earth as well as accurate information about our ozone, dust, cloud cover, vegetation, and volcanic ash—all important aspects in our study of climate change. Most significantly, DSCOVR provides for the first time a complete energy budget for the Earth, and monitors how much of the planet's energy from the sun is sent back out into space.

All these elements are what led to the idea of the DSCOVR satellite. Not just the desire for full pictures of our planet and our home, but also the amazing scientific data gathering that can be achieved from that special point in space. We had a real opportunity in the 1990s to start building enough public support to really get on track to solving the climate crisis. We lost that opportunity and we cannot afford to lose it again.

Just like Apollo 17 did several decades ago with the *Blue Marble* photograph, DSCOVR and satellites like it give us the means of getting an accurate view of our planet, and the data and inspiration we need to protect it. Let's use it. ◉

**DSCOVR'S POSITION RELATIVE
TO THE EARTH**

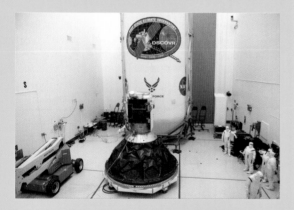

**Engineers prepare to launch
the DSCOVR satellite.**

TRUTH TO POWER

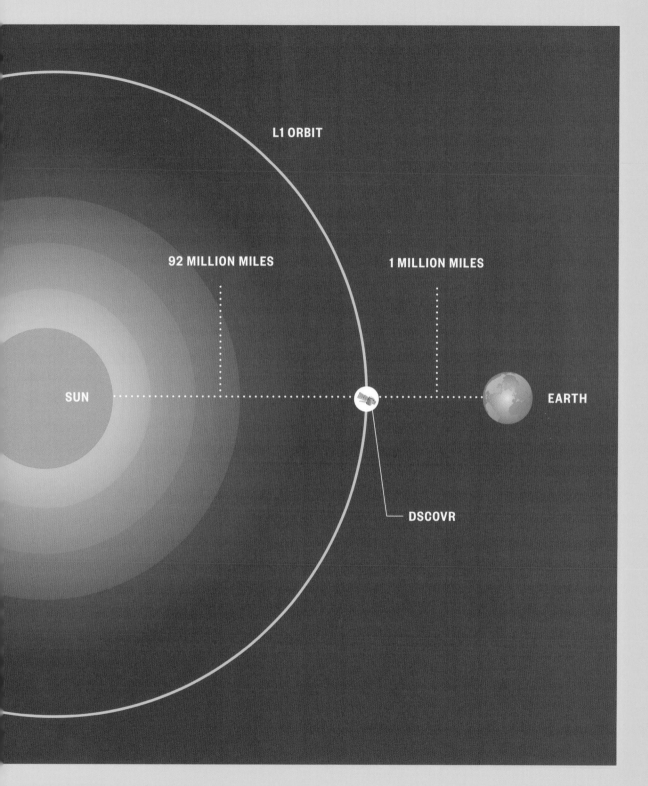

L1 ORBIT

92 MILLION MILES

1 MILLION MILES

SUN

EARTH

DSCOVR

Accord De Paris c'est

In December 2015, representatives of virtually every nation in the world gathered in Paris to address the climate crisis. They all pledged to work together to achieve net zero greenhouse gas emissions as early in the second half of this century as possible. This was a historic agreement.

I was relieved when I got to Paris because there were influential men and women from countries around the world with whom I'd had the privilege of working, some of whom had been through my training program. They asked me to help make the conference a success.

To celebrate the Paris Agreement's entering into force, the Eiffel Tower is lit up with the words "The Paris Accord is done."

Paris, France
November 4, 2016

169

What is the Paris Climate Agreement?

195 countries signed a pledge to keep global temperature rise below 2°C (3.6°F), and, if possible, below 1.5°C (2.7°F).

▶ All countries agree to reduce global greenhouse gas emissions to net zero as soon as possible in the second half of the century.

▶ The U.S. pledged to reduce greenhouse gas emissions by 26 to 28 percent below 2005 levels by 2025.

▶ India aims to install 175 gigawatts of renewable energy capacity by 2022.

▶ China will peak its CO_2 emissions by 2030.

▶ Developed countries will provide $100 billion in climate finance by 2020.

▶ Countries should raise the ambition of their initial commitments over time to make sure we meet the goals of the Paris Agreement.

▶ The Paris Agreement entered into force on November 4, 2016.

Celebrating the successful
conclusion of negotiations.

Le Bourget, Paris, France
December 12, 2015

Christiana Figueres

Former Executive Secretary of the United Nations Framework Convention on Climate Change (UNFCCC) and a Climate Reality Leader

SAN JOSÉ, COSTA RICA

IN THE EARLY 1990S, when Christiana Figueres's daughters were young, she became preoccupied by the extinction of *Incilius periglenes*, better known as the golden toad. The golden toad had been a beautiful, bright-orange species native to the forests of Figueres's home country, Costa Rica, and its loss seemed to her emblematic of the deteriorating Earth she would someday pass on to her children.

"I was profoundly impacted by having witnessed the disappearance of a species," she said. "It was then that I started learning about climate change, and I have been passionate about it ever since."

Figueres had been thinking about sustainable lifestyles for a long time. Years earlier, before she studied social anthropology at the London School of Economics, her undergraduate work at Swarthmore College in Pennsylvania brought her to a remote Costa Rican village in the Talamanca Mountains, where she spent time with the indigenous residents. The experience, working with people who had no electricity or running water, permanently informed her outlook on the environment.

"Indigenous populations are some of the most vulnerable populations to climate change, but they are also treasure troves of responsible land use and water management practices," she said. "We can all learn from their wisdom and long-standing experience. We can all gather insights from them on the

natural resource balance which we have destroyed and must reestablish."

But it was the episode with the golden toad that galvanized Figueres, whose mother had been an ambassador and legislator, and whose father served as the president of Costa Rica for three periods between the 1940s and the 1970s. In her parents' footsteps, she set out to become a leader for environmental progress.

To do so, Figueres chose a life of diplomacy. In 1995, she joined Costa Rica's climate change negotiating team at the United Nations Framework Convention on Climate Change (UNFCCC)—the group tasked, essentially, with negotiating a way for the world to avoid environmental collapse. Simultaneously, she founded the Center for Sustainable Development of the Americas, a nonprofit that advocated for financial systems that would promote sustainable development in the Caribbean and Latin America.

In 2007, Figueres attended the second-ever Climate Reality Training in Nashville, Tennessee. In 2010, she was appointed to run the Secretariat, the group that runs the UNFCCC. In that position, Figueres has acquired a reputation as a dynamo—skilled in the art of diplomacy but willing to push hard to convince the group's 195 member nations that the climate crisis is genuine and immediate.

The now-extinct golden toad.

"I'm very comfortable with the word 'revolution,'" Figueres told *The New Yorker* in 2015. "In my experience, revolutions have been very positive."

A key component of Figueres's strategy in that position has been empathy. She understands that Costa Rica's hydropower and wind resources give it an incentive to promote climate progress that not every country enjoys—especially not those with significant fossil fuel resources.

Figueres is known as an avid distance runner and dancer who tends to take public transit to work. In the wake of the Paris Agreement, she has set her sights on convincing world leaders to seize control of climate emissions by 2020, a year that scientists see as the deadline to accelerate CO_2 reductions in order to protect the world's most vulnerable populations from the worst impacts of climate change.

"We have not reached the turning point of greenhouse gas emissions," she said. "Industrialized countries must continue to decrease their emissions."

In sum, she sees the global community as having earned a mixed report card over the past 25 years. On one hand, she sees the implementation of the Kyoto Protocol and the Paris Agreement and the substantial investments and price reductions in renewable technologies as triumphs. On the other, she worries that the slowing of the temperature increase hasn't been enough to avoid the worst of the global climate change fallout.

Remembering the golden toad, she says, she draws hope from the legacy of the Earth that she'll leave behind for her children.

"We cannot afford the luxury of not being hopeful," she said. "This is a challenge we must face and conquer. Succeeding in arresting climate change is the only option we have. And success always starts with optimism." ◉

Even though President Trump has slashed federal programs to reduce emissions, U.S. businesses are moving ahead on their own. Many cities—and 36 states—have set renewable energy portfolio standards or goals.

CHANGE IN CALIFORNIA GDP AND GHG EMISSIONS SINCE 2000

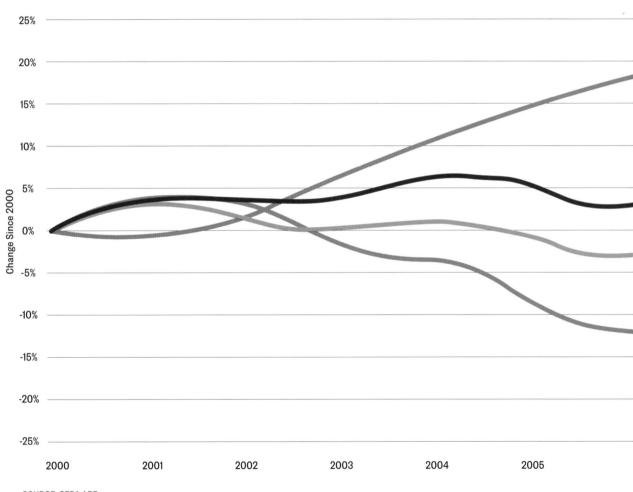

Change Since 2000

SOURCE: CEPA ARB

Their actions show that economies
can reduce emissions and still
grow. California leads the way—
as its economy and population
have grown, its greenhouse gas
emissions have fallen. The state
has pledged to reduce emissions
by 40 percent by 2030, compared
to its 1990 levels.

■ GDP
■ GHG EMISSIONS
■ GHG EMISSIONS PER CAPITA
■ GHG EMISSIONS PER GDP

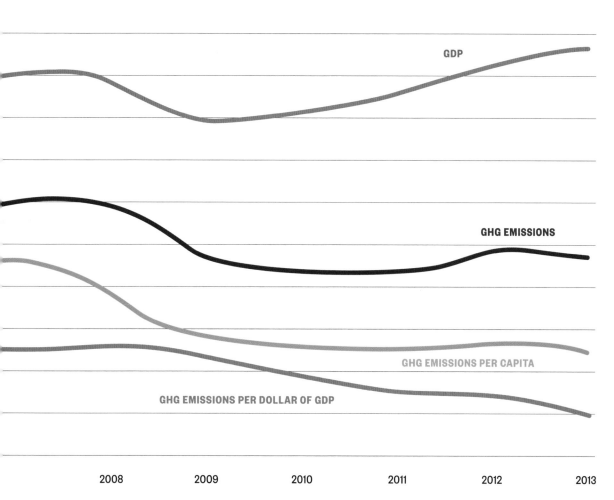

GDP

GHG EMISSIONS

GHG EMISSIONS PER CAPITA

GHG EMISSIONS PER DOLLAR OF GDP

2008   2009   2010   2011   2012   2013

TRUTH T

O POWER

This section presents a blueprint for what you can do personally to hasten the solution to the climate crisis. As you may have noticed, the year 2017 has already been marked by an enormous upsurge in political activism in the United States, especially on the part of the many millions of Americans who strongly oppose the policies and proposals of the Trump administration.

The first part of this book presented the evidence for why it is so important that we quickly shift from dirty, highly polluting, fossil fuel–powered electricity generation to renewable sources of energy. The existential threat we are facing also makes it important that we shift to sustainable agriculture, sustainable forestry, electric vehicles, LEDs, efficient and affordable energy storage, and the introduction of hyper-efficiency in the way we use energy and materials. But in order to accomplish this transformation of human civilization in time to avoid the catastrophic consequences of the climate crisis, it is imperative that individual citizens become actively engaged in the struggle for the future of humanity.

Political will is a renewable resource, but it can only be renewed with the passionate involvement of individuals around the world who are willing to put time and energy toward learning the best ways to encourage political and business leaders at every level of society

It is imperative that individual citizens become actively engaged in the struggle for the future of humanity.

to make these changes a priority—and then take action.

This section of the book is designed to be a "how to" guide for those who want to become effective advocates for solving the climate crisis. It includes sections on how to encourage others to vote, how to most effectively influence the elected officials that represent you at the local, state, and national level, how to translate your passion into a successful strategy for changing minds and hearts—and how to persuasively press for the changing of laws and policies.

There continues to be a lot of resistance to doing the right thing, and it is important to understand the reasons so many are still reluctant to accept the urgency of the changes we must make. For starters, many people choose inaction because it is simply easier to embrace any available doubt that

Demonstrators from around the globe demand world leaders take climate change seriously.

New York, New York
September 21, 2014

serious change is truly necessary.

Unfortunately, powerful and wealthy special interests whose business models would be severely harmed by a speedy reduction in our dependence on fossil fuels have a sophisticated understanding of our vulnerability to this doubt. And in order to exploit that vulnerability, they have spent enormous sums of money to sow confusion by distributing an endless stream of falsehoods about the crisis and about the availability of solutions.

Scholars have documented the cynical process by which the carbon polluters have pursued this massive disinformation campaign. We can see with great granularity how the deniers have adapted the blueprint from a similar effort decades earlier by the cigarette manufacturers who, for 40 years, successfully delayed recognition of the scientific and medical consensus linking smoking to lung cancer and other diseases of the lungs and heart.

In their ongoing effort to cultivate paralyzing doubt about the reality of the growing disruption of the Earth's climate pattern, carbon polluters have also developed a robust alliance with ideologically motivated advocates for radical reductions in the role of government at all levels—or, as President Donald Trump's controversial associate Stephen Bannon said in early 2017, "the deconstruction of the administrative state."

Ironically, special interests have such an unhealthy degree of influence over governments at every level that the "administrative state" now subsidizes the burning of fossil fuels in the U.S. at a rate 25 times larger than the meager subsidies for renewables, and often impedes the transition to a sustainable future. As a result, the changes we need will not necessarily result in an increase in the role of government at all, but require instead a redefinition and redirection of the role government plays.

In order to bring about the changes we need, activists need to focus not only on communicating the truth about the climate crisis and the readily available solutions, but they must also focus on learning how to wield political power—the healthy and liberating form of power that democracy puts in the hands and hearts of every citizen who wants to exercise it.

Take, for example, the laws now in place in the state of Florida that were written by lobbyists for the powerful

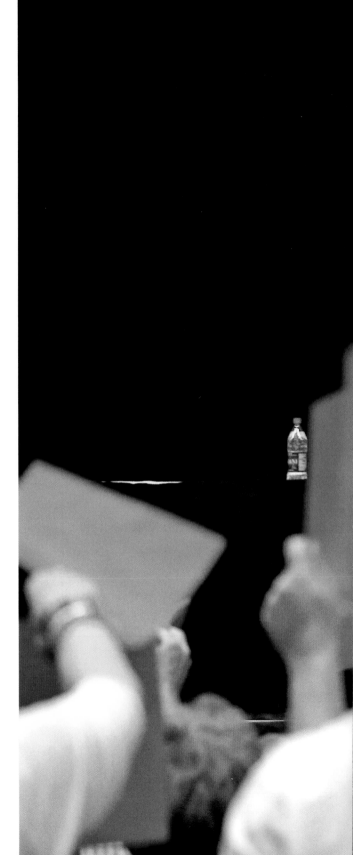

Arizona Senator Jeff Flake
answers questions at a town
hall while the audience holds up
red cards in disagreement.

Mesa, Arizona
April 13, 2017

181

fossil fuel–burning utilities there. At the present time, if an individual homeowner wishes to lease solar panels for his or her rooftop, Florida's state government forces them under power of law to abandon any such dream—unless they contact the fossil fuel–burning utility that serves their neighborhood, asks them for permission to lease a solar panel, and then pays money to the utility. If citizens of Florida can find a way to eliminate that onerous and ridiculous law, they will diminish the role of government, rather than increasing it. It is, again, a question of power. Who has the power? Voters or special interests?

Recently, when Floridians eager to generate their own electricity from their own rooftops—and exert their independence from the monopoly power of the utilities—complained that Florida is, after all, the "Sunshine State," the head of one of the two largest utilities replied, "We are the Sunshine State, but we're also the partly cloudy state."

American democracy has been hacked. Elected representatives of the people have too often become obedient, obsequious servants of the utility companies. At the same time, the utilities also spend large sums of money to flood the airwaves with deceptive television and radio advertisements intended to brainwash viewers into passivity and fool them into thinking that the utilities have their best interests at heart—when actually, the utilities are simply using falsehoods to increase their profits and executive bonuses.

There are many other examples of what is happening to Florida throughout the United States and in many nations around the world. And tragically, many legislators have learned that if they stay on the "gravy train" provided by special interests, they can rely on those interests to fool voters into thinking that they are being well represented, and persuade them to reelect their dishonest representatives over and over again—even if those representatives never lift a finger to serve the public interest.

However, in the dawning age of the Internet and social media, individual voters are beginning to awaken to the way special interests have taken advantage of the general public. As a result, we are now witnessing the beginnings of a nonviolent political revolution in which

Rex Tillerson, former CEO of ExxonMobil, after being sworn in as Secretary of State.

—

Washington, D.C.
February 1, 2017

TRUTH TO POWER

American democracy has been hacked.

citizens are starting to take back control of their own destiny and are demanding that those they elect to serve the public interest actually do so.

If you want to join this revolution—and I hope you do—what follows is a practical guide to how you can save the future. As you will see, different people find different paths. Each of us has our own areas of interest and we all naturally choose different ways to help win the battle for our future.

Once you make the basic decision to get involved, you will discover the best ways that you can be effective. But remember, as Goethe once wrote, "It is not enough to know; we must also apply; it is not enough to will, we must also do." The truth can set us free, and once free, we must act. ◉

Be an Involved Citizen

There are a number of ways individuals can have a surprisingly big impact on elected officials at every level of government. I used to be an elected official, and I know a little bit about what works. The secret is to make it unmistakably clear that their positions and actions related to solving the climate crisis will absolutely determine whether you (and everyone you can influence) will either:

A strongly support them for election or reelection

B do everything in your power to make certain they are defeated in the next election.

Delegates voting to nominate
candidates for the 2016 election.

1. Register to vote and help get others to vote too.

Over 40 percent of the eligible voting population did not vote in the 2016 presidential election. Stay registered no matter what—every election counts.

▶ Find out how you can register at usa.gov/register-to-vote.

Encourage all of your friends and other people in your social network to register, and then make sure they vote on election day. You can consult resources like Rock the Vote, Project Vote, NextGen Climate, and League of Conservation Voters to learn more about getting out the vote.

2. Find your elected officials.

In addition to the president, you are represented by members of the U.S. House and Senate at the federal level, your governor and state legislators at the state level, and your mayor and local officials in your city and county.

▶ To learn who represents you at each level, visit usa.gov/elected-officials.

3. Learn how they vote.

It's important to understand how your representatives vote on climate issues. This will help you better understand their commitments and dictate how you engage them.

▶ Visit online voting scorecards such as Scorecard.LCV.org or GovTrack.us.

4. Call, tweet, and write to your elected officials.

Once you've learned the names of your lawmakers, you can reach them through the congressional switchboard by calling (202) 225-3121 and telling the operator to whom you wish to be connected. Save this number in your phone so that you can call them regularly.

Calling members of Congress is one of the most effective things you can do as an engaged citizen. Congressional staffers will tell you how important these calls are in helping lawmakers understand where their constituents stand. The number of calls an office receives has a significant impact on how a representative votes on a piece of legislation. With that said, any sort of contact with your officials strengthens our democracy.

Republican Congressman Rodney Davis now supports finding solutions for the climate crisis.

Springfield, Illinois
August 14, 2014

Call your elected officials.

Very rarely, you will be able to talk directly to an elected official, but it's most likely that you will speak to a staff person. When calling, it's important to let them know exactly what issue you're calling about and concisely tell them your position. Most of the time the staffer will simply be recording the number of calls they receive on a given issue, so there is no need to speak at length and you shouldn't feel pressured to carry on a conversation. Be polite, but by all means be forceful and make it unmistakably clear that you are passionate about this issue and that your network of friends will be tuned in to exactly what the elected official does or does not do relevant to climate. And get others to call too. Numbers matter.

SAMPLE CALL SCRIPT

TO CALL REGARDING A GENERAL ISSUE

"Hello, my name is [YOUR NAME], from [YOUR CITY], and I'm calling to urge Representative/Senator/Governor/Mayor etc. [   ] to advocate for genuine solutions to climate change. This is important to me because [VERY SHORT REASON]."

TO CALL REGARDING A VOTE ON A BILL

"Hello, my name is [YOUR NAME], from [YOUR CITY]. I'm a constituent and I'm calling to urge Representative/Senator/Governor/Mayor etc. [   ] to vote yes/no on bill [####]. This is important to me because [VERY SHORT REASON]."

A man holding a ballot gets ready to vote.

Cottonwood Falls, Kansas
November 8, 2016

Tweet your elected officials.
Members of Congress and other elected officials also pay careful attention to replies and mentions on their Twitter accounts, especially when they come from people who clearly identify themselves as constituents. One study showed that even a few dozen tweets from constituents on a given issue was enough to get the office's attention. ◉

SAMPLE TWEET

Dear @[YOUR OFFICIAL'S TWITTER HANDLE], I'm a constituent. Please vote NO on any bill that would lead to more burning of dirty coal.

See page 204 for more about using social media as a climate activist.

Senator Lamar Alexander
455 Dirksen Senate Office Building
Washington, DC 20510

July 28, 2017

Clearly state the bill name or number you are writing about in the first sentence

Dear Senator Alexander,

Identify yourself as a constituent and include relevant information about yourself, like profession, if you're a parent, veteran, etc.

I'm writing to urge you to support the Global Warming Solutions Act of 2017, which takes an important step toward reducing carbon emissions that cause climate change.

As a constituent and parent of young children, I am very concerned about the future of our planet.

NASA recently confirmed that the Earth has set record high temperatures for three years in a row. There is no time to waste. Congress must take bold action to hold corporations accountable and move toward renewable energy sources, which will be a boon to our economy as well as our environment.

Tie it to current news

We are making progress to solve the climate crisis, but our political leaders must act. Please take the next step by voting yes on the Global Warming Solutions Act.

Sincerely,
Jefferson Smith
350 Green Terrace
Nashville, TN 37221

Make sure your voice is heard.

Win the conversation.

A woman asks a question of Senator Lindsey Graham at a town hall meeting.

—

Columbia, South Carolina
March 25, 2017

Speak at a Town Hall Meeting or Forum

One of the most effective ways to influence your elected officials is to speak to them face-to-face in town hall meetings or at other open forums. Members of Congress and local elected leaders want to know which issues are most important to their constituents, and taking the time to show up in person communicates to them that you are serious about addressing climate change at the municipal, state, and federal level. Even if you're a little nervous about public speaking, with a little preparation you can make a big impact. This is what speaking truth to power is all about.

1. Make your concern about the climate personal.

Successful climate activists are experts at connecting their personal stories and concerns to the greater issues of climate change. It's important you pick an issue that affects you and your community personally.

Here are some ideas:
▶ Promote clean air by asking that municipal vehicles be transitioned to electric vehicles or hybrids.
▶ Make sure your tax money isn't contributing to climate change by asking that municipal buildings transition to solar or wind power.

Paying attention to the climate and environmental issues being discussed in your community and at the state and national levels may provide some good ideas for how you can get involved.

One example is The Climate Reality Project's 100% Committed campaign: encourage your city, business, or university to commit to using 100 percent renewable electricity.

▶ Learn more at climaterealityproject .org/content/roadmap-100.

Governments everywhere should put a price on carbon that reflects the true costs we all pay for global warming pollution and incentivizes the transition to a clean energy economy.

▶ To learn more about this, visit the Climate Reality website at climaterealityproject.org for best practices on designing such a policy.

You can also focus on related issues, but remember to mention climate early in your remarks.

QUICK TIP

If your city doesn't have a climate task force, maybe it's time to form one! *See page 252 for information on running for office.*

2. Find the right opportunities to speak and engage with elected officials.

Organize or join local groups, like the Indivisible chapter in your community (see page 284), to engage the political system at town halls, public events, district offices, rallies, marches, and relevant city council or committee meetings. See if there is a specific municipal council or body focused on issues related to energy and the climate. Find out if you need to do anything in advance to speak at these events or just show up ready to contribute.

3. Prepare to speak.

Remember that in most town hall meetings and local forums like city council meetings, speakers are typically expected to speak for only a few minutes, so make your point quickly and effectively. In order to have the most impact, you may want to consider doing the following to prepare:

▶ Plan out your remarks ahead of time, and write them down to help commit them to memory. Make your most important point early in your remarks.
▶ Practice in front of friends or family to get feedback, and time yourself to make sure you're within the time constraints.
▶ It's important the committee knows you're an active member of the community. If you're a business owner, parent, veteran, faith leader, medical professional, or educator, make sure to include this information in your presentation.
▶ Bring a visual aid or two, whether it's a prop or a poster board with some key facts or graphs, to help you make your point.

▶ You want to feel confident and make a good impression. You don't need to wear a suit, but dress professionally and avoid wearing political T-shirts or buttons unrelated to the cause you are speaking about.

4. Bring backup. There's strength in numbers.

In order to win over your officials, you've got to persuade them that this issue is not only important to you, but to many others in your community. If possible, it's a good idea to bring friends and family to show support for your presentation. Don't be shy about asking them to clap or vocally agree during and immediately following your presentation.

5. Then, when the time is right, speak up!

There's nothing to worry about. As a climate activist, you know the science is on your side. Arrive early and take a seat somewhere with easy access to the aisle. When your name is called or when your raised hand is called upon, take a deep breath, and give your presentation. The more you speak up, the more comfortable you will get, and the more effective you will be. ◉

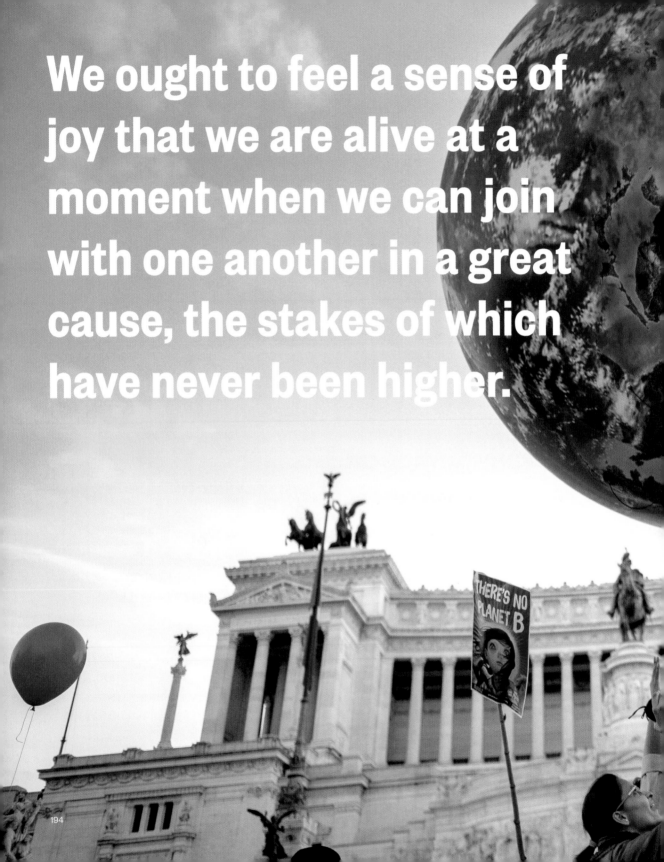

We ought to feel a sense of joy that we are alive at a moment when we can join with one another in a great cause, the stakes of which have never been higher.

Demonstrators throw a giant
Earth balloon during the COP21
climate change meetings.

Rome, Italy
November 29, 2015

The Greenville News

Paris Agreement Can Grow U.S. Jobs

By Ryan Popple
CEO, Proterra – Guest

Two actions inside of the Trump White House are converging: First, President Trump has met with leading CEOs several times since his term began. Why? Because he wants to restore U.S. manufacturing jobs, a message he forcefully reiterated during his address to Congress in February. Second, Trump's recent Energy Independence executive order, while dialing back some of former President Obama's climate policies, did not specifically address the US's participation in the Paris Agreement. What do these two seemingly unconnected events have in common? Everything.

I'm the CEO of the leading manufacturer of electric buses, Proterra. We employ 150 talented South Carolinians to manufacture American-made, all-electric city transit buses that out-perform our Chinese competitors. Buses manufactured in Greenville are now serving mass transit routes throughout the country – riders in Nashville, Seattle, Louisville, Stockton, Los Angeles County, Park City, Tallahassee and Seneca, SC are all safely transported on clean, quiet Proterra buses. In 2016 alone, our six buses in South Carolina drove 175,000 miles while saving nearly 44,000 gallons of diesel. And with a backlog that totals nearly 300 buses, we've developed the future of the U.S. transit market. Within 10 years, I doubt any city in the U.S. will buy a fossil-fuel transit bus. EV is just too efficient, too good, too affordable. South Carolina should be very proud that the EV transit trend started right here, with great engineers and manufacturing.

In addition to the 150 people employed at our Greenville manufacturing facility, Proterra has helped to create hundreds of other manufacturing jobs indirectly in South Carolina. We are American-made, through and through. Proterra buys approximately 22% of all components from within South Carolina. If we expand to the entire South East, Proterra buys approximately 36% of all components locally. Nearly 80% of all of our components come from other American companies. Buy America is in our DNA.

We're not alone in this jobs effort. Newer and cleaner technologies are producing thousands of more U.S. jobs, including in manufacturing. Indeed, clean energy jobs are booming—employing now over 3 million Americans. According to one recent source, there are more jobs now in the renewable energy space in 41 states and Washington, DC than in the coal, oil and gas sectors. Over 100,000 U.S. workers now manufacture, construct and maintain the U.S. wind turbine fleet. The solar workforce increased by 25% in 2016, while wind employment increased by 32%. Manufacturing jobs within the solar industry rose 26% in 2016 and now total nearly 40,000 jobs. And projections are that the growing demand for electric vehicles will mean tens of thousands of more jobs for Americans.

A lot of our neighbor companies and institutions in South Carolina are already competing effectively in the global energy technology market that is expected to grow to $6 trillion. As an example, South Carolina is a leader in hybrid and electric vehicle production. The vehicles that BMW manufactures in Spartanburg, SC use advanced materials, state-of-the-art batteries and energy efficiency software to lower fuel consumption without reducing driving performance. And several firms manufacture components and equipment that are vital to the generation and distribution of clean energy.

More locally, the Upstate is a case study in why restoring manufacturing is the key to economic health. Thanks to forward-thinking leaders, the region decades ago invested in and attracted value-added manufacturing. The results have been phenomenal, and have led to a synergy among business, community and universities. We are proud to be part of this success story.

Unfortunately, outside of the clean energy sector, we have seen a tremendous loss of manufacturing jobs. As President Trump has noted, since 2000, the United States has lost more than 5 million manufacturing jobs and witnessed the closing of more than 60,000 factories. I agree with the President that we cannot afford to lose any more manufacturing jobs. But I disagree that more coal is the answer.

The Palmetto State agrees. In its September 2015 Final Report, the SC Clean Energy Industry Manufacturing Market Development Advisory Commission found that the State "is advantageously poised to capture a considerable portion of the growing clean energy manufacturing sector thanks to its skilled and growing manufacturing workforce, strategic location on the east coast and world renowned research infrastructure." Notably, the Report made clear that U.S. manufacturing and sustainability efforts were not mutually exclusive.

So what does any of this have to do with the Paris Agreement? It means that 190 countries have committed, in writing, to reducing their greenhouse gas emissions based on their own national plans. They will need to buy clean energy products (solar panels, wind turbines, electric vehicles and more) to meet their commitments under the Agreement—and those products should be made in the U.S. American companies like Proterra and thousands of others can employ millions of U.S. workers—including South Carolinians—to build advanced energy products and stamp them "Made in America" for export around the globe.

For all of these reasons, CEOs like me believe the U.S. should remain a part of the Paris Agreement, which involves action by all countries. I also am committed to increasing U.S. manufacturing jobs, in the Upstate and across our operations in the U.S. The two objectives are inextricably linked. Instead of allowing our global competitors to take advantage of the Paris Agreement, selling foreign products to countries that are trying to meet their emissions reductions goals, we should be out there competing for that work. Our foreign competitors are playing to win. We should be too.

(The piece originally appeared in The Greenville News, Sunday, April 2, 2017)

Write about Climate Effectively

By writing articles, opinion pieces, and letters to the editor, your reasonable, science-based arguments and personal stories can reach a massive audience and help counter misinformation about climate change—especially if your writing goes viral online. Influence and impact is within the reach of anyone who can write persuasively and passionately. Lawmakers, CEOs, and other leaders pay careful attention to the opinion pages of local and national papers, making them an important venue for persuading powerful people and affecting public discourse.

Even though special interests have more influence in our democracy than ever before, the opinions of voters can still carry the day—if enough people speak out passionately. You don't need any special qualifications or even a lot of experience to get published. Here are some best practices that will dramatically increase your chances.

1. Be timely.

The first question any opinion editor will ask when you submit a piece is, "Why is this relevant now?" With few exceptions, most pieces that are accepted are tied to a breaking news story or a hot-button issue that is generating discussion locally or globally. Look for opportunities to enter the conversation quickly, before the public focus moves on to the next topic. Pick a topic that you're passionate about and that you have something to add to. Here are some ideas:

▶ A local ballot measure, piece of legislation, or other policy issue.
▶ A personal story about what you are doing to reduce your own carbon footprint.
▶ An important racial, social, or economic justice issue that intersects with climate change and environmental protection.
▶ Criticism for elected officials who are failing to address climate issues or praise for those who are showing courage and leadership.

2. Be concise.

Research guidelines for letters to the editor and other pieces before submitting one. For an op-ed, 600 to 800 words

Even though special interests have more influence in our democracy than ever before, the opinions of voters can still carry the day— if enough people speak out passionately.

is standard, while letters to the editor are generally 100 to 300 words. Lengthy pieces may be dismissed outright, no matter how good your writing or argument. Some outlets accept longer-form pieces, but often not as unsolicited submissions. More important is your reader's attention span. You're more likely to reach a broad audience with a piece that is short, clear, and to the point.

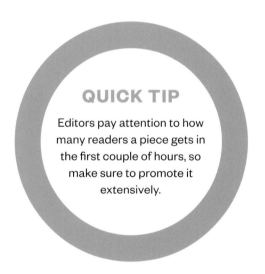

QUICK TIP

Editors pay attention to how many readers a piece gets in the first couple of hours, so make sure to promote it extensively.

3. Support your argument.

Back up your points with concrete examples and evidence. Avoid hyperbole and exaggeration. If you state your points clearly and calmly while providing proof for your claims, your argument will be more convincing, especially for the most skeptical readers. It's also a good idea to refer to your personal experience and story.

4. Know your audience.

Put yourself in your audience's shoes and think about the arguments, sources, and tone that would be most convincing to them.

5. Pick the best outlet.

Choose your publication well. Which outlet will be most credible to your audience? Members of Congress, for example, are influenced by pieces appearing in local papers within their district as well as Beltway outlets like *The Hill* and *Politico*. *The Huffington Post* and *The Guardian* are well respected, but if you're reaching across the aisle, they may not be the best home for your op-ed. National papers like *The New York Times* and *The Washington Post* have a wide reach, but submitting to them is extremely competitive.

6. Get feedback.

Always try to get a second opinion before submitting your piece. If you're trying to reach a specific audience, get feedback from a member of that group. Even just having a friend or family member look over your piece can ensure an editor doesn't pass you over because of a simple spelling or grammatical error. If you don't have someone else who can review it, sleep on it and take a second look in the morning before you hit send. ◉

Start a Petition

The First Amendment says that no law shall prohibit the right of people "to petition the government for a redress of grievances." Nowadays, it has become common practice for people to unite in an expression of support or reproach for a government official or organization. Petitions can directly affect policies or signal to leaders how strongly constituents or customers feel about a particular issue. Every signature adds weight to the concern. If you're a budding climate activist, petitions are also a great way to build a community of like-minded people.

The Climate Reality Project helps deliver these 2.1 million comments to the EPA.

Washington, D.C.
June 25, 2012

2.1 MILLION COMMENTS
to Cut Carbon Pollution

1. Identify your target.

Direct your petition to whoever has the most direct influence on the issue. For government concerns, this might be a representative voting on a bill. For corporate concerns, this might be a CEO, large shareholder, or the company's sustainability department.

2. Craft a compelling and concise message.

State the problem and desired outcome clearly, so everyone understands the "so what." Use short sentences and don't go over 200 words. Offer a deadline to create urgency and news clips to show the issue is a subject of public interest.

3. Circulate widely.

Your petition's success lies in getting it out there. Use social media networks to post and share the link. Share around your school or office as well. Bring paper petitions to meetings, or organize signature drives at local businesses, farmers' markets, and events.

4. Deliver.

If your petition is online, it is easy to bring your message to its recipient: hit send. Make sure your petitioners use their social media to follow up with the person or organization you are petitioning. If you have paper to deliver, mailing is an option. Or consider delivering it at an important event, like a shareholders meeting or a press conference.

Taken together, these steps can drive great momentum for your cause and your community. Keep your petitioners close, thank them for their participation, and constantly involve them in your future projects. ◉

Americans exercise their right to petition in opposition to a bank merger.

San Francisco, California
February 2, 2015

Establish Yourself as a Climate Activist Online

The Internet has changed the face of activism. Some of the most popular modern political movements started online through social media, blog posts, and email campaigns. You don't need to rearrange your life to be a climate activist. You can start or join a community of climate activists around the globe from your sofa, and then work together to encourage good science and advocate for protecting the Earth.

Ed Stafford updates his blog during his record-breaking 859-day Amazon River walk.

Amazon Jungle, Peru

1. Create social media accounts.

Social media sites provide powerful platforms for change-makers to educate the general public and influence political leaders. Facebook, Twitter, Instagram, Snapchat, Pinterest, and Tumblr all have their value, but you may not have time to maintain a presence on all of them. Keep your finger on the pulse: different platforms rise and fall in popularity, and different demographic audiences tend to prefer certain platforms over others.

2. Choose your best outlets.

Online activism takes many forms in many venues these days. Social media is a necessity; beyond those platforms, you may also want to establish a blog, create an email newsletter or mailing list, publish on a writing platform such as Medium, or explore new outlets and platforms just launching.

3. Show that you're a climate activist.

As you set up your accounts, establish yourself as an outspoken climate activist by putting your climate advocacy front and center in your username, profile picture, and bio. You can identify yourself as part of the broader movement by using a profile image "filter" like the Climate Reality Project's green ring.

▶ Include a link in your bio to your blog, if you have one, or to an informative climate-related website like climaterealityproject.org.

4. Use strong visuals.

Especially when you're starting out, photographs, videos, infographics, and memes help grab people's attention and increase sharing.

5. Follow other influencers.

Pay attention to what prominent climate experts, political leaders, NGOs, and journalists are saying and amplify their messages or reply with a different opinion.

6. Be creative.

Humor, wit, and creativity can go a long way in helping you reach an audience beyond your immediate circles.

7. Share facts and breaking news.

Become a source where your followers can find important news and analysis on local and national climate issues.

8. Post frequently.

There are best practices for each platform as to how often you should post, but at least a few times a day is usually safe. During key moments like a State of the Union address or a vote in Congress, you should post several times using appropriate hashtags, as many more people will be paying attention. ◉

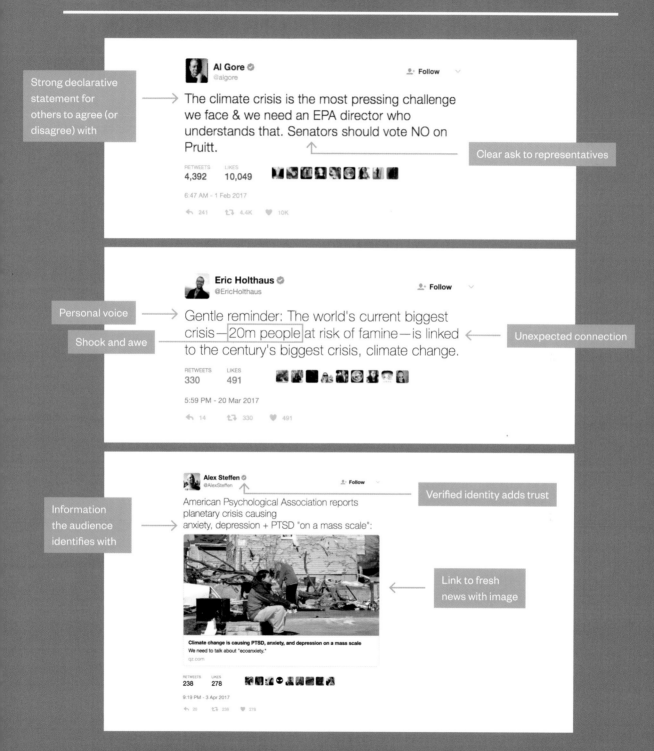

Strong declarative statement for others to agree (or disagree) with

Al Gore ✔
@algore

⬝ Follow ⌄

The climate crisis is the most pressing challenge we face & we need an EPA director who understands that. Senators should vote NO on Pruitt.

Clear ask to representatives

RETWEETS 4,392
LIKES 10,049

6:47 AM - 1 Feb 2017

↩ 241   ⟲ 4.4K   ♥ 10K

Eric Holthaus ✔
@EricHolthaus

⬝ Follow ⌄

Personal voice

Gentle reminder: The world's current biggest crisis—20m people at risk of famine—is linked to the century's biggest crisis, climate change.

Shock and awe

Unexpected connection

RETWEETS 330
LIKES 491

5:59 PM - 20 Mar 2017

↩ 14   ⟲ 330   ♥ 491

Alex Steffen ✔
@AlexSteffen

⬝ Follow ⌄

American Psychological Association reports planetary crisis causing anxiety, depression + PTSD "on a mass scale":

Verified identity adds trust

Information the audience identifies with

Climate change is causing PTSD, anxiety, and depression on a mass scale
We need to talk about "ecoanxiety."
qz.com

Link to fresh news with image

RETWEETS 238
LIKES 278

9:19 PM - 3 Apr 2017

↩ 20   ⟲ 236   ♥ 278

John Cook

Founder of Skeptical Science

BRISBANE, AUSTRALIA

BY 2007, JOHN COOK had grown so frustrated by endless arguments with his family over the existence of climate change that he began to maintain a list of dubious talking points they used against him, complete with counterexamples he could use to cut the altercations short.

The technique was so successful that he started to wonder if his list might be useful to others. After some consideration, he turned it into a remarkable website called Skeptical Science, which assembles common myths about climate change. Think "Then why is it cold out?" and "There is no consensus"—alongside meticulously researched rebuttals.

The site touched a cultural nerve, and it was just beginning to pick up steam when Cook got an email that would permanently alter the course of his life. The message was from a cognitive scientist, who praised the site, but forwarded a selection of psychological research on how to construct an argument that's maximally effective at changing hearts and minds.

For Cook, it was an epiphany. He realized that there was an entire body of research that studied the question of how to communicate complex ideas most effectively. Embarrassingly, it soon became clear that he'd been making missteps that an expert in the field would consider rather basic.

"I was doing what almost everyone does when they debunk myths," he said. "They emphasize the myth first. They usually use it as the headline, then talk about the facts later. What that does is make the myth more prominent, and it risks strengthening it."

Cook, who exudes a quiet intelligence, started to study with passion. At first he was just looking for tips to make entries on Skeptical Science more convincing, but he soon started to wonder if he might have found his calling. Eventually, he enrolled in a doctoral program at the University of Western Australia where he dove into intricate questions of communication theory—while continuing to maintain Skeptical Science on the side.

In the university system, Cook approached the challenge of communicating effectively with the same fervor he'd employed regarding climate change. He co-authored two books and penned a thesis about closing the "consensus gap" between the scientific case for climate change and public perception. He also served as the lead author on an influential paper, later tweeted by U.S. President Barack Obama, that quantified support for global warming among researchers.

Cook also developed a set of three guidelines that he believes are key to framing an argument as effectively as possible.

The first is to know your target readers. "The best audience is often not people who hold a different

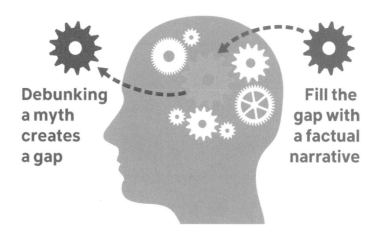

Debunking a myth creates a gap

Fill the gap with a factual narrative

Cook's website features visual aids like this illustration to help people address climate denial.

view," he said. "It's the undecided majority. Trying to convince a hardcore disbeliever is unlikely to have much impact."

The second is to carefully consider the key facts you want to communicate and to boil them down to their absolute essence. Cook uses the phrase "simple and sticky" to describe facts that have been reduced to a form so pure that they cut through the spin and lodge in readers' memories.

To describe his third guideline, Cook uses an example from immunology. Cook has found that if you explain to someone why a faulty argument is weak, the effect can be akin to vaccination. When they eventually come across a stronger form of the obfuscation, they'll be better equipped to argue against it.

For instance, researchers in 2017 found that if they'd exposed subjects to the idea that politically motivated groups use misleading tactics to convince the public that there's wide disagreement among scientists about global warming, those subjects

became less likely to believe similar false claims in the future.

"You need to inoculate people against misinformation," he said. "It's about exposing them to a weak form of the misinformation, so that the strong form won't influence them."

If you want to promote climate science in the public sphere, Cook recommends that you follow his guidelines—and, hearkening back to the roots of Skeptical Science, suggests that you take the issue up with those closest to you.

"One of the most trusted sources of information about climate change is friends and family," he said. "I would suggest that people speak from the heart on why this issue is important to them." ◉

To learn more about Cook's work, visit SkepticalScience.com.

I believe we have the capacity, at moments of great challenge, to set aside the causes of distraction and rise to the challenge that history is presenting.

Magnify Your Impact with Press Coverage

Understanding the media landscape, including knowing the prominent climate publications and journalists, is vital for driving attention to your activism. Take note of how journalists cover various causes to get a feel for what piques their interest. Use this insight to organize creative, attention-grabbing campaigns that journalists will be unable to ignore.

1. Build relationships with journalists—it's easier than you think.

Send an email or letter to the reporters who cover the environment in your area, or even those at national outlets who cover the environment. Follow them on Twitter, comment on their articles, or send them a quick email to thank them for their reporting on an important issue. They'll be more likely to remember you later when you ask them to cover your event or petition.

2. Alert the press.

If you are planning some newsworthy statement or event, keep reporters informed and give them notice so they can plan ahead. Remember that journalists are inundated with story ideas, so sometimes a quick email with just the key facts is as effective as a formal press release. Don't pester, but if you don't hear back after sending an email or release, follow up with a phone call to make sure they saw it.

3. Prepare for the possibility that you might be interviewed.

What is the most important message that you want people to take away from a radio interview or article in which you are quoted? Write down three or four key talking points, rehearse them, and stick to them no matter what. If a reporter asks you a question to which you don't know the answer, or that seems off topic, find a way to transition back to your talking points. They should be no more than a sentence or two long. Avoid rambling.

Sometimes you will be dealing with a reporter who is hostile to your position. Maintain your composure and don't show anger or frustration. If you stay calm, you'll look like the reasonable one to anyone watching. ◉

A demonstrator is interviewed during a sit-in coordinated by the Campaign Against Climate Change.

London, England
March 7, 2015

213

Tais Gadea Lara

Journalist and
Climate Reality Leader

BUENOS AIRES, ARGENTINA

WHEN TAIS GADEA LARA was a young girl living near Buenos Aires, she told her mother that she intended to be a journalist when she grew up.

Gadea Lara, now 29, has emerged over the past decade as an award-winning environmental journalist in Argentina's independent media: she's the co-founder of media project Conexión Coral, a TV reporter for *Efecto Mariposa* and *Hoy Nos Toca*, and writes for newspapers and magazines including *La Nación* and *Sophia*.

Gadea Lara now lives in Buenos Aires proper, though when we spoke she had just returned from an expedition to report on conservationists in Patagonia who are working to protect the hooded grebe, a critically endangered migratory bird. It's the type of story that epitomizes her wide-ranging oeuvre, mixing a deep concern for sustainability and the environment with a hopeful view of the role the public can take in shaping the future of the planet.

"What I try to do in every article is to be optimistic," she said. "There are a lot of people working on climate action, and it's helpful to show readers that there are people in their communities who are working on that."

That outlook underlies Gadea Lara's ethos as a journalist. She reports on the grave realities of climate change, but tries to counterbalance each story with examples of governments and citizens that have taken action for the public good.

Last year, for instance, Gadea Lara visited vulnerable communities on the outskirts of Buenos Aires that lacked access to electricity or hot water. She saw that community groups had stepped in to provide photovoltaic panels and bathing facilities, and she ended up writing a newspaper feature about efforts in Argentina to fight poverty by harnessing renewable resources.

This positivity is key, she believes, to engaging citizens of a developing economy who might otherwise see environmentalism as a luxury for wealthier nations. It's the same viewpoint that appealed to Gadea Lara when she attended South America's first Climate Reality Leadership Corps training program in Rio de Janeiro in 2014—the idea that, if we work together, it's not too late to save the world.

"I think the main job we have as journalists," she said, "is to tell people what they can do." ◉

To learn more about Gadea Lara's work, visit her website at TaisGadeaLara.com.

Gadea Lara interviews a man about the impact of climate change on his life during the COP22 Climate Conference.

Marrakesh, Morocco
November 6, 2016

When children ask questions about what's being done to their planet, parents are often moved to make changes.

Children take part in a country-wide effort to break the world record for most number of people planting trees simultaneously.

—

Catequilla Hill, Ecuador
May 16, 2015

Talk to Children about Climate Change

When I was a young child, my father taught me about soil conservation on our family farm. For me, that was the beginning of my awareness of and concern about the impact people have on the environment. If we can help children make sense of the environmental problems they're inheriting, they'll be better equipped to solve them. Start early, with simple concepts, and make sure to nurture an ongoing conversation.

1. Foster a love of nature.

Children who care for nature are more likely to become adults who do too. Teach children to respect the Earth and take responsibility for keeping it healthy by getting them outside as much as possible.

WHAT HAPPENED TO PLAYING OUTDOORS?
Almost three-quarters of today's mothers in the U.S. say they played outdoors every day as children, but only one-quarter say their kids do.

SOURCE: CONTEMPORARY ISSUES IN EARLY CHILDHOOD (2004)

Give children time and space to play.
Despite our culture's preference for cramming schedules with sports, music lessons, and playdates, children thrive on unstructured play. When left to their own devices outdoors, imagination takes off. Kids who feel free to love what they love, whether it's digging in the dirt or staring at clouds, are more likely to see outside time as something to look forward to rather than a boring activity.

Listen for and support children's preferences.
Talking to children about their time outside can be as important as discussing what they learned at school. When a child feels your interest, it helps them understand that outdoor experiences matter and will help them find creative ways to celebrate it.

Empower kids to find nature anywhere.
It's true that all cities are not created equal when it comes to open space. However, having lived both on a farm and in cities, and having helped raise children in both kinds of settings, I know what most parents know—that nature is all around us if we just take the time to look.

▶ Stroll around the neighborhood, listening for birds, watching for insects, and collecting "treasures" like leaves and rocks.
▶ Encourage activities like tree climbing and stargazing.
▶ Avoid the "look, don't touch" mentality. Promote a healthy curiosity about the natural world.
▶ Plan special trips to outdoor-oriented institutions like botanic gardens, arboretums, and parks.

2. Track your family's carbon footprint and waste.

Even young children can learn the basics of a carbon footprint. You can turn individual lessons and chores into a meaningful family activity by discussing your household's larger impact on the Earth.

Frame the discussion.
Explain the big picture of how household energy use adds up within the home as well as how individual homes contribute to the collective problem of global climate change. Impress upon children the importance of individual responsibility when it comes to ethical energy consumption. Teach them the basics about the global energy system, including the importance of energy efficiency and the advantages of renewable sources of energy compared to dirty fossil fuels.

Discuss how your household currently measures up.
Review your utility bills to find your average monthly usage. Visit an online carbon calculator like the one provided by the Environmental Protection Agency to learn the carbon footprint of your home. Based on what you find, set a goal for future savings.

Map out where you use energy.
Make it a game to seek out every way your house uses electricity. Watch for standby energy devices like computers or cable boxes, which suck energy even when they're not in use. *See page 261 to learn what to do with this problem.*

▶ For information visit: youth.zerofootprint.net and climatekids.nasa.gov.

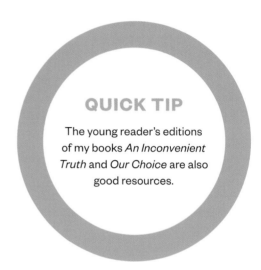

QUICK TIP

The young reader's editions of my books *An Inconvenient Truth* and *Our Choice* are also good resources.

3. Promote climate change education.

Over the past 20 years, environmental education programs have had major benefits, from improved critical thinking to increased civic engagement. Unfortunately, more often than not, climate change education is lacking. A recent survey found that 30 percent of science teachers who teach climate change tell students that it is "likely due to natural causes," while another

31 percent teach the issue as unsettled science. Parents should encourage teachers to resist the effort by climate deniers to undermine science.

Here are some suggestions you can make to your children's teachers, or use if you're a teacher yourself:

Turn to technology.
Teachers can bring science to life with engaging apps, like BBC's *Earth*, NASA's *Earth Now*, or WWF's *Together*, available on iTunes, Apple TV, Google Play, or your local cable television.

Bring in the arts.
Climate change is interdisciplinary. Art teachers can assign climate change posters. Creative writing teachers can assign poems on the subject.

Explore these climate and energy curriculum resources.
▶ climatekids.nasa.gov/menu/teach
▶ nwf.org/Eco-Schools
▶ eia.gov/kids/energy.cfm?page =teacher_guide ◉

Haven Coleman, a young Climate Reality Leader, asks her congressman about renewable energy policy at a town hall meeting.

—

Colorado Springs, Colorado
April 13, 2017

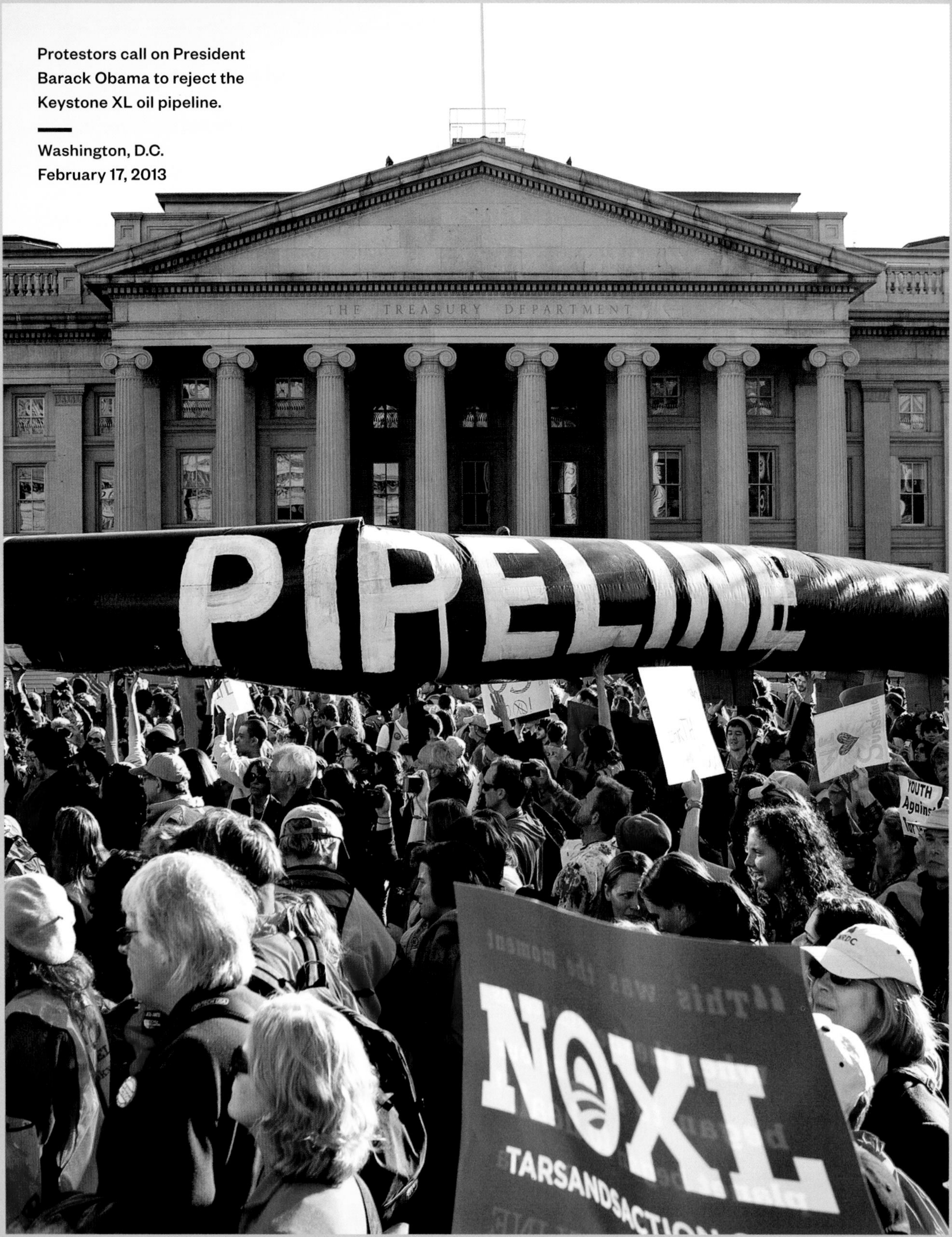

Protestors call on President Barack Obama to reject the Keystone XL oil pipeline.

Washington, D.C.
February 17, 2013

Harriet Shugarman

Founder of Climate Mama
and Climate Reality Leader

WYCKOFF, NEW JERSEY

HARRIET SHUGARMAN SPENT years building a career at the United Nations and the International Monetary Fund, where her environmental work included helping organize the first Earth Summit. But it wasn't until the births of her children that the magnitude of the climate crisis washed over her in full force.

"There was so much happiness, but also such a sense of responsibility," said Shugarman, who grew up in Alberta, where oil and gas are a large part of the economy. "Learning about the climate crisis, you might want to forget it, but you know it's real."

After the release of *An Inconvenient Truth*, Shugarman attended one of the first Climate Reality trainings in Nashville. When she returned to New York to deliver her own presentations at schools and community centers, she discovered that her identity as a mother gave her a powerful ethos as a speaker.

Though she'd spent many years working with diplomats and officials at the UN and the IMF, Shugarman recalls that her climate presentations gave her a new sense of effecting direct change in the world.

"It took me a year or two after giving presentations in my community to realize that I could speak in this really personal voice as a parent," she said. "I felt empowered."

As she discovered that voice, Shugarman founded an organization called Climate Mama that publishes information about environmentalism and advocacy aimed at parents—and has been recognized by the White House and the Environmental Protection Agency for its outreach efforts.

Shugarman also keeps busy as an activist. In 2011, she was arrested in Washington, D.C., at a protest against the Keystone XL Pipeline. She also teaches about climate change policy at New Jersey's Ramapo College, writes for national outlets including MSNBC and *The Huffington Post*, and until recently chaired the Environmental Commission and Green Team in the New Jersey town where her family lives.

"I am hopeful," she said, "because of the many amazing people I meet from the climate movement and the environmental movement and beyond. I'm hopeful because of my children. I can't let myself not be hopeful." ◉

To learn more about Shugarman's work, visit ClimateMama.com.

Tactics and Strategies of the Anti-Smoking Movement

HOW CAN CLIMATE ACTIVISTS challenge and counteract the propaganda coming from billion-dollar fossil fuel industries, as well as the constant denial from "skeptics"? The campaign against tobacco use shows us how difficult the challenge can be— but also what success can look like.

In 1998, the "truth" campaign was launched, with the goal of ending teen tobacco use. The theme of the campaign was exposing tobacco industry tactics that manipulated teen consumers—tactics that we now know were also adopted by large carbon polluters in the fossil fuels industry to mislead the public about the true causes of climate change. (Fittingly, the first years of funding came from a massive settlement between 46 U.S. states and the biggest tobacco companies.)

The truth campaign marked a significant change from prior anti-smoking campaigns, which had focused on negative health effects. Extensive research had shown that teens were not dissuaded from smoking by warnings about lung cancer and other consequences. So the truth campaign used a different approach in radio, television, and billboard advertising to cleverly highlight the blatant falsehoods of the tobacco companies and provoke teens to ask themselves a subversive question: "Am I being played for a fool and taken advantage of by these giant corporations?"

Additionally, it used "horizontal influence," meaning not a top-down, but peer-to-peer approach. The campaign coordinated regional youth-led groups called SWAT, Students Working Against Tobacco. According to a 2009 issue of the American Journal of Preventative Medicine, truth prevented 450,000 youth from starting to smoke within the first four years of the campaign.

In 2014, the Centers for Disease Control and Prevention launched the "TIPS" campaign to urge adult smokers to quit. The ads showcased former smokers suffering from tobacco-related illnesses giving "tips" to current smokers for how to handle the ailments when they start suffering from them. The campaign inspired almost two million people to quit over three years.

Corporate Accountability International (CAI) found success using boycotts against tobacco companies. CAI launched a boycott against Kraft products, owned by cigarette producer Philip Morris (now Altria; the campaign was so effective that the company changed its name!). The campaign particularly focused on boycotting Kraft Macaroni and Cheese to put pressure on the tobacco industry to end marketing targeted at young people. The boycott tarnished Kraft's image as a family brand. Boycotts have been effective in the climate movement too—for example a "switch your account" campaign led Bank of America to limit its financing of mountaintop removal coal mining practices.

The fossil fuel industry has misled much of the public into thinking climate change is not real— much like the cigarette companies promised us their product wasn't dangerous. The truth campaign show that through innovative and emotional activism and marketing, people can be persuaded. This achievement provides hope for making the truth about the climate crisis just as persuasive. ◉

Images from "The Sunny Side of Truth" campaign, launched in 2008.

Talk with Climate Deniers

Even though climate science is peer-reviewed, comprehensive, and well established, I know all too well that it is still a deeply polarizing subject. Climate deniers and those of us who accept the facts are sometimes pitted against one another at family gatherings, social occasions, and in the larger public discourse. It's important that you not only understand why this controversy persists (hint: it's manufactured) but also that you can confidently and meaningfully address these skeptics.

It is important to remember that this divisiveness has been purposefully engineered by oil, coal, and gas companies—and the politicians whose pockets they line. In Tennessee, we have an old saying, "If you see a turtle on top of a fencepost, you can be pretty sure it didn't get there by itself." In the same way, when you hear all the climate denial in the U.S., you can be pretty sure it didn't get there by itself either. Over the past few decades, large carbon polluters have invested heavily to "manufacture doubt" and advance obfuscation instead of science—in much the

same way the tobacco lobby successfully created doubt in the public's mind as to whether or not cigarettes cause cancer. Ultimately, they lost that battle, but not before they delayed public health responses to cigarette smoking by over 40 years. The carbon-polluting lobby is using their playbook to do the same where global warming is concerned.

It's now clear that Exxon Mobil knew about the climate consequences of burning fossil fuels beginning in the late 1970s—but instead of changing course based on its own research, the company instead poured millions into efforts to dupe the public about those consequences. We also know that President Donald Trump once called climate change a Chinese hoax (although he later claimed he was joking), and the man he appointed to head the Environmental Protection Agency, Scott Pruitt, even denied the most basic scientific finding concerning global warming: that CO_2 emissions trap heat in the atmosphere. That fact was proven by scientists more than 150 years ago!

These misinformation efforts have thus far been all too effective. They've obstructed progress by normalizing outright denial of science so effectively that the U.S. has more climate change deniers than any other country.

Don't be dissuaded if some denier says, "I don't want to talk about it." Don't let that stop you.

Speak up.

And they have created a political and cultural divide so deep that the very topic of global warming has become almost taboo for some to discuss in polite company. According to a 2015 study, 74 percent of Americans rarely, if ever, discuss climate change. It is difficult to dispel misinformation about something you are not supposed to talk about. This makes it all the more important for climate activists to break the silence and engage in civil debate with those who have been misled.

The goal of this section is not to encourage you to convince every climate denier you run into; it is to make you feel confident that if a lively debate is occurring, you're armed with the facts and reasoning to set the record straight. Rest assured that the science is on your side. You just have to remember some basic questions and responses, brought to you in part by the Climate Reality Project. SkepticalScience.com is also a fantastic resource for novel and effective ways of interacting with climate deniers.

1. How can there be global warming when it's snowing outside?

We still have winter—and we still have "natural variability." This means that the fluctuations from season to season and from day to day still exist. And that means that some days will still be cold. But if you look at the bell curves on pages 46 and 47, you will see that, on average, there has been an enormous increase in hot days and extremely hot days, while there has been a sharp decrease in the number of cold days. In fact, some say that's one of the reasons we notice the cold days a lot more when they do show up.

Global warming is about broader, long-term climate trends scientists are seeing around the world, as opposed to local weather patterns. Daily temperatures may rise and fall, but it's the long-term heating trend that matters. There are multiple signals of this long-term trend: winter comes later and spring comes earlier. Summers are longer and hotter. All of the natural systems of the Earth—including plants and animals—are forced to adjust to the dramatic changes underway. All of the ice-covered regions of the world are melting and sea level is rising. It is getting so hot in some regions of North Africa and the Middle East that scientists are now predicting that parts of the Earth that are now heavily populated will become uninhabitable.

2. Why do some deniers claim that the Earth has been cooling since 1998?

To begin with, all the temperature records around the world demonstrate very clearly that this assertion is completely false. It's true that 1998 was a warm year, and for a few years after 1998, its temperature record was not broken. However, the record set in 1998 has since been broken many times. The hottest year of all was 2016; the second hottest was the year before; the third hottest was the year before that. You can find the graph on pages 50–51. If the person claiming the world is cooling also tells you that the moon landing was faked, it might be time to end the conversation. But do

it respectfully and politely—just don't waste any more time.

3. How do you explain the fact that not all scientists agree the climate is changing?

Multiple peer-reviewed studies confirm that 97 percent of the world's top climate scientists publishing articles in peer-reviewed journals agree that man-made pollution is the principal cause of global

DENIERS CAN MISLEAD BY CHERRY-PICKING SHORT TIME FRAMES

Realist's view of global warming
Denier's view of global warming

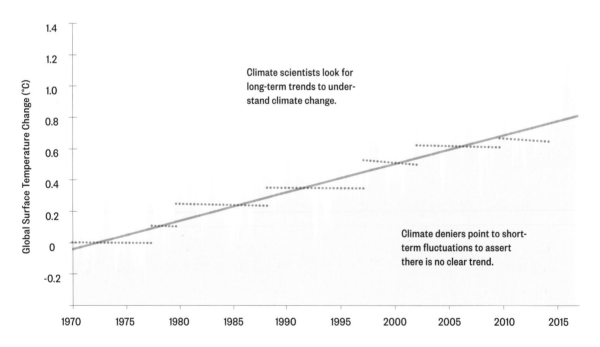

Climate scientists look for long-term trends to understand climate change.

Climate deniers point to short-term fluctuations to assert there is no clear trend.

SOURCE: SKEPTICALSCIENCE.COM

warming. In fact, during the past few years, less than 0.1 percent of climate research rejects the consensus. Every national academy of science in the world agrees, as does every major scientific organization. Several of the tiny group of scientists who disagree with the consensus have shadowy financial ties to the fossil fuel industry.

Here, I find an analogy works well. For example, if you have chest pains and were somehow able to get advice from the 100 leading heart doctors in the world, what would you do if 97 of the 100 expressed alarm and told you that you needed to go to the hospital right away? Would you do nothing because three of the 100 doctors say they just aren't sure and you don't need to do anything?

4. Natural cycles have always influenced planetary climate. How can you really believe humans could possibly have that much impact?

Humanity has become the largest force of nature affecting the ecological system of the Earth because of three factors working together: First, we have quadrupled our population in less than a century; second, we now have at our disposal technologies far more powerful than any that people in prior eras could

have dreamed of; and third, our obsession with short-term thinking in the new hyper-global economy has served to blind us to the impact of what we are doing—most of all in using the most vulnerable part of the Earth's system, the atmosphere, as an open sewer.

While it's true that natural cycles have an impact on climate, human activities are now overwhelming all of those natural cycles—primarily because we are spewing 110 million tons of man-made global warming pollution into the atmosphere every 24 hours and it is trapping as much extra heat energy as 400,000 Hiroshima-class atomic bombs exploding every day. But again, man-made global warming pollution now overwhelms all the natural factors put together.

5. Plants need carbon dioxide, and we need plants. So how is more CO_2 supposed to be a bad thing?

Carbon dioxide is necessary for life on Earth. We all need it to help retain the sun's heat, and plants of course need it to "breathe." Some plants, it's true, do appreciate an extra dose of carbon dioxide. But others are damaged by excess CO_2, which reduces the level of nutrients in many food crops and increases the damage done by many plant pests.

A person looks out at Glacier Blomstrandbreen in the high Arctic.

Svalbard, Norway
1922

A Greenpeace campaigner looks
out at the now retreated Glacier
Blomstrandbreen in the high Arctic.

Svalbard, Norway
July 2002

Unnamed glacier, southwest Greenland.

Ujaraannaq Valley, Greenland
Summer 1935

Same location, southwest Greenland.

Ujaraannaq Valley, Greenland
Summer 2013

Moreover, even those trees and other plants that can theoretically grow faster with more CO_2 cannot do so without concomitant increases in soil nutrients and other factors also necessary for a higher growth rate.

In addition, the disruption of the water cycle by excessive CO_2 levels in the atmosphere hurts many food crops. Already, we're seeing major devastation to many valuable food crops, including reduced yields from corn and wheat due to the heat stress directly linked to excessive CO_2.

6. We all breathe out carbon dioxide. Are you saying we should all stop doing that, too?

Let's all take a breath here—because breathing has nothing to do with global warming.

Each of us breathes out about 2.2 pounds of carbon dioxide a day, which might sound like a problem when you consider there are more than 7 billion of us doing it all day, every day.

But that's not the case, because we are participating in a closed cycle. That is, the carbon we breathe out comes from the food we eat, whether directly from plants, which take it in via photosynthesis, or indirectly from meat. So we get carbon from plants, breathe it out, and they take it in again.

Burning dirty energy is a completely different story. When we dig up and burn coal, oil, or gas, we are bringing carbon into the air that has been stored underground for millions of years. And once we've released that carbon genie from the bottle and into the atmosphere, it can remain there for hundreds of years—some of it for thousands of years.

7. How can a couple of degrees be such a big deal?

The average human body temperature, at 37°C (98.6°F), is much higher than the current average global surface temperature on Earth—14.8°C (58.7°F). The 20th century average was 13.9°C (57°F), and yet an increase of 2°C (3.6°F) in your body temperature is a reason to go to the doctor and see what's wrong. And if it's not a temporary increase but a long-lasting one, and if it continues to increase day after day, the doctor is likely to tell you that you have a serious health problem. The same is true for the Earth. We have given it a fever, and the fever keeps going up. All of the delicately balanced ecological systems are stressed by the increasing temperatures.

A scientist releases a weather balloon, which measures atmospheric pressure, temperature, and humidity.

Antarctica

Climatologists predict that a 2°C (3.6°F) rise above the pre-industrial average would have devastating effects on plants and animals, food crops, and public health. And unfortunately, that is exactly where we are heading in just another 30 years. Unless we stop loading the atmosphere with even more heat-trapping pollution, temperatures could increase by 4°C to 5°C (7.2°F to 9°F) in the lifetime of the millennial generation.

Also, bear in mind that the problem is not just a problem of surface temperature—it is also about the many other consequences of a 2°C (3.6°F) increase, such as the disruption of the water cycle, the accelerated melting of ice leading to sea level rise, and all the other consequences described in Part I of this book. What's more, a quick review of historical climate trends shows us that even the increase of less than 1°C (1.8°F) since 1980 has already caused a dramatic increase in extreme weather events, from intense rainstorms and severe droughts to more frequent heat waves.

These events will only worsen unless we act now.

8. Won't limiting emissions also limit jobs and economic growth?

A fast growing category of new jobs is in renewable energy, efficiency improvements, and the Sustainability Revolution. For example, solar jobs in the United States are growing 17 times faster than average job growth, and the fastest-growing job occupation is wind turbine technician. Numerous economic studies have now proven that limiting emissions does not limit economic dynamism. The good news is that exactly the opposite is true.

And the economic losses of climate change are mounting, already costing the world as much as $1.2 trillion per year. Every year, climate change is responsible for 400,000 lives lost, from mega-storms like Superstorm Sandy and Typhoon Haiyan to the impact of vector-borne diseases—not to mention the millions of deaths from conventional air pollution generated by the burning of fossil fuels.

Maintaining our dependence on dirty fossil fuels would not only devastate public health and the environment, it would also prevent us from gaining the many economic benefits of the job-intensive transformation to a clean energy economy.

One study, for example, found that decarbonizing the electric system would boost global GDP by $19 trillion between now and 2050.

9. If warming is inevitable, even if we went 100 percent renewable, then what is the point?

Yes, climate change is happening. We have already suffered some regrettable losses, and unfortunately, we cannot go back in time to stop what we have started. However, we can still prevent the catastrophic damage that we would otherwise suffer by acting boldly and quickly to limit and then reduce greenhouse gas emissions.

"Obstructionist attitudes, even on the part of believers, can range from denial of the problem to indifference, nonchalant resignation or blind confidence in technical solutions. We require a new and universal solidarity."

—Pope Francis

10. For the sake of argument, let's say I get on board with climate science. What can one person do?

The good news is that there is plenty we can do now to help reduce the impact of climate change.

Each of us can take steps individually, but all of us must act as citizens to ensure that our government—and others around the world—takes collective action to reduce our dependence on fossil fuels and move to a clean energy economy. This means that we not only have to change our light bulbs, we have to change our laws. We can also choose the products we buy with an eye to minimizing the impact on the climate. This sends a powerful signal to business and industry that they need to offer more climate-friendly goods and services.

For more information

▶ Check out the "Truth in 10" slideshow at inconvenientsequel.com
▶ Look for the Skeptical Science app on iTunes or Google Play for on-the-go, science-based responses to skeptics.
▶ You can back up your arguments with graphs and charts available from NASA at climate.nasa.gov/earth-apps.
▶ The Climate Reality Project has answers for questions from deniers at climaterealityproject.org/content/12-questions-every-climate-activist-hears-and-what-say. ◉

Oren Lyons Jr.

Faithkeeper of the Turtle Clan of the
Onondaga Nation of the Iroquois Confederacy

ONONDAGA, NEW YORK

OREN LYONS JR. WAS THE ELDEST of seven siblings who grew up on an Onondaga reservation in upstate New York. In the early 1940s, when he was a young teen and his father left the family, it became his responsibility to provide for the family by hunting, fishing, and gathering firewood.

"I was pretty much hunting for the family," said Lyons, who is now 87 years old. "Our life was tough, hard, but we had a lot of fun. We got to a certain age where we were in the woods all day long."

From early on, it was clear that Lyons was a talented artist. After serving as a heavy machine gunner in the 82nd Airborne Division during the 1950s, he was accepted to Syracuse University on a lacrosse scholarship, where he studied at the College of Fine Arts. He was an all-American, on the same team with the legendary Jim Brown. Lacrosse, of course, was invented by the Iroquois. When he graduated, he moved to New York City and stayed at the YMCA, determined to become a professional artist.

He eventually found a job as a commercial artist for Norcross Greeting Cards, where he rose through the ranks to become the director of art and planning. He married and bought a house in New Jersey.

Everything changed when his aunt, who served as a Clan Mother back home, asked if he could take a leadership role in the Turtle Clan of the Onondaga Nation of the Iroquois Confederacy. Lyons was taken aback; in many ways, he'd traded that life for the American Dream. He took a year to research the history, culture, and cosmology of his ancestors, then decided to accept a position on the Council of Chiefs.

In the end, the combined workload of his corporate job and Council responsibilities was too much. "I thought I could stay in New York and do it, but it didn't work out," he said. "It was too much, and I had to go home."

In the wake of that decision, he embraced his role as an advocate for the Iroquois. He became a professor of Native American history and culture at the University of Buffalo, protested development projects on indigenous land, and attracted the attention of John Lennon and Yoko Ono, both of whom visited Lyons in Onondaga in 1971.

Lyons also helped found the Traditional Circle of Indian Elders and Youth and traveled internationally to learn about issues facing indigenous people around the world. He wrote multiple books, edited a magazine called *Daybreak*, and in 1977 joined a delegation in Geneva that successfully lobbied the United Nations to recognize the status of indigenous people.

Over the years, Lyons's attention turned to the environment, and to the connections between

Lyons participates in the People's Climate March.

New York, New York
September 21, 2014

climate change and the rights of native people.

"I think the point of no return for global warming is much closer than people think," he said. "I've been up to Greenland twice now. You want to get scared, take a look at what's going on up there."

Lyons points to the Onondaga's yearly cycle of ceremonies—when the sap begins to flow from the maple tree, when planting begins, at the first harvest, at the midwinter—as the type of touchstone that has kept the Iroquois society in harmony with the Earth for thousands of years.

Native people have suffered terribly during centuries of colonialism, he argues, and the effects of environmental degradation are likely to be the most severe for disenfranchised populations. Lyons wonders whether the world's policy makers might benefit from the traditional wisdom of indigenous groups. He reflects sometimes on an ancient Iroquois law that suggests considering the effects of current actions on the people who will be alive in seven generations.

"When I was growing up as a kid, seven generations were easy to see," he said, sighing. "It was like forever. Now, it's pretty god darn murky."

Lyons takes strength, he says, in his memories of his close-to-the-Earth childhood on the Onondaga reservation and in the rich tribal traditions he rediscovered over the course of his life.

"We were instructed as leaders: never take hope from the people," he said. "So regardless, you've got to strive on." ◉

An employee checks a cable on a Vestas wind turbine.

Osterild, Denmark
April 18, 2016

Find a Career in Renewable Energy

You can dedicate your life to fighting climate change without becoming a full-time volunteer or sacrificing your livelihood. For example, solar jobs in the United States are growing 17 times faster than average job growth, and the fastest-growing occupation is wind turbine technician. Whether you're in corporate headquarters or out on the solar or wind farm, a job in renewable energy is a great way to fight climate change every day.

There are two main ways to break into this exciting industry:

1. Use your technical talents.

Are you an electrical contractor and want to diversify your skills? If so, there are exciting new opportunities to adapt your technical abilities to the clean energy revolution. Many have found it valuable to become certified as a solar technician.

▶ The U.S. Department of Energy lists places across the country where people can get various types of training for renewable energy jobs at energy.gov/eere/education/find-trainings.

▶ If you wish to pursue certification, solar installers should visit nabcep .org/certification and wind installers can explore energy.gov/eere/wind/wind-testing-and-certification.

2. Use your other skills.

Renewable energy companies have many needs beyond technical expertise—from sales and marketing to human resources. This means there are many opportunities to work for firms helping to solve the climate crisis even if you do not have technical skills.

▶ Non-technical types of renewable energy careers include:
    – Accounting and administration
    – Research and data analysis
    – Procurement and outsourcing
    – Construction
    – Sales and marketing
    – Support services from facilities management to legal support and recruitment

QUICK TIP

Get inspired by real-world stories of people joining the solar economy at *www.stories.solar*, a project of the Southern Environmental Law Center.

Once you've chosen a direction, make the switch:

Network.
Attend renewable energy events and conferences to educate yourself about the industry and meet new people. Learn from and introduce yourself to the experts; show them you are curious and motivated to participate.

Follow industry news.
Read industry publications and follow leaders on social media. This will help you to show depth of knowledge in your cover letters and interviews.

Go to school.
Consider taking an elective in sustainable business at your local college or through an online course.

Be an activist.
Your skills may speak for themselves, but your passion for advancing climate solutions can help set you apart from other candidates in your field. Practice explaining why you want to work in this industry. Stand out as a well-informed, well-intentioned activist who is as excited about fighting climate change as you are about being productive in the business side of companies that are part of the solution. ◉

A solar technician at work.

We are going to win this; we are going to solve this crisis.

The key is solving it quickly enough. That's why it matters that so many people are organizing to accelerate the solutions.

Wei-Tai Kwok

COO of Amber Kinetics, Inc. and Climate Reality Leader

LAFAYETTE, CALIFORNIA

WEI-TAI KWOK SHOULD HAVE been happy. His family life, with a wife and two school-age children, was fulfilling. He had built his Bay Area firm, Dae Advertising, into an industry power player with a client list that included Disney and Apple.

But when he saw *An Inconvenient Truth*, it set him on a course that would come to change everything. In the days after the screening, he found himself preoccupied by the ways global climate change would affect the lives of his kids, then aged nine and six. As he tends to do, he confronted his concerns by researching them meticulously—and what he found angered him. He was perturbed not just at the policy makers who, he came to believe, weren't doing enough to cut carbon emissions, but also at himself for a lifetime of complacency.

"I got mad," he said. "I realized that not only was I not part of the solution, but I was part of the problem. It became an ethical issue to me that was intolerable. I could not enjoy being at work anymore."

Kwok attended my 2013 Climate Reality Leadership training in Chicago, where he learned to apply his experience in corporate communications to giving presentations about climate science. Afterward, he set the goal of reaching 1,000 people in his hometown of Lafayette, Louisiana, and when he met it, he doubled his goal—and reached it—the following year.

Kwok also decided to dedicate his professional life to climate progress by leaving his advertising firm for a series of jobs in the clean energy sector, including stints at Suntech Power, NRG Energy, and Andalay Solar. He's currently serving as the chief operating officer for Amber Kinetics, a Union City, California, startup working on a mechanical battery that stores energy using a flywheel.

Now, working with renewable energy during the day and as a Climate Leader after hours, Kwok has turned the climate crisis into an opportunity to build a brighter future for the Earth. He credits that growth to the diversity and camaraderie of his fellow climate leaders in Chicago.

"It was so inspiring," he said, "to sit with people of all ages and genders and creeds and work together to solve this problem. It filled me with hope." ◉

To learn more about becoming a Climate Reality Leader, see page 297.

Make Your Business More Sustainable

Businesses have the opportunity to be on the front lines of the Sustainability Revolution. Whether you are a business owner who can make the decisions yourself or a dedicated employee willing to push for change from within, every business can and should pollute less and help fight the climate crisis by achieving maximum efficiency and leveraging the passions of its employees to make it happen.

1. Make the business case.

From those with entry-level jobs all the way up to those in the C-suites, every employee of a company can encourage more sustainability. In most cases, success depends upon winning support from colleagues, managers, and other stakeholders. Here are some arguments that can help you explain how sustainability efforts benefit the business where you work:

Sustainability can reduce operating costs and improve business intelligence.
By using smart building technology to facilitate and monitor energy use, operations managers can not only ensure that systems like heating and cooling run more efficiently, they can also use predictive analytics to drive future performance and planning.

Attracting consumers and employees.
In a recent poll, 64 percent of global CEOs said that Corporate Social Responsibility goals were core to their business, in part because they help drive public and partner trust. Furthermore, brands with demonstrated sustainability goals are seeing a growth in consumer sales. That means promoting a climate agenda can improve your reputation and support profitability at the same time. This is also important for attracting and retaining employees who want their work to reflect their values, an increasingly important factor for job satisfaction among younger employees.

Sustainability is more affordable than you think.
Renewables and "smart building" technology—everything from lighting sensors to solar systems—are getting

Solar panels mounted above a parking area serve double-duty providing shade for the cars below.

A new cycle bridge called "The Bicycle Snake" provides increased accessibility and safety for cyclists.

Copenhagen, Denmark
July 14, 2014

less expensive every year. Plus, there are many valuable legal and financial incentives for energy efficiency programs, such as tax credits, fee reductions, waivers, and even expedited building permits.

Turn wasted space into energy and value.
An empty rooftop or vacant parking lot sizzling in the sun can be covered with solar panels.

▶ More details for building your case can be found at usgbc.org/articles/business-case-green-building.

Position yourself as an early leader.
The need for businesses to embrace a sustainable approach is growing due to increasing external forces, including policy changes like a price on carbon, pressure from large investors to disclose climate risk (especially if their supply chains are vulnerable) and to identify opportunities for emissions reductions, and rapid technological changes that are undermining existing business models. This is why major corporations worldwide are moving quickly to adopt renewable energy and to innovate with new products that address fast-growing markets focused on sustainability.

2. Invest in clean energy and efficiency.

Buildings use about 40 percent of the total energy consumed in the U.S., making them a vital place to focus our efforts. Here are some ways to improve energy use and reduce your organization's carbon footprint:

Assess the situation.
Start by understanding where you are now. Benchmark your energy use by identifying the ratio of economic output to emissions or researching the ratio of electricity consumption to employees in your company.

▶ A great resource for per-employee benchmarks is g20-energy-efficiency.enerdata.net/indicators/unit-electricity-consumption-of-services-per-employee.html.

▶ You can also use a carbon footprint calculator to assess your baseline; try the one at coolclimate.berkeley.edu/business-calculator.

Identify areas of opportunity.
Approximately 30 percent of energy used in buildings is wasted, so there are likely many ways you could improve efficiency. Here are a few places to look:

The building envelope.

Leaky or poorly insulated walls, windows, and doors waste energy. Updating these thermal barriers can keep the building operating at higher efficiency. An EnergyStar roof can reduce peak cooling demand by 10 to 15 percent.

Building systems.

Heating, cooling, and ventilation (HVAC) comprises about 34 percent of an average commercial building's energy use. EnergyStar systems typically use 10 to 20 percent less energy than conventional products. Lighting and computers also require a lot of energy, so look for savings potential here, too, from ensuring the use of LED bulbs to investing in "smart lighting."

Energy supply.

If onsite development of renewables is not an option, look at your utility's green power options. Your firm may also be able to purchase renewable energy credits.

▶ Check for potential incentives in your state through the Database of State Incentives for Renewables and Efficiency at dsireusa.org.

Build your strategy.

Set clear goals for energy savings, tactics, and timelines. Identify project stakeholders, communicate the plan clearly, and work together—for example, to research HVAC systems that would work for your office. Decide who will be responsible for advancing the plan and how to measure progress. When you reach your goal, celebrate!

3. Make it easy to be green.

While energy systems for buildings are a huge part of the equation, day-to-day use also adds up. Try these ideas to make your workplace more conducive to climate-friendly behavior:

Empower recycling.

Make sure your workplace has easily accessible recycling bins.

Choose green supplies.

Make sure the supply closet is stocked with environmentally friendly options, such as refillable toner and inkjet cartridges, reusable dishes, and Forest Stewardship Council–certified paper. Buy in bulk to save on packaging.

Reduce paper waste.

Encourage colleagues to reduce paper use in simple ways, such as printing double-sided and using online collaboration tools that reduce the need for paper documents.

Prevent e-waste.

Most electronics include harmful materials that can be recycled safely.

"What is the business case for an economic system that says it is cheaper to destroy the Earth than to take care of it? How did such a fantasy system that defies common sense even come to be? How did we—all of us—get swept up in its siren's song?"

—Ray Anderson, late chairman of Interface, Inc.

▶ The EPA lists major nationwide retailers that offer computer, battery, and cell phone recycling options at epa.gov/recycle /electronics-donation-and-recycling.

Engage with your colleagues.
Survey people to find out what actions they think are important, then use that knowledge to design a program that best reflects your organization's values. Ongoing idea exchanges via internal meetings as well as lunch-and-learn seminars with experts will keep your colleagues connected.

Create a climate action team.
Form a group that brings together the most passionate people from across the organization, ideally including at least one person from each department. Define your purpose, outline key goals and tactics, and designate roles.

Organize actions and initiatives.
Rally people around special events, such as Bike to Work day. Look for creative ways to incentivize participation.

Promote climate-friendly benefits.
Among the employee benefits that can also help the planet are pretax public transportation passes, tuition support, climate-related performance bonuses, and socially responsible investment choices within a pension or 401(k) program. ◉

Run for Office

You might be surprised to learn how many opportunities there are to become an elected government official. While there are only 537 federal offices in the U.S., there are more than half a million opportunities to run for office in the more than 90,000 government units, including city and county positions, school boards, water districts, and so on.

You don't need a degree in political science or a track record in local politics to get elected. In fact, the House of Representatives is made up of an increasingly large share of people from business backgrounds, and a broad mix of professions can be found in any public office, from English teachers to scientists. Each office comes with its own opportunity to influence.

1. Assess your prospects.

Visit your city, county, or state Board of Elections to learn which offices will be on the ballot soon. When choosing the office you'd like to run for, consider whether factors like your skills, experience, and network could resonate with voters for one particular office over another. It's also worth considering whether you are

A woman waves a flag at a presidential rally at the Santa Monica High School Football Field.

Santa Monica, California
May 23, 2016

interested in challenging an incumbent, or running for an open office. Then think about your answers to some relevant questions, such as: Can you meet the eligibility requirements? Are you ready to look people in the eye and ask them for their support?

Although running for office has in recent years required a lot of fundraising, this appears to be changing. Some candidates for office during the last election—including one prominent candidate for U.S. president— demonstrated that it is now possible

"Progress occurs when courageous, skillful leaders seize the opportunity to change things for the better."

—Harry S. Truman, Former U.S. President

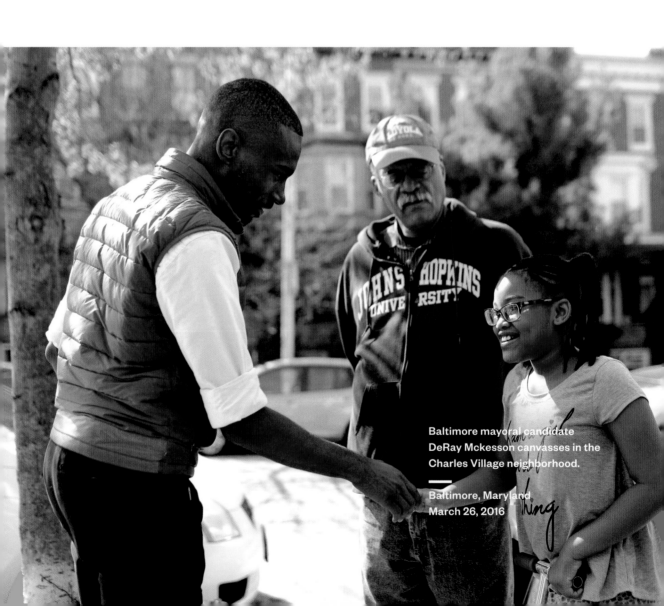

Baltimore mayoral candidate DeRay Mckesson canvasses in the Charles Village neighborhood.

Baltimore, Maryland
March 26, 2016

to raise money on the Internet in small amounts from lots of people. In addition, campaigns for local offices typically cost much less. Many candidates have been elected on shoestring budgets. Make sure that you have support from your family and others who could be personally affected by your decision to run for office.

2. Lay the groundwork.

Get organized well in advance of making any formal announcement of your candidacy. It is critical that you become visibly active in the community, attending important events, meeting with influencers, and talking with people about the issues you and they care about. If you are new to town, or have been otherwise engaged, it is never too late to get involved. Act now, enlisting your family and close friends to help you in these early days.

3. Build your campaign team.

Campaign teams vary in size depending on the campaign. The key roles you may need to fill include a campaign manager, directors in charge of finance, communications, politics, and outreach, as well as a volunteer coordinator and a treasurer.

4. Craft your message.

Why should you win? What are your goals while in office? How will you see them through? These are questions you and your campaign will have to answer every day, in every encounter. Create a simple, memorable, and unified campaign message to ensure voters know who you are and what you stand for.

To develop that message, you need a strong sense of who your target voters are, and how to appeal to them. Study voter demographics in your area. Who do you need to win over?

5. Rally support.

Once you have a campaign strategy, it is time to get the word out there and connect with as many voters as possible.

Do this by prioritizing:

▶ Door-to-door canvassing and phone banking
▶ Online engagement
▶ Town halls and other public speaking events
▶ Fundraisers
▶ Coalitions and endorsements
▶ Advertising and PR

Running for office is hard work—as is being a public official. In terms of making direct and lasting impacts in the fight against climate change, though, there's hardly a better choice to make.

One more thing—and it's actually the most important thing—always remember why you got involved in your campaign in the first place and hold true to your values. Don't ever compromise your integrity. Stay focused on your objectives to bring positive change. ◉

Talking with voters during my first U.S. Congressional campaign.

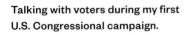

**Rural Middle Tennessee
July 29, 1976**

Steven Miles

Minister for Environment and Heritage
Protection, Minister for National Parks and the
Great Barrier Reef, and a Climate Reality Leader

QUEENSLAND, AUSTRALIA

ABOUT 10 YEARS AGO, when Steven Miles's wife was pregnant with their first child, he started to worry about climate change. The couple intended to raise a family in Australia's coastal Queensland, and the threat of rising sea levels began to alarm him.

"Climate change is already affecting Queensland," Miles said. "We're having hotter and hotter days, more cyclones. My motivation in politics was always about future generations—like education and the economy—but when you think about it, all of those things will be impacted if we can't stop the planet from getting hotter."

After Miles saw *An Inconvenient Truth*, he traveled to Melbourne to take part in the Climate Reality Training program I led there in 2007. Afterward, while working day jobs for trade unions and nonprofits and completing a PhD in political science, he became engrossed with Queensland's lush coastal biosphere—and how it has come to be menaced by the changing climate.

He became especially concerned with the Great Barrier Reef, a marvel of the natural world that runs down the length of Queensland's shoreline. Scientists believe it to be the largest structure on Earth made of living organisms, and its rich ecosystem shelters many endangered and vulnerable species of whales and sea turtles.

The reef is also, Miles learned, straining under unprecedented environmental stress. The warming ocean has caused a series of catastrophic "bleaching events," which occur when higher temperatures cause the disruption of a symbiotic relationship between the coral and beneficial organisms called zooxanthellae, which provide nutrients to the coral. If the damage continues unchecked, the entire ecosystem could collapse. The bleaching started in 1998 and continues to this day; in the summer of 2016, the reef suffered its most serious bleaching event in history.

"It was catastrophic," Miles said. "The amount of coral that hasn't recovered is enormous."

By 2014, Miles and his wife had three children, and it was on their behalf that he mounted a successful campaign for parliament under the slogan "Miles Better for the Reef." His former colleagues were supportive of his environmental message, with one union leader from his days in labor advocacy quipping that "there ain't no jobs on a dead planet."

When he was elected in early 2015, Miles was appointed environmental minister, and he immediately dedicated himself to protecting Queensland's natural habitats. He increased spending on koala conservation, pushed for mining and land rehabilitation reform, and, of course, worked diligently to protect the Great Barrier Reef.

Bleached coral from a mass-bleaching event in 2017. Pixie Reef, near Cairns Australia, March 3, 2017

Queensland alone can't change the global climate, but Miles hopes that if the state can reduce strain on the reef through local legislation that fights fertilizer runoff and other threats, it will buy the reef enough time for countries around the world to unite against carbon emissions and stop or reverse the coral bleaching for good.

"We're actually putting a lot of stress on the reef through localized pollution," he said. "The scientists tell me that if we can take the pressure off from that, we can give the reef extra time to confront global warming."

With the reef's future teetering on the brink, he also hopes that Queensland can reduce its own carbon footprint. Australia is largely dependent on fossil fuels for electricity and transportation, but Miles believes the country is poised for an energy revolution as it invests in a mix of photovoltaic, solar-thermal, and wind infrastructure for a greener future.

In the service of those goals, Miles maintains a frenetic schedule. When we spoke on the phone for this book, he had to take a short break in the middle for a live interview with a local radio station about water-quality testing in the Fitzroy River Basin. Miles sees the Paris Agreement, which Australia ratified late last year, as a watershed moment in the international struggle for climate progress. He senses a momentum that he's never felt before, especially among business leaders, who, he believes, are starting to see environmental responsibility as a corporate duty.

"I've felt a real shift post-Paris in the business sector," he said. "Multinational companies want to be in business in 2050, so they have long-term plans, and they're building into their plans the targets that were set in Paris."

Miles's advice for climate activists around the world who want to make a change in their home communities is simple: start educating yourself on how to run for office, even if it's just a local position, in order to push for positive change at a grassroots level.

"I am optimistic," he said. "I think you have to be." ◉

Walk the Walk

While it's great to encourage your family, friends, and community to be more climate conscious, it's important you, yourself, practice what you preach. You should lead by example by shrinking your carbon footprint and making climate-friendlier consumer choices. People will expect it, and they should. Furthermore, it will help you understand the intricacies of sustainable living and better inform your decisions.

1. Evaluate your current impact and set a target.

Calculate how much energy you use by looking at your utility bills and setting a specific goal for reducing it: for example, 10 percent in six months.

▶ It might help to use the EPA's Carbon Footprint Calculator at epa.gov /carbon-footprint-calculator.

2. Audit your home.

Search your home for opportunities to reach your goal. Inspect each room, making a list of everything that is plugged in. Look for and note any outright energy drains, such as drafts.

Consider bringing in a professional to conduct an even more thorough evaluation, including inspecting major

QUICK TIP

Use power strips to cut the flow of electricity to standby devices, like TVs and computers, which can suck up energy even when they are off.

appliances and identifying areas that are missing insulation. The Department of Energy estimates that following a professional auditor's recommendations for efficiency upgrades can result in saving up to 30 percent on your energy bill.

▶ Learn more at energy.gov/energysaver /professional-home-energy-audits.

3. Look for ways to save.

Heating, cooling, and hot water. Keeping a home heated and cooled comprises about half of the energy use in a typical American house, while water heating represents about 18 percent. There are simple ways to lower those figures. Use a programmable thermostat and make sure your water heater is insulated against heat loss. You may want to go further and invest in new, more efficient systems, which can often save more money than the purchase price in just a few years. In addition, solar water heaters are eligible for tax credits through 2021.

Any place with an outlet. The average household owns dozens of consumer electronics, which add up to 12 percent of a home's electricity use.

▶ Consider updating to more efficient options, which you can find at energystar.gov.

It is estimated that if every TV sold in the U.S. was EnergyStar–certified, 9 billion pounds of greenhouse gas emissions would be averted each year.

Garden.
Planting the right trees around your home will help clean the air—and can add valuable shade that can reduce energy bills. Tree cover can naturally trim summer air-conditioning bills by up to 35 percent. Consider starting a compost pile, which helps save the energy used to transport food waste and keeps decaying organic matter from contributing methane emissions to a landfill.

Garage or driveway.
First, leave the car behind as often as you can. There are also several ways to improve your carbon footprint when

Preschool students plant apple trees in an event organized by the German Forest Protection Community for Day of the Forest.

Near Baerenthoren, Germany
March 21, 2017

using your vehicle, such as avoiding idling and keeping your tires inflated to the right pressure, which can save up to 10 percent on fuel. When it is time to replace your current vehicle, choose a more efficient option, ideally an electric vehicle.

▶ Research available federal tax credits for EVs at fueleconomy.gov /feg/taxevb.shtml.

4. Make the switch: consider going solar at home.

You should start by asking your electric utility to switch to clean energy. Google has a great tool called Project Sunroof which shows you your solar options.

▶ To learn more, visit google.com/get/sunroof.

A tractor pulling a weed harrow
on farmland.

June 19, 2012

Eat with the Planet in Mind

The EPA has reported that all the emissions from the "electric power, transportation, industrial, and agricultural sectors associated with growing, processing, transporting, and disposing of food" account for a significant percentage of U.S. emissions. Whether it's by eating less meat or buying local, you should consider agriculture and its pollutant by-products whenever shopping or eating out.

1. Eat less meat, especially red meat.

Eating a lot of meat results in more greenhouse gas (GHG) emissions due to the inefficient transfer of plant energy to animal energy, which creates a larger impact on the climate per calorie. Cutting down on the amount of meat you eat, especially red meat, can have a significant effect on emissions—and, doctors say, also improve your health.

2. Make plant-based food a bigger part of your diet.

Because of meat's heavy GHG emissions, lowering your intake even slightly can have an impact. Going one or two days a week without meat is a good start. Plant-based foods like lentils, beans, and whole grains are great sources of protein. If you do want to eat meat, try swapping out beef and pork for chicken, dairy, eggs, or fish, which have much lower carbon footprints.

3. Go local.

Transportation makes up of about 11 percent of food-related emissions. Eating only local foods for a year would avert the carbon emissions associated with driving 1,000 miles in a passenger vehicle.

▶ Use localharvest.org to find nearby sources of local foods, including farmers' markets.

4. Buy foods that don't contribute to deforestation.

Deforestation contributes 10 percent of all GHG emissions. Check the websites of the brands you use to be sure they have pledged to deforestation-free supply chains, and check Greenpeace's scorecards of how they are really doing.

5. Buy in bulk.

After you've found your favorite low-emission food items, consider buying more of them. Buying more food at one time, assuming you eat it all, will save you trips to the grocery store, and, in turn, reduce your emissions.

6. Buy organic.

A study found that organic agriculture uses 30 to 50 percent less energy than traditional agriculture. ◉

The Boqueria market.

Barcelona, Spain
March 1, 2014

"Food production is a main driver of biodiversity loss and a large contributor to climate change and pollution, so our food choices matter."

—Bojana Bajzelj, Researcher at University of Cambridge

**Morning at the Rodale Institute,
an organic farm since 1947.**

—

**Kutztown, Pennsylvania
October 18, 2016**

Support Organic Agriculture

FARMERS STAND ON THE FRONT LINES of the climate struggle—not only because they often feel the brunt of severe weather and drought, but also because they have the power to help reverse climate change with every crop they grow.

Since humans began farming the earth, the world's soils have lost 30 percent to 75 percent of their carbon content. Not only does this mean that some of that carbon is now in the atmosphere, contributing to the climate crisis, but it also means less fertile soil and lower yields. Depletion of soil carbon has worsened with intensive, modern farming practices like the dependence on synthetic nitrogen fertilizer, tillage, and monocropping, all of which disrupt soil's natural carbon storage capabilities.

The good news is that the soil offers a truly down-to-earth opportunity to fight climate change. According to the Rodale Institute, an agricultural research nonprofit based in Kutztown, Pennsylvania, by using organic, regenerative soil management methods, farmers can play a significant role in taking carbon out of the atmosphere and putting it in the ground, converting it from a greenhouse gas into a food-producing asset. The organization's research shows that by switching current croplands and pastures to organic management practices, we could potentially sequester a nontrivial percentage of current annual CO_2 emissions.

Regenerative organic agriculture comprises a range of time-tested practices that contribute to soil's ability to retain carbon. Many of these are easy and relatively inexpensive to adopt. For example, cover cropping, mulching, and composting all help keep organic matter (i.e., carbon) in the soil. They also include conservation tillage or no-till farming, which can play a vital role in keeping plant residue in the soil and reducing erosion. Regenerative, organic agriculture can be economical too because it helps farmers maintain yields and improve farm profitability.

Meanwhile, demand for organic produce has been rising dramatically over the past decade, with pesticide-free fare now sold in most mainstream grocery stores. According to the Organic Trade Association, in 2015, Americans spent more than $43 billion on organic products, and nearly 22,000 businesses earned organic certification, up a record 12 percent from the year before.

Still, the organic market is dwarfed by conventional food production which currently accounts for more than three quarters of all fruit and vegetable sales. So it's important that we use our hard-won dollars to help show the broader industry that organic is not just a nice-to-have—it's better for the Earth and, for many consumers, it's a must-have.

Restructuring our global food system is a massive undertaking, and one that each of us can contribute to by voting with our forks and our wallets. Educate yourself on where your food comes from by reading labels, getting online to learn more, and talking with your local farmers about their climate-friendly practices. ◉

Learn more at rodaleinstitute.org/regenerative-organic-agriculture-and-climate-change.

when you insist on buying the most climate-friendly goods and services, you add to the pressure on businesses to continue leading the Sustainability Revolution.

A customer browses produce in a local grocery store.

—

Yangon, Myanmar
March 11, 2017

Cotton scraps collected by the TAL Garment Manufacturing group and remade into reclaimed cotton clothing by Patagonia.

Vote with Your Dollars

The industries that profit from the destruction of our planet rely on your hard-earned money to justify their fossil fuel habits. One of the most basic and potent forms of power we have is our ability to decide where and how we spend our money. Regardless of your financial situation, there are some simple ways to make sure you're supporting businesses that are part of the solution rather than the problem.

1. Study before you buy.

You already research the products and brands you buy for price. You can also examine their business practices. Look for companies that have made an explicit and authentic commitment to sustainability and eco-friendly practices.

2. Invest with climate in mind.

Investment is a powerful tool to support eco-friendly companies. And if you have investments in polluting companies,

Yvon Chouinard, founder of Patagonia, has proven that corporations can be sustainable as well as profitable.

Ventura, California
January 23, 2010

divesting can be a strong form of protest, as well as a wise move. Over the past few years, large investment fund companies have lost billions due to their investments in fossil fuels. Seek out financial advisers and investment firms that have made a strong commitment to eco-friendly values. Look closely at your investment portfolio to make sure all the companies you invest in follow meaningful "Environmental, Social, Governance" (ESG) criteria. Companies that meet rigorous ESG criteria are more likely to be socially responsible environmental stewards and have an ethical corporate culture.

3. Make more efficient travel plans.

Travel is an area where almost every family can easily reduce its carbon footprint.

▶ Look for hotels that have green business practices, such as those who participate in the Green Hotels Association, which you can learn about at greenhotels.com.

Some airlines are better than others, or offer carbon offset options. Try to fly less overall. Consider exploring national forests or state parks near your home-town for vacation.

TRUTH TO POWER

The manufacturing of Nike Air bags, where 90 percent of waste is recycled and reused.

Nike Air Manufacturing Innovation Facility
February 2017

4. Green your banking.

Keep your money with institutions that support climate advocacy work. Some organizations, including CREDO Action, the Sierra Club, and the League of Conservation Voters, offer their own credit cards, so your interest payments go to support environmental activism instead of Wall Street. Smaller banks and credit unions are more likely to fund clean energy and local advocacy work.

5. Give to the movement.

Reducing your own environmental impact is just a start. We all need to support the groups and nonprofits that spend every day fighting for the future of our planet. Set personal goals for how much you can donate every month. Pick organizations that are doing work you believe in, and where your money will make the greatest difference. ⊚

How to Create and Host Events

The author Malcolm Gladwell wrote an influential essay a few years ago called "Small Change," which perceptively described the relative weakness of any strategy for organizing that puts its sole emphasis on clicking boxes on the Internet. Online organizing plays a crucial role, but in order to develop a stronger sense of cohesion and commitment among those you are organizing, it is essential to hold in-person events. Marches, concerts, film screenings, town hall and city council meetings, teach-ins, and student rallies can have enormous impacts—including recruiting new activists, generating media coverage, and putting pressure on decision makers.

The Live Earth concert, which inspired people to find and act on solutions to climate change.

Rio De Janiero, Brazil
July 7, 2007

277

1. Have a Strategy.

Getting 100, 500, or 1,000 people to come to a rally or other event is great, but if you don't have a plan to leverage that attendance into political power and action, it might be a waste of time. Before you start organizing, take the time to identify some clear goals, such as recruiting 5-10 new members or volunteers, collecting 100 postcards to send to legislators, raising a certain amount of money, or gathering 50 new email addresses or phone numbers.

Think about how achieving these short-term goals will help you achieve your longer-term goals, like getting a policy changed or dramatically increasing public awareness of a climate issue.

2. Choose what kind of event you'd like to put on.

Rallies, marches, and demonstrations.
Be sure to set reasonable goals. Think of how you can make the event visually

Demonstrators march on the British parliament as part of the Time to Act march.

———

London, England
March 7, 2015

compelling and successful even if only a small number of people show up. You don't need large numbers of people to get attention for your cause. Get creative and consider using costumes, props, and theatrics to convey your message. Most importantly, make sure that your demonstration is seen and heard by the people you're trying to influence and inspire. You can mobilize on the sidewalk outside a corporate headquarters or on the steps of your city hall. If possible, organize the demonstration during business hours so that the decision makers you are trying to influence will see it. If you choose a weekend to increase attendance, be sure to alert the media and collect photos and video to send to your target and the press and to share on social media. The Climate Reality Project also hosts regular Days of Action—try planning an event on one of these days to increase attention by linking to a larger organization.

In the U.S., the First Amendment protects the right to assemble. In most cities, you can organize demonstrations on public sidewalks without any need for a permit. Larger demonstrations and marches that take over the street often do require a permit. Most city government websites have some information about permits for public events, so do your research to avoid any conflict.

Boycotts.
If a business in your community is engaging in irresponsible practices that are harmful to the planet, you may want to take the extraordinary step of organizing a boycott.

However, once you call for a boycott, you need to back it up. Organize a picket line outside the business you are boycotting and have volunteers pass out leaflets encouraging customers to spend their money elsewhere. Make sure to have clear, achievable demands so that the company knows what they need to do to get the boycott to stop. Your goal is to make it more economically or politically costly for them to continue the negative practice than it is for them to agree to your demands.

Letter-writing parties and phone banking.
As noted on pages 186–189, it's important to regularly contact your elected officials and other decision makers, but it's a lot more fun—and a lot more effective—to organize an event with a group of people who are doing the same. Provide materials for people to use to write letters or send postcards to their representatives, or printed scripts for people who want to make phone calls. Serve refreshments, and keep it light and fun.

Women grab postcards during a
local postcard-writing event.

Boulder, Colorado
January 29, 2017

"We cannot condemn our children,
and their children, to a future that is
beyond their capacity to repair."

—Barack Obama, Former U.S. President

Help others learn more about the climate crisis and its solutions.
Show your support for climate action by going to see *An Inconvenient Sequel: Truth to Power* at your local theater. Bring your family, friends, and peers to share the experience and start a conversation about how your community can get involved.

After *An Inconvenient Sequel: Truth to Power* is released for home viewing, host a movie party with your friends or family. Be sure to open the floor to discussion after the film, and have a facilitator or expert there who can keep the conversation productive and offer concrete action steps. If you would like to host a public screening of either of my films, contact Paramount Pictures at (323) 956-5000 and ask for the Repertory/Non-Theatrical Department.

Climate Reality presentations.
The Climate Reality Project gives presentations focused on climate science and climate action. At a Climate Reality Leader presentation, participants learn about the impacts of climate change on a local and global level, solutions to solving the climate crisis, and what you and your organization can do to fight climate change and create a better future for the planet.

▶ You can request a free Climate Reality presentation by going to realityhub. climaterealityproject.org/events /attendpresentation. Once you've requested a presentation, follow the event hosting advice above to promote it.

Benefit parties.
You probably already have organizing experience, even if you have only hosted a small gathering of friends. A benefit party isn't much different—you just ask your guests to make a donation to the cause. You can have someone collect donations at the door or "pass the hat." Offer refreshments, put on music, and tell your friends to invite their friends. These events can be casual, but take some time to talk to the guests one-on-one and as a group. Explain what you're raising money for, why it's important, and how they can get more involved.

QUICK TIP

See page 297 to learn how to become a Climate Reality Leader and make your own climate presentations.

Fundraising meals.

Consider organizing a breakfast, lunch, or dinner event to raise funds. Cook a tasty and inexpensive meal yourself, or ask local restaurants to donate or offer discounted food to support the cause. Charge a flat rate or sliding scale donation for entry to the meal, and give your guests opportunities to contribute more if they can. Some restaurants will let you host fundraising events in their space, and donate a portion of their profits.

Concerts and performances.

Partner with local or national artists who are sympathetic to your cause and who can draw a crowd. They may be willing to donate their labor, but you will often want to offer them a percentage of the money raised or an honorarium. If you treat the artists well, they will be more likely to promote your event to their fan base. It's often helpful to partner with a local venue or a promoter who has experience with local venues, sound equipment, and local music press.

Just because there's music doesn't mean your event can't also include short, upbeat speeches or announcements from local groups between musical acts. Have a charismatic host to remind the audience of the purpose of the event and give them ways to take action or get involved. If you're partnering with a well-known artist or band, contact local media outlets and offer them an interview with your performer before or during the event. Prep the performers with talking points ahead of time.

3. Get people to come.

Every event is different, and you'll need to make decisions based on your goals, your audience, and your resources. But there are some key "best practices" that apply to almost any event, whether it's a loud demonstration or a black-tie gala. Every organizer who has hosted events has had the fear, "What if no one comes?" To avoid this scenario, it's important to recognize how much work it takes to turn large numbers of people out to an event. You'll need to use every tool in the toolbox, whether you're trying to fill a venue that holds 50 people or 5,000.

Here are some basics for every event:

Don't go it alone.

Your events will be more successful if you have help organizing them. Find collaborators who can bring their own ideas and social networks to the table. Partner with other organizations and divide up the responsibilities related to the event.

Pick the right venue.

Where your event happens is important.

Continued on p. 286.

Indivisible

Leah Greenberg and Ezra Levin, Co-Founders

WASHINGTON, D.C.

LEAH GREENBERG AND EZRA LEVIN are two of the former congressional staffers behind the Indivisible Guide, an online handbook and website dedicated to empowering activists to resist the Trump administration's agenda. It's an effective group: in fact, my youngest daughter, Sarah Maiani, is a member of the Indivisible group in Santa Barbara, California. Earlier this year, Greenberg and Levin, a married couple, sat down with me to talk about the origins of Indivisible and the most effective ways you can engage with your local representatives.

AL GORE: You've cited the Tea Party as an inspiration for Indivisible. Why do you think the Tea Party was so effective, and what can other activists learn from it?

EZRA LEVIN: After the election, we realized that, putting aside the Tea Party's racism and violence, they were smart on strategy. They implemented a defensive strategy focused on their own representatives. They went to public events and town halls and made calls. It worked. They took down a lot of the agenda of Barack Obama, a historically popular president with an enormous congressional majority.

LEAH GREENBERG: When I was working for Representative Tom Perriello (D-Virginia), the Tea Party took up a lot of mental space in the office. Whatever we were doing, you had to think about what their response was going to be.

AG: What are some examples of effective activism you've seen since the 2016 election?
EL: One thing that blew us away was the first congressional recess, in February 2017, when every member of Congress goes back home to listen to their constituents. Local Indivisible groups have been doing phenomenal work in helping people organize and attend town halls. In response, many Republican members have actually refused to hold town halls. We've even seen people holding their own town halls: if their representative showed up, great; otherwise, they were ready with a cardboard cutout or an empty chair.

LG: The thing that has struck me is the power of stories. In early January, a group of constituents brought into Virginia Representative Barbara Comstock's office a family that was threatened by the repeal of the Affordable Care Act. This family had a 10-year-old daughter who has a preexisting condition; without treatment, she would die. These stories can change what is seen as possible.

Indivisible volunteers hold hands at the Women's March.

———

Washington, D.C.
January 21, 2017

AG: What's the story behind the name "Indivisible"?

LG: We were trying to think of something that was rooted in American history, but also encompassed the full diversity of America today. The only way to respond to a demagogue who is threatening components of our civic society is to treat an attack on one as an attack on all.

AG: How can the way a congressional office responds to an outcry by its constituents have an impact on the way elected officials make decisions?

EL: Members of Congress want to be reelected. That means they care about how their constituents view them and how the local press treats them. Our theory of change here is that any individual member of Congress cares much more about their image back home than about any one thing that President Trump is trying to get done.

AG: What steps can activists take to avoid burnout?

EL: That's front and center in our minds right now. The scenario we want to avoid is that two years from now, the story becomes, "Remember back in 2017, when we all did activism for a while?" These are everyday citizens who are giving up their nights and weekends to fight for things they believe in. It's important to build a sense of community.

AG: If someone reading this book wants to become politically active, what should they do?

EL: Go and get involved in your local Indivisible group. Go to IndivisibleGuide.com and type in your zip code. No matter where you are in the country, you will find a group near you. Get involved on your own turf. ◉

Remember the old rule of thumb: make sure you can fill the space. A large crowd overflowing a small space sends a powerful message. The same size crowd, dwarfed by a large venue with lots of empty seats sends a weak message. Pick a central location that's easily accessible by public transportation and/or has ample parking available. Spaces that are already well known to the activist community, like progressive churches (or other houses of worship), bookstores, music venues, or community centers, are often best. College campuses may have a variety of spaces that you can rent or reserve for free through a student organization or friendly professor.

Promote shamelessly.
You need to be a champion of your event. Create a Facebook event and invite all your connections. Then message the guests and ask them to invite their friends. Post the link to your

During the COP21 conference, demonstrators paint the roads surrounding the Arc de Triomphe with non-polluting water-based paint to create the image of a sun.

Paris, France
December 11, 2015

event in relevant online groups and forums, email it to your mailing list, and ask local organizations to share it with their members. You can also create an online form using a service like Action Network, NationBuilder, or Google Forms where people can RSVP for your event by providing their name and contact information. That way you can email them the day before the event to remind them or send them relevant information. For larger events like mass

demonstrations, you may want to set up a custom webpage with information about the event and an easy way for people to sign up for updates. Hand out flyers or postcards at other similar happenings, on college campuses, or at the grocery store.

Leverage word of mouth.
Directly invite as many people as possible, and get commitments from them that they'll be there. Telephone

"We are the first generation that can put an end to poverty and we are the last generation that can put an end to climate change."

—Ban Ki-Moon, Former Secretary General of the U.N.

trees also work extremely well. Asking someone to bring something, like snacks, or to play a volunteer role at the event is a great way to make them feel more connected—and committed.

Utilize advertising and media.
If you have a budget, even a small one, consider Facebook or Twitter ads to promote your event to a targeted audience, or consider taking out an ad in your local paper or on your local radio station. Often, local TV stations will mention your event as a public service, if you let them know about it in advance. Then move on to getting media coverage. Most local outlets have event listings that you can submit to for free. Contact local journalists who cover politics and the environment and encourage them to write about your event in advance, or make it one of their "weekly picks." See page 211 for more tips on getting press coverage.

Create compelling visuals.
Make your event stand out. Take the time to create attractive posters, handbills, and online graphics. You don't need to be a designer—free online services like Canva.com have templates that make this easy for anyone (though it won't hurt to enlist a designer on your team). Don't crowd your outreach materials with information—just provide the key details, and direct people to an email address or website where they can learn more. See pages 290–291 for Shepard Fairey's advice for designing fantastic demonstration materials.

3. Manage a successful event.

Regardless of size, the day of the event will probably be a little stressful and require some running around to take care of logistics. Make sure you have a good team of volunteers to help, and that everyone knows what they are responsible for ahead of time. If a few people show up to your event early, put them to work. Here are some roles you will likely need to fill:

▶ Greeters to welcome people as they come in, ask them to sign in with their name, email, and phone number, and collect donations if applicable.

▶ Hosts and emcees to make announcements, keep the program running smoothly, and keep the crowd energized and engaged.

▶ Servers and bartenders to help sell or give away food or drinks.

▶ Canvassers to work the crowd asking people to take various types of actions like signing a postcard to local lawmakers, opting in to receive text messages, or signing a paper petition. This may not be necessary at smaller events, but it is key for larger and outdoor events.

▶ Security might be needed if you're concerned about counter-demonstrators or someone disrupting your event. It's always good to have a few people who are on the lookout for potential problems, and they should be trained in de-escalation and conflict management to help quickly address anything that comes up.

▶ Stage managers to make sure that speakers, performers, and others are where they need to be when you need them there, and to keep things running smoothly.

5. Design great event materials.

Put your message front and center at every event. Be sure to have signs, banners, stickers, buttons, or T-shirts available for your audience to show their support. You can also provide posterboard and markers for people to make their own signs.

Here are some basic tips for designing effective materials:

▶ Keep it simple: you want your message to be immediately understandable and legible from a distance, so keep it short, to the point, and bold.

▶ Use large fonts and contrast to make your words stand out. Black letters on a white background, or vice versa, are always a good way to go.

▶ Get creative: humor, compelling images, and memorable slogans will help you reach more people. Spend some time brainstorming ideas with others.

▶ Don't break the bank: you can get banners, signs, and other materials professionally printed, but it's expensive. Consider hosting a banner-painting or sign-making party a week before your demonstration or event. Not only will you save money, you'll build excitement for the event itself. ◉

INTERVIEW

Shepard Fairey

Artist and Founder of OBEY Clothing

LOS ANGELES, CALIFORNIA

SHEPARD FAIREY IS A PIONEERING figure in the street art movement and an outspoken advocate for social and environmental justice. His work has achieved near ubiquity both through his company, OBEY, and the now famous 2008 "Hope" poster depicting Barack Obama. Early in 2017, we sat down to discuss ways that artists and activists can work together to fight climate change.

AL GORE: How did you first become concerned with the climate movement?
SHEPARD FAIREY: I had an abstract understanding of how our growing population, on a planet with finite resources, was a problem. But really, it was seeing *An Inconvenient Truth*. It had a dramatic impact on me. The entire presentation was very persuasive, and it led me to do more research, and it woke me up to the urgency of addressing climate change.

AG: Your work has raised awareness of the most pressing social issues of our time. Based on your experience, what is the role of art in inspiring social activism?
SF: I think the great thing about art is that it affects people emotionally, so it can break through predispositions. If a verbal or written argument doesn't

register, it's easy to block it out. When art connects to something human, that's where the magic is.

Shepard Fairey painting "Liberté, Égalité, Fraternité" mural in Paris, 2016.

Fairey paints a Project C:Change
Mural called "Peace Elephant."

Hong Kong
October 25, 2016

AG: What advice would you give to climate activists who want to incorporate art and design into their activism?

SF: One of the challenges with climate change is that it's a big issue with a lot of different variables. It's hard to nail down just one symbol for it, and people often try to get too many ideas into one piece. I'd encourage people to convey something relatable. Let a smokestack be a symbol. Let rising sea levels be a symbol.

AG: You've used the word "propaganda" to describe your work. What do you mean by that? And to turn our last question around, how can a person create effective propaganda?

SF: I try to be very transparent about what I'm doing. I use the word "propaganda" to encourage people

to be realistic about analyzing everything that comes at them, including what I'm sending their way. When a corporation or politician is saying that the science isn't solid enough on climate change, you need to look at what their real reason for that is.

AG: If you're using art to build momentum behind a movement, what's more important: quantity or quality?

SF: I have a whole section in my biggest monograph, *Supply & Demand*, called "Repetition Works." What's fascinating about virally transmitting images is that people subconsciously understand which way the tide is moving. I think pop cultural symbols, like the peace sign, had a lot to do with the move away from supporting the Vietnam War. I want to see the same thing happen with climate change. ◉

BE INCONVENIENT.

aninconvenientsequel
TRUTH TO POWER

TOP: A participant at the Global Climate March in Berlin, on the eve of the opening of the U.N. climate summit in Paris.

BOTTOM: Shepard Fairey's poster for the 2014 People's Climate March.

LEFT PAGE TOP ROW (RIGHT): A movie poster for *An Inconvenient Sequel*.

LEFT PAGE TOP ROW (LEFT): A San Diego rally against climate change on February 21, 2017.

LEFT PAGE MIDDLE ROW (RIGHT): A protester displays a sign at the 2017 San Diego rally.

LEFT PAGE MIDDLE ROW (LEFT): In opposition to the policies of Donald Trump, Greenpeace protesters hang a banner reading "Resist" from a crane behind the White House.

LEFT PAGE BOTTOM ROW (RIGHT): A 2015 climate march in Berlin.

LEFT PAGE BOTTOM ROW (LEFT): Over 1,000 activists protest the Dakota Access Pipeline at the U.S. District Court in Washington, D.C.

It is wrong to pollute this Earth and destroy the climate balance.

It is right to give hope **to the future generation.**

Climate Reality Leadership
Corps training.

Shenzhen, China
June 2016

Become a Climate Reality Leader

The Climate Reality Leadership Corps is a diverse, global network of passionate people dedicated to fighting climate change through informative presentations, events, policies, and action.

Each of the more than 12,000 Climate Reality Leaders have been through my trainings—multiday events that present not only the science of global warming, but also teach leaders essential skills in communicating the challenges and solutions to the crisis. By giving their own presentations to organizations around the world, they are building a 21st-century movement for climate action.

The Climate Reality Project's mission is to catalyze a global solution to the climate crisis by making urgent action a necessity across every level of society. One of the main ways it does this is by training a network of cultural leaders, organizers, scientists, storytellers, and other citizens around the world to explain the climate crisis and its various solutions. This book provides a glimpse of the training that Climate Reality Leaders get at two- and three-day workshops—but there is so much more to experience and learn at these events.

In the Climate Reality Leadership Corps, exceptional leaders are trained through a suite of in-depth programming on science, communications, and organizing.

1. What does it mean to be a Climate Reality Leader?

A Climate Reality Leader is a changemaker who is committed to promoting understanding of the climate crisis and its solutions—and stimulating action by those who want to help solve it. Each one has been trained by a set of experts to speak truth to power, to stand up to anti-science climate denial and the well-funded dirty energy lobby, and to motivate their friends, colleagues, and neighbors to help solve the crisis. As of this writing there are more than

12,000 Climate Reality Leaders making a difference through action and engagement with their local networks. They are inspiring communities around the world to take climate action now.

By the way, 100 percent of the profits I would have otherwise received from *An Inconvenient Truth* and the book of the same name went to finance the founding of the Climate Reality Project. The same is true of the profits from this book and the movie of the same name.

One of the principal ways Climate Leaders serve is by giving their own version of the updated slideshow about the impacts of—and solutions to—the climate crisis. They also inform their audiences about what they can do to support the shift to clean, renewable energy. We need more people involved in this fight, and spreading this information through free, engaging, targeted presentations is a crucial action.

2. How can I attend a Climate Reality Leader's presentation?

Customized Climate Reality presentations can be organized anywhere, from a library or city hall to a local influencer's living room. When you attend one of these regularly updated, multimedia presentations, you will learn about the global climate crisis, the clean

Give us three days, we'll give you the tools to change the world.

—The Climate Reality Leadership Corps motto

energy revolution, and local issues and opportunities.

▶ To learn about presentations near you, visit Climate Reality at realityhub .climaterealityproject.org/events /attendpresentation.

Here, you can sort by Title, Venue, or Description, or explore an interactive map of upcoming presentations. If you find an event you would like to attend, take a second to register for a free account, then RSVP to the presentation in your area.

3. How can I train to be a Climate Reality Leader?

Are you ready to help lead the movement? Attend a multiday Climate Reality Leadership Corps training session to learn the ropes from renowned climate scientists and communicators. I personally attend all three days of these training programs as well. Since 2006, 35 of these inspiring, hands-on training events have been held in cities from Istanbul to

Shenzhen, Jakarta to Rio de Janeiro—and of course, in cities throughout the United States.

While each training is unique, depending on when and where it takes place, they all offer in-depth learning about what is happening to our planet, as well as the real-world storytelling skills it takes to inspire others to take action.

4. What will I learn?

Several speakers and panelists are lined up for each training, from leading climate scientists who will offer the latest in data and predictive analytics, to communications experts who will train you in the skills of persuasive speaking, in-person outreach, digital activism, and media relations. A mix of hands-on workshopping, expert lectures, and meaningful networking prepare you to build broad grassroots support for your endeavors.

▶ To learn when the next training will be taking place, visit climaterealityproject.org/training.

5. What happens when the training is over?

Within a year of completing the training, each Climate Leader is expected to perform 10 "Acts of Leadership." Of course, some Climate Leaders end up performing more than 100 acts of leadership each year. These acts can take a variety of forms. For example, giving a presentation, writing a blog or letter to the editor, organizing a film screening, meeting with local, state, or federal leaders, or taking part in a day of action. Some speaking events may be arranged for you through the Climate Reality Project, but for the most part, Climate Leaders are responsible for seeking out opportunities.

Leaders can keep in touch with one another by using the Reality Hub, an online community of Climate Reality Leaders and other changemakers.

▶ Visit realityhub.climaterealityproject .org to explore and connect with a global community of climate activists. ◉

Attendees of The Climate Reality Project's 24th Climate Reality Leadership Corps training.

▬

Johannesburg, South Africa
March 12, 2014

Give Your Own Climate Change Presentation

The most important task for Climate Reality Leaders is to spread the word: to give free and engaging climate change presentations to their own audiences. Much of the Leaders' training is focused on these presentations.

In conjunction with the release of this book and the film *An Inconvenient Sequel*, I am making available a compact, 10-minute version of the slideshow for you to download and use in your own climate presentations. The fight against the climate crisis needs more people—including you.

1. Get the presentation.

► Download the "Truth in 10" slideshow at InconvenientSequel.com.

2. Find your audience.

Your book club, your church, your family, your company—you probably already have several natural audiences for a presentation. Starting small is a good strategy, but don't be afraid to bring the presentation to bigger groups; they may be even more interested.

3. Be prepared.

This book and *An Inconvenient Sequel* are both great training for giving the presentation. Be sure to rehearse before you present. Find the right pace and try narrating it out loud, by yourself. Think about the questions you may get and be prepared with answers.

4. Make it personal.

A good presentation tells a story. While the facts of the climate crisis are compelling, your own connection to the issue and your suggestions for actions you and the audience can take are what people will remember most. Add personal observations where you can to make it clear that you have a stake in the fight. Explain (and show) why solving the climate crisis means so much to you, and how its impacts and solutions will affect your audience.

5. Manage your time, hope, and complexity budgets.

You'll have three budgets with an audience, make sure you use them carefully.

Time.
People will give you only a certain amount of their time. The more personal and interesting your story is though, the more time they will allow.

Hope.
You never want your audience to lose hope. Yet in telling the climate change story, some truths are hard to hear. Before showing examples of the suffering climate-related events are causing, I warn my audience that these examples are hard to see, but to hold on—hope is coming.

Complexity.
Everyone has a threshold for processing complex information. Tailor the overall complexity of your message to your audience, and be sure to alternate difficult concepts with information that's easier to absorb.

6. Use an array of visuals.

There are a variety of ways to make the data and your story more powerful, entertaining, and informative. Here are some examples of the types of slides I include in every presentation, and why I use them. You may want to adopt these practices when making your own slideshow.

Set the stage.
I always start my slideshows with this photo. It was the first full-disk view of Earth we ever saw, and it helped to spark a new era of environmental protections. This view reminds us that we are all connected, and all in this fight together.

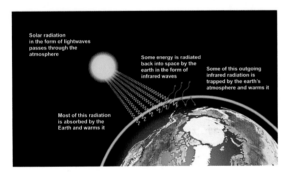

Explain the science.
Infographics like this can help to explain complicated systems or concepts clearly. Step-by-step illustrations can help to engage audience members who might tune out a complex message delivered only through text or pictures.

Stay within the "hope budget."
Photos of recent extreme weather- or climate-related events remind people of the urgency of the crisis and the need to solve it quickly. But be judicious in the number of examples you give. It's easy to deplete your audience's "hope budget."

Isolate startling facts.

Important points sometimes deserve to stand on their own. At other times, pairing them with a relevant image can convey a deeper meaning. Here the text is enhanced with a photo of an endangered species (the golden poison frog).

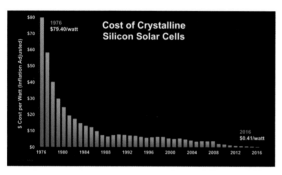

Show the proof.

Choose your charts wisely, using relatively simple examples that illustrate a dramatic change. Going overboard with charts and graphs can quickly exhaust the "complexity budget."

Use appropriate imagery.

Combine text with images that reflect a similar tone. Here, the photo gives a sense of place while the open sky and dramatic lighting signify hope. The moving boat conveys the idea that we are all moving forward, together.

7. Do it again.

Once isn't enough. You'll get better and more comfortable each time you give the presentation. It's important that we spread the truth about the climate crisis as widely as we can. The more you do it, the larger your network and influence will grow, and the more effective you will be in the fight to protect our planet. ◉

The fight against climate change will not be easy. We will encounter a series of NO's.

The great American poet Wallace Stevens wrote one of my favorite lines:

"After the final no
there comes a yes
and on that yes
the future world depends."

Those of us who are privileged to be alive in these early decades of the 21st century are called upon to make decisions of great consequence. Indeed, it is not an overstatement to say that the entire future of humanity depends upon whether or not we rise to the challenge before us.

The climate crisis is the most serious and threatening manifestation of an underlying collision between human civilization as it is presently organized and the ecological system of the Earth—upon which the fortunes and future prospects of our civilization, and our species, depend.

Our population has quadrupled in less than a century and is predicted to continue growing in the present century from 7.4 billion in 2017 to 9.7 billion in the next 33 years, and to 11 billion or more by 2100. Population growth is slowly stabilizing as girls are educated, women are empowered, fertility management is made widely available and child mortality continues to decline. This aspect of our relationship to the Earth is, in spite of the great challenges growing populations will pose in some regions, a success story unfolding in slow motion.

But the impact we have on the natural systems of the Earth is magnified enormously by the awesome power of the technologies that have become available to us since the Industrial and Scientific Revolutions. In particular, any decision to continue relying on dirty and polluting carbon fuels threatens to massively disrupt the climate conditions that have given rise to the flourishing of civilization and have supported the rich and diverse web of life that is integral to our survival. Global warming is the most threatening part of our ecological crisis because the thin shell of atmosphere surrounding our planet is the most vulnerable part of the Earth's system.

But there is a third factor that has led to this crisis, one that is more consequential than either population or technology. It is our way of thinking and the values on which we base the decisions we make. In particular, short-term decision-making is now commonplace in politics, culture, business, and industry. And it is now abundantly clear that

A march to protest the Dakota Access Pipeline.

Standing Rock Sioux Reservation, North Dakota
September 9, 2016

if we continue to ignore the long-range consequences of our present actions and behaviors, we will put our future at dire risk.

The good news—the exciting news—is that we already know that we can change the way we think. We know it with certainty because we have made historic changes in our ways of thinking before. Every great moral cause in human history was initially launched at a time when the overwhelming majority of men and women believed that the change called for was not only impractical but completely implausible. As the late Nelson Mandela said, "It is always impossible until it is done."

This aphorism is true for the abolition movement, the women's suffrage movement, the civil rights movement in the United States, the anti-apartheid movement in South Africa, and more recently, the gay rights movement in the United States and in nations around the world. As each of these moral causes gained more supporters, the changes they called for were met with increasingly fierce opposition. Each renewed

call to do the right thing was met with a resounding "No!"

And in every one of these historic struggles, those fighting for justice, faced with a seemingly endless and implacable resistance, came to doubt that victory would ever come. In the bleakest hours of the U.S. civil rights struggle, Martin Luther King Jr. answered some of his followers who plaintively asked how long it would be before they won.

"How long?" he replied, "Not long! Because no lie can live forever.... How long? Not long! Because the arc of the moral universe is long but it bends towards justice. How long? Not long!"

A mere five years ago, if someone had predicted that in the year 2017 gay marriage would be legal throughout the United States and would be not only supported but honored and celebrated by two-thirds of the American people, I would have responded by saying, "I hope so, but I'm afraid that is extremely wishful thinking."

The pattern is always the same: once the underbrush of obfuscation, straw men, and distractions are cleared away and the underlying issue is resolved into a binary choice between what is clearly right and what is clearly wrong, then the outcome becomes preordained—because of who we are as human beings. And then the change comes quickly. As the late economist Rudi Dornbusch once observed, "Things take longer to happen than you think they will, and then they happen faster than you thought they could."

We are close—very close—to a similar tipping point in the great moral cause that is the climate movement. Every day now, millions more are awakening to the realization that it is wrong to destroy the future of the human race, and it is right to give future generations the well-being, justice, prosperity, and hope to which they are rightfully entitled.

It is also important to note the relationship between solutions to the climate crisis and the current state of the global economy. There is, at present, a growing concern about the weakness of "secular demand" throughout the global economy. The recovery from the Great Recession, which began in early 2009, has not created enough new jobs

to boost incomes—and spending—in the U.S. and in many other countries. As a result, many economists have expressed concern that the global economy is in danger of slipping into another recession. Moreover, the stagnation of wages since the mid-1970s is believed by most to be a principal underlying cause of the political unrest fueling the rise of populist authoritarianism.

Meanwhile, in addition to the impact of hyper-globalization, the accelerating impact of intelligent automation is continuing to exert downward pressure on wages and is continuing to eliminate jobs in a pattern that convinces many observers that conventional economic theory—which tells us that automation always creates more jobs than it eliminates—may no longer be valid. And the reason seems to be that the extension of cognitive capacities along with physical capacities is a game changer.

In these unusual and new economic circumstances, what is most needed to restore strength to the global economy and restore confidence in the efficacy of self-governance is a coordinated global initiative to create tens of millions of new jobs throughout the world—jobs that are not vulnerable to either outsourcing or intelligent automation.

As luck would have it, the steps necessary to solve the climate crisis are exactly the same steps that would save democracy and economic prosperity. They include: a coordinated effort to retrofit buildings in communities throughout the world; an acceleration of the transition to renewable sources of energy and higher levels of efficiency in industry and business; and a shift to sustainable transportation, agriculture, and forestry. An initiative including these steps would simultaneously heal the climate crisis and become the smartest global economic strategy we could follow.

The generation of young people who will fill these new jobs are even now joining this struggle and bringing fresh resolve—reminding us of the special role that young people have so often played in focusing the attention of their elders on the clear distinction between right and wrong.

I vividly remember when I was 13 years old, hearing President John F. Kennedy commit the United States to the inspiring goal of putting a man on the moon within 10 years. And I remember how many of my elders in 1961 felt that goal was unrealistic and perhaps even impossible. But eight years and two months later, Neil Armstrong put his foot on the surface of the moon. Two seconds later, when the news of that history-making step reached NASA's mission control center in Houston, Texas, a great cheer went up—and the average age of the systems engineers cheering in that room was 26—which means that when they heard President Kennedy's challenge, they were 18 years old.

They changed their lives to gain the skills to match their inspiration and become a part of history. And many of today's 18-year-olds are doing the same. Many years from now, when they reach the age of their parents today, they will inherit the Earth we bequeath to them. And depending on the circumstances in which they find themselves, they will ask one of two questions.

If they live in a world of stronger storms, worsening floods, deeper droughts, mega-fires, tropical diseases spreading throughout vulnerable populations in all parts of the Earth, melting ice caps flooding coastal cities, unsurvivable heat extremes in the tropics and subtropics, hundreds of millions of climate refugees generating political disruptions and threatening the collapse of governance—if they face these horrors and the others of which scientists are now warning, they would be justified in looking back at us and asking,

Hundreds of thousands take part in the People's Climate March.

New York, New York
September 21, 2014

"What were you thinking? How could you have done this to us?"

But if they live in a world filled with a sense of renewal, with hundreds of millions of new jobs created in the Sustainability Revolution, with cleaner air and water and the growing prospect of restoring the climate balance—if they have hope in their hearts and can experience the joy of telling their own children that their lives will be better still—then they will ask a different question of us: "How did you find the moral courage to change, boldly and quickly, and save our future?"

The time for us to answer that question is now—by seeking the truth about the reality we are confronting, by using the power we all have to bring about the necessary and urgent changes, and by never forgetting that the will to change is itself a renewable resource. ◉

It's time to speak truth to power.

These are some of the 12,000 Climate Leaders giving the presentation around the world.

Join the fight at
InconvenientSequel.com.

ACKNOWLEDGMENTS

There are a great many people without whose help I could not have written this book. First of all, Liz Keadle has helped me throughout the entire process. I am also grateful to each of my children, Karenna Gore, Kristin Gore, Sarah Gore Maiani, and Albert Gore III, for advice and counsel.

I benefitted from the invaluable research by my personal staff, particularly Brad Hall and Alex Lamballe, without whom this book would never have been possible. Jill Martin worked tirelessly with me on the design of the graphs, pictures, and other graphic material. The entire staff in my Nashville office, led by my superb Chief of Staff, Beth Prichard Geer, helped enormously. And thanks to Joby Gaudet, who has worked extremely hard to ensure the constant flow of information between me and my team. Special thanks as well to Betsy McManus for all of her help and advice.

The climate scientists and other experts who have done the research on which much of this book is based are too numerous to list by name here, though many of their names are in the credits at the bottom of graphs and quotations from studies throughout the book. I would like to single out Jim Hansen, whose scientific work has been especially compelling to me for many years. I would also like to once again acknowledge the seminal work of the late Roger Revelle, who first enlightened and inspired me in the late 1960s and whose path-finding research, along with that of Charles David Keeling, is considered by many to be the baseline for modern climate science.

This book was brilliantly edited, produced, and art directed by Melcher Media. I have worked with the CEO and founder, Charles Melcher, for many years. This is our third book together, and each project has deepened our friendship. It has been a joy to work with Charlie and his skillful team, including especially Josh Raab, David Brown, and Victoria Spencer. I would also like to thank MGMT. for their art direction and beautiful design of the book, especially Alicia Cheng, Sarah Gephart, Sarah Mohammadi, Ian Keliher, Olivia de Salve Villedieu, and Federico Pérez Villoro.

I am particularly grateful to my publisher, Rodale, Inc., and to its talented CEO, Maria Rodale. This is also my third book with Rodale. Their commitment to the environment has been legendary for many years. The Rodale team with whom I worked, including Gail Gonzales, Jennifer Levesque, Yelena Nesbit, Aly Mostel, and Angie Giammarino, did an excellent job. Thank you!

My agent, Andrew Wylie, has, as always, provided extremely valuable guidance and help. Those who are privileged to work with Andrew know that his assistance invariably goes well above and beyond the normal course of duty. Thanks also to Charles Buchan at the Wylie Agency.

This book is a companion to the movie of the same title, *An Inconvenient Sequel: Truth to Power,* which is being released simultaneously. As a result, it has naturally benefitted enormously from the wisdom of the movie's amazing codirectors, Bonni Cohen and Jon Shenk, from its hard-working producers, Diane Weyermann and Richard Berge, and from Sara Dosa and the other talented professionals at Actual Films.

Moreover, none of this would have been possible without the incredible team at Jeff Skoll's Participant Media, including CEO David Linde, the aforementioned Diane Weyermann, Christina Kounelias, and Sam Neswick.

I want to give special personal thanks to Jeff Skoll. Without his encouragement and advice, neither the movie nor the book would have emerged. In addition, I want to thank Lindsey Spindle at the Jeff Skoll Group for the invaluable help that she has provided.

I also want to thank the very able team at Paramount Pictures, headed by Jim Gianopulos. Megan Colligan has played an especially important role. Thanks also to Peter Giannascoli and Katie Martin Kelly.

I also want to thank Mike Feldman, Jason Miner, and Deb Greenspan at the Glover Park Group for all of their help and advice over the past two years on both this book and the companion movie.

My partners and colleagues at Generation Investment Management have been extremely helpful in developing the understandings presented in this book of the Sustainability Revolution, market and investment trends, and the speed with which technologies for renewable energy production, energy storage, electric vehicles, efficiency improvements, and related technologies are developing and spreading worldwide.

Likewise, I am grateful for the help and advice of my partners at Kleiner, Perkins, Caulfield and Byers for their advice. I have also learned a great deal about commitment to sustainability in the marketplace from the men and women at Apple, Inc., with whom it has been my privilege to work for many years.

(In the interest of full disclosure, I have a small indirect investment in two of the companies mentioned in the text, Proterra and ChargePoint, and larger, direct investments in Apple and Google, both of which are also mentioned in the book.)

The Climate Reality Project, headed by Ken Berlin, has been enormously helpful throughout this project. I am very grateful to the board members, professional staff, donors and supporters, and the more than 12,000 trained Climate Reality Leaders around the world for their inspiration. One hundred percent of my share of the profits from the sale of this book (and from the movie) is being donated to The Climate Reality Project.

PHOTO CREDITS

Nicklen/National Geographic Creative; p. 238: Courtesy of Oren Lyons; p. 239: AP Photo/Craig Ruttle; p. 240: Chris Ratcliffe/Bloomberg/Getty Images; p. 243: Dave and Les Jacobs/Getty Images; p. 245: Courtesy of Wei-Tai Kwok; p. 247: Reed Kaestner/Getty Images; p. 248: Rasmus Hjortshøj - COAST Studio; p. 253: Joseph Sohm/Shutterstock.com; p. 254: AP Photo/Patrick Semansky; pp. 256–257: Jeffrey Markowitz/Sygma via Getty Images; p. 258: Courtesy of Steven Miles; p. 259: © Brett Monroe Garner; pp. 262–263: Klaus-Dietmar Gabbert/picture-alliance/dpa/AP Images; p.264: Arterra/UIG via Getty Images; p. 267: Artur Debat/Getty Images; p. 268: Cynthia van Elk/De Beeldunie; pp. 270–271: Bloomberg/Getty Images; p. 272: Courtesy of TAL Apparel; p. 274: Lucia Griggi/Redux; p. 275: Nike; p. 277: Luisa De Paola/AFP/Getty Images; pp. 278–279: Niklas Halle'n/AFP/Getty Images; p. 281: Daily Camera; p. 284: KK Ottesen; p. 285: Melissa Bender Photography; pp. 286–287: © Greenpeace; pp. 290–291: Jon Furlong/jonfurlong.com; p. 292 (clockwise from top left): Sandy Huffaker/AFP/Getty Images, Courtesy of Paramount, Sandy Huffaker/AFP/Getty Images, Paul Abernethy/Global Citizen, Michael Nigro/Pacific Press/LightRocket via Getty Images, Saul Loeb/AFP/Getty Images; p. 293 (top): John MacDougall/AFP/Getty Images, (bottom): Illustration courtesy of Shepard Fairey/obeygiant.com; p. 296: Courtesy of The Climate Reality Project; pp. 300–301: Courtesy of The Climate Reality Project; p. 304 (top): NASA; p. 306 (from top): DarrenRD CC BY-SA 4.0, Dirk Ercken/Shutterstock.com, © SevArt/Pond5; p. 309: Terray Sylvester; p. 310: Azuri Technologies Ltd.; p. 313: Reuters/Adrees Latif; pp. 314–315 (first row, from left): Courtesy of Lina Carrascal, Rafsanul Hoque, Kara Jess Rondina, Courtesy of Rituraj "Raj" Phukan, Michael Dawson, Courtesy of Sankalp Mohan Sharma, Fundación Global Democracia y Desarrollo, FUNGLODE, Courtesy of Lina Carrascal, Sahin Kumar Lohani; (second row, from left): Courtesy of Rituraj "Raj" Phukan, Courtesy of Nana Firman, Thai PBS, Jennifer Smith, Rehia Qais; (third row, from left): Courtesy of Nana Firman, Courtesy of Nora J. Coker, Courtesy of Guilherme Sortino, John Leo Algo, Joe Douthwright; (fourth row, from left): Courtesy of Eric Novak, CREO-ANTOFAGASTA, Courtesy of Jess Reese, Jyoti Bhandari, Courtesy of Rohit Prakash; (fifth row, from left): Courtesy of Mehak Masood, Dan Brannan EdGlenToday.com, Courtesy of Duncan Noble, Fundación Éforo; (sixth row, from left): Courtesy of Rituraj "Raj" Phukan, Clearwater Bay School, Mean Mustard of Cebu City, Courtesy of Sankalp Mohan Sharma, Marc R. Caratao, Julianne Reynolds, Bruce Bekkar; (seventh row, from left): Jay Wilson, Adopt a Native Elder; (eighth row, from left): Explora Science Museum, Courtesy of Brian Ettling, IEEE SEECS, Rehia Qais, Courtesy of Andrea McGimsey; (ninth row, from left): JP Santos, SEREMI MINVU LOS LAGOS, Courtesy of CB Ramkumar, WESA 2017, Courtesy of Rashida Atthar, Nat Giambalvo, Courtesy of Allison Arteaga

Thank you to these Climate Reality Leaders featured on pp. 314–315: Alice Giambalvo, Allison Arteaga, Andrea McGimsey, Brian Ettling, Bruce Bekkar, CB Ramkumar, Claudia Cedano Belliard, Delaney Reynolds, Duncan Noble, Eden Vitoff, Eric Novak, Erica Largen, Guilherme Sortino, Hernan Silva, Jacqueline Lucero, Janice Kirsch, Javaria Qais Joiya, Jess Reese, John Leo Algo, Katarina Hazuchova, Lina Carrascal, Mara Cantonao, Martin Rabbia, Mehak Masood, Michele Douglas Eleta, Nana Firman, Nora Foster-Coker, Patricia McArdle, Pragya Ghimire, Raj Phukan, Rashida Atthar, Rohit Prakash, Rubina Karki, Ryan Anthony Bestre, Sankalp Mohan Sharma, Stephen Bieda, Stuart Scott, Syeda Nishat Naila, Umay Salma, Viveik Saigal, and Wei-Tai Kwok.

Text on p. 196 courtesy of The Greenville News.

This book was produced by

MELCHER MEDIA

124 West 13th Street, New York, NY 10011
melcher.com

President and CEO: Charles Melcher
Vice President and COO: Bonnie Eldon
Executive Editor/Producer: Lauren Nathan
Production Director: Susan Lynch
Editor/Producer: Josh Raab
Assistant Editor/Producer: Victoria Spencer
Consulting Editor: David E. Brown

Designed by MGMT. design
Illustrations by Danaiphan Washareewongse
Information graphics by MGMT. design

Melcher Media would like to thank:
Mary Bakija, Callie Barlow, Jess Bass, Emma
Blackwood, Tova Carlin, Amelie Cherlin, Jon
Christian, Karl Daum, Michel Diniz de Carvalho,
Shannon Fanuko, Barbara Gogan, Ashita Gona,
Evan Greer, Mary Hart, Luke Jarvis, Aaron Kenedi,
Karolina Manko, Emma McIntosh, Kate Osba,
Nola Romano, Rachel Schlotfeldt, Daisy Simmons,
Michelle Wolfe, Megan Worman, Katy Yudin, and
Gabe Zetter.

Christ Our Life

God Guides Us

Authors

Sisters of Notre Dame
Chardon, Ohio

Reviewers

Sister Mary Judith Bucco, S.N.D.

Sister Margaret Mary Friel, S.N.D.

Sister Mary Jean Hoelke, S.N.D.

Sister Mary Cordell Kopec, S.N.D.

Sister Mary Charlotte Manzo, S.N.D.

Sister Ann Mary McLaughlin, S.N.D.

Sister Mary Donnalee Resar, S.N.D.

Sister Katherine Mary Skrabec, S.N.D.

Sister Eileen Marie Skutt, S.N.D.

Sister Mary Jane Vovk, S.N.D.

LOYOLA PRESS.
A JESUIT MINISTRY
Chicago

Nihil Obstat
Reverend John G. Lodge, S.S.L., S.T.D.
Censor Deputatus
May 22, 2007

Imprimatur
Reverend John F. Canary, S.T.L., D.Min.
Vicar General, Archdiocese of Chicago
May 25, 2007

Christ Our Life
found to be in conformity

The Ad Hoc Committee to Oversee the Use of the Catechism, United States Conference of Catholic Bishops, has found the doctrinal content of this catechetical series, copyright 2009, to be in conformity with the *Catechism of the Catholic Church*.

The *Nihil Obstat* and *Imprimatur* are official declarations that a book is free of doctrinal and moral error. No implication is contained therein that those who have granted the *Nihil Obstat* and *Imprimatur* agree with the content, opinions, or statements expressed. Nor do they assume any legal responsibility associated with publication.

Acknowledgments

Excerpts from the *New American Bible* with Revised New Testament and Psalms Copyright © 1991, 1986, 1970 Confraternity of Christian Doctrine, Inc., Washington, DC. All rights reserved. No portion of the *New American Bible* may be reprinted without permission in writing from the copyright holder.

Excerpts from the English translation of *The Roman Missal* © 2010, International Commission on English in the Liturgy Corporation (ICEL); excerpts from English translation of *Rite of Penance* © 1974, ICEL; excerpts from the English translation of *A Book of Prayers* © 1982, ICEL; excerpts from the English translation of *Book of Blessings* © 1988, ICEL. All rights reserved.

English translation of the Apostles' Creed and the Nicene Creed by the International Consultation on English Texts.

Loyola Press has made every effort to locate the copyright holders for the cited works used in this publication and to make full acknowledgment for their use. In the case of any omissions, the publisher will be pleased to make suitable acknowledgments in future editions.

Cover art: Lori Lohstoeter
Cover design: Loyola Press and Think Design Group
Interior design: Think Design Group and Kathryn Seckman Kirsch, Loyola Press

ISBN 13: 978-0-8294-2413-3, ISBN 10: 0-8294-2413-X

© 2009 Loyola Press and Sisters of Notre Dame, Chardon, Ohio

For more information related to the English translation of the *Roman Missal, Third Edition,* see www.loyolapress.com/romanmissal.

Dedicated to St. Julie Billiart, foundress of the Sisters of Notre Dame, in gratitude for her inspiration and example

LOYOLAPRESS.
A JESUIT MINISTRY

3441 N. Ashland Avenue
Chicago, Illinois 60657
(800) 621-1008
www.loyolapress.com

14 15 16 Web 10 9 8 7

Contents

(continued next page)

(continued from previous page)

Note to Families

Goals of This Year's Program

This year your child will be learning how God calls us to live with him forever. The commandments are taught as signs of God's love, and the Beatitudes are introduced as Jesus' way to happiness. Your child is led to a greater appreciation of the sacraments and is encouraged to respond joyfully to God's call to live in the spirit of his love.

A Family Program

Because your faith makes a profound impact on your child, the *Christ Our Life* series provides a Building Family Faith feature at the end of chapters. Usually one chapter is presented in class each week. The activities in the Building Family Faith encourage you to nurture your child's faith by sharing your own response to God. Building Family Faith begins by stating the goals of the chapter. Family activities that promote these aims are listed under four topics:

Reflect
suggests a Scripture reference related to the topic of the chapter.

Discuss as a Family
provides questions to help you apply the Scripture reading to daily life.

Pray
sums up the message for the week in a short prayer that everyone can pray daily. This prayer can be copied and posted on the refrigerator or a mirror. You may add it to meal prayers or other family prayer times.

Do
provides ideas for sharing at meals and for other family activities related to the message of the chapter. You may wish to read all the suggestions to the family and then decide which to do that week. You may also wish to choose other activities that family members suggest.

You are urged to help your child evaluate his or her growth at the end of each unit by discussing with your child the goals on the Looking Back page at the end of each unit.

Each of the units in this book ends with four Family Feature pages that suggest ways to engage the entire family through fun projects, discussion, and review activities.

You can also help your child refer to What Every Catholic Should Know on pages 183–204 and the We Remember sections at the end of chapters.

Note to Families

Ten Principles to Nurture Your Child's Faith

1. Listen with your heart as well as with your head.

2. Encourage wonder and curiosity in your child.

3. Coach your child in empathy early. It's a building block for morality.

4. Display religious artwork in your home. This will serve as a steady witness that faith is an important part of life.

5. Gently guide your child to a life of honesty.

6. Whenever appropriate, model for your child how to say "I'm sorry."

7. Eat meals together regularly as a family. It will be an anchor for your child in days to come.

8. Pray together in good times and bad. Worship together regularly as a family.

9. Be generous to those who need help. Make helping others an important focus of your life as a family.

10. See your child for the wonder that God made. Communicate your conviction that your child was created for a noble purpose—to serve God and others in this life and to be happy with God forever in the next.

Visit **www.christourlife.org/family** for more family resources.

We Come to Know God

See what love the Father has bestowed on us that we may be called the children of God.

1 John 3:1

A Letter Home

Dear Parents and Family,

Welcome! You have an exciting role ahead in supporting your child's learning about the faith. Your interest, participation, and discussion will expand your fourth grader's understanding of these lessons and convey their importance.

In Unit One, the children will discover the many ways God is reaching out to us. They first learn how God reveals himself in creation and especially in his Son, Jesus. Not only does God speak through Jesus, but Jesus is God, speaking and acting. The children will grow to see God's hand in creation and to respond to his call with a real desire to learn more about him. You can help them identify God's handiwork in the world around them.

The children will learn that the key message of the Bible is that God loves us. A better understanding of Scripture will help them develop a devotion to and a new respect for the Word of God. You, too, can gain insight into the readings at Mass with the Sunday Connection found in the Resources section at www.christourlife.org/family.

This first unit also describes how God continues to reach out to us through the Church. The authority that Jesus gave to the apostles is the same authority handed down to today's pope and bishops. The children will be encouraged to show their appreciation for Church leaders as well as to use their own talents to help spread the good news of Jesus' Resurrection through prayer; through their efforts at school, at home, and in the community; and through their example. This is a worthy goal for your whole family.

At the end of each chapter in this unit, the children will bring home a review of the chapter along with either the Building Family Faith page or the Family Feature section. These features give you a quick review of what your child learned and offer practical ways to reinforce the lesson at home so that the whole family may benefit.

Visit **www.christourlife.org/family** for more family resources.

God Reveals Himself to Us Through His Son

God Calls Us to Be His Friends

"Jack, come over here," Matthew called excitedly as Jack walked into the classroom the first day back to school after vacation. "Wait till you hear what I did this summer!"

- What may Matthew have wanted to tell Jack?

- Why are we so eager to tell our friends about our summer?

God calls us friends. He reveals himself to us because he loves us. God reveals himself as three Persons—Father, Son, and Holy Spirit. We call this the Trinity. God wants us to come to know him better so that we will love him more. You will come to know God in many ways, but especially through Jesus.

Jesus calls each of us to share God's friendship. This year you will learn how to live the way a friend of God does. You will study the commandments he gave, which guide us to happiness here and to perfect happiness with God forever.

God Reveals Himself in Creation

None of us has seen God. How can we know him? We listen to God as he reveals, or tells us about, himself. God reveals himself to us in many ways.

All the things God has created tell us something about him. They tell us that God is great and good and loving!

God created everything for us to use and to enjoy. How good God is!

O Lord, How Great and Good You Are!

O Lord, my God, how great you are! You put springs of cool water in the valleys, where the wild animals come to drink. The birds make their nests in the trees.

You make fresh grass grow for the cattle and bring forth crops from the soil so that people may have food to eat. How many are your works, O Lord God!

adapted from Psalm 104:1, 10–12, 14, 24

Write a postcard to a friend describing a nice place to play outdoors near your home.

Postcard

postage

To:_____

What does your description of creation tell you about God?

God Reveals Himself Through Jesus

God reveals himself in the words he speaks to us and in the deeds he does for us. God reveals himself perfectly through Jesus.

Two thousand years ago the Son of God became man. This mystery is called the Incarnation. Jesus is both God and man. Why did God become man? The Bible tells us:

> "For God so loved the world that he gave his only Son, so that everyone who believes in him might not perish but might have eternal life."
>
> John 3:16

> At the Last Supper, Philip said to Jesus, "Master, show us the Father, and that will be enough for us!" Jesus answered, "Have I been with you for so long a time and you still do not know me, Philip? Whoever has seen me has seen the Father. . . . The words that I speak to you I do not speak on my own. The Father who dwells in me is doing his works. Believe me that I am in the Father and the Father is in me."
>
> adapted from John 14:8–11

In many ways, Jesus reveals how much God our Father loves us. Jesus' words and deeds tell us how great and good God is. He shows us God's kindness, forgiveness, and love for the poor. God wants us to show loving concern and care for those who are poor too.

5

Jesus Invites Us to Believe

On the first Easter evening, when Jesus came to the apostles, Thomas was not with them. Thomas did not believe the apostles when they told him that Jesus was risen from the dead. Thomas said, "Unless I see the mark of the nails in his hands and put my finger into the nailmarks and put my hand into his side, I will not believe."

A week later Jesus came to the apostles again, and Thomas was with them. Then Jesus said to Thomas, "Put your finger here and see my hands, and bring your hand and put it into my side, and do not be unbelieving, but believe."

Thomas answered, "My Lord and my God!"

Jesus said,

> "Have you come to believe because you have seen me? Blessed are those who have not seen and have believed."
>
> adapted from John 20:24–29

We believe without seeing because we have faith. Faith is a precious gift from God that helps us to believe in him. It makes us able to trust in him. God is always truthful; he cannot deceive us.

When we were baptized, God gave us the gift of faith and a share in his own life. Faith leads us to enjoy eternal life with God. Through his Church, Jesus helps our faith to deepen. Our faith becomes stronger when we pray and celebrate the sacraments, when we listen to God's Word and study the Church's teachings, and when we do what God tells us to do.

A Moment with Jesus

Think about the postcard you wrote earlier in the chapter. Invite Jesus to join you in that special place you described. Thank him for his awesome gifts of creation. Ask him to help you deepen your faith. Tell him how much you love him, and enjoy knowing how much he loves you.

How We Come to Know Jesus Today

Draw lines to the words that complete the sentences.

We meet Jesus in the   •   • Scripture.

We read about Jesus in   •   • people.

Jesus teaches us through the   •   • sacraments.

We see Jesus in other   •   • Church.

Think of how you and your family do things together in your home that help you know Jesus better, such as reading, praying, or helping someone. In the house, draw yourself and your family doing that activity.

Review

A Faith Puzzle

Fill in the puzzle with the missing words.

1. Faith leads us to eternal l _____ .

2. In Baptism we s _____ God's life.

3. Faith is the power to b _____ .

4. When we believe, we t _____ in God.

5. God tells only the t _____ , not lies.

We Remember

How does God reveal himself?

God reveals himself through creation, Scripture, and perfectly through Jesus.

How can we help God's gift of faith to grow?

We can help our faith to grow by praying, celebrating the sacraments, listening to God's Word, studying the Church's teachings, and doing what God tells us.

We Respond

Act of Faith

O my God, I firmly believe that you are one God in three divine Persons: Father, Son, and Holy Spirit. I believe that your divine Son became man and died for our sins, and that he will come to judge the living and the dead. I believe these and all the truths which the holy Catholic Church teaches, because you have revealed them, who can neither deceive nor be deceived. Amen.

Building Family Faith

CHAPTER SUMMARY We believe God created us out of love, and we come to know God through creation, his words and deeds, and his Son, Jesus. We respond to God's love with faith.

REFLECT

For God so loved the world that he gave his only Son, so that everyone who believes in him might not perish but might have eternal life.

John 3:16–17

DISCUSS AS A FAMILY

*   how God reveals himself through nature, other people, the Church, and Jesus.
*   some ways your family can grow in faith.

PRAY

Lord, help me grow strong in my faith.

DO

*   Notice what amazes or delights you at a park, a nature conservatory, or even in your own backyard and realize that these are signs of God.

*   At mealtime name one person, place, thing, or experience that helped you realize God's love.

*   Read a story or watch a family movie about believing, such as *Field of Dreams*.

Visit **www.christourlife.org/family** for more family resources.

God Speaks to Us in Scripture

God Reveals Himself in Scripture

At every celebration of the Eucharist, the Scripture is read aloud. At the end of the first reading, the reader says, "The Word of the Lord." We answer, "Thanks be to God." A deacon or priest reads from the Gospels. He ends with the words, "The Gospel of the Lord," and we answer, "Praise to you, Lord Jesus Christ!"

The Bible is a very special book. The Church tells us that God reveals himself to us in Scripture. We call the Bible *Sacred Scripture*, which means "holy writing."

Sacred Scripture is made up of many books written over hundreds of years. The Church teaches us that God **inspired,** or worked within the minds of, the Scripture writers. That is why we believe Scripture is the Word of God.

The Bible is separated into two parts. The Old Testament is about what God did for his people during the time before Jesus came. The New Testament is about the words and deeds of Jesus and the early Church.

> In Scripture God comes to meet his children with great love and speaks with them.
>
> adapted from *Dogmatic Constitution on Divine Revelation*, Chapter VI, Article 2

Scripture Tells God's Message of Love

Both parts of the Bible tell us about God's love for us.

The Old Testament

The Old Testament is full of stories about God's love for his chosen people. Some of the books show how God revealed himself to the **Hebrews**, led them out of Egypt, and gave them his laws of love, making them his own people.

Parts of the Old Testament tell how God wanted his people to live. Many books record the messages God gave his people through the **prophets**, who were sent by God to teach his people.

In the Book of Psalms, God shows his people how to pray. The psalms are prayers of praise, thanksgiving, petition, and sorrow. God's people sang the psalms. So did Jesus. We say them or sing them at Mass.

The New Testament

The New Testament tells how Jesus showed us God's love. There are four Gospels, according to Matthew, Mark, Luke, and John. The Gospels have a central place in the New Testament because they have Jesus Christ at their center. The Gospel is the "Good News" of Jesus, our Savior, who offers us eternal life. We hear the Gospel read every time we go to Mass.

In addition to the Gospels, the New Testament contains the Acts of the Apostles. The Acts of the Apostles tells how the Holy Spirit guided the early Church. It has stories that show how the first Christians loved and followed Jesus Christ. The writer of the Gospel of Luke is also the author of the Acts of the Apostles.

The New Testament also has letters that were meant to teach the early Christians about Jesus. Now the letters teach us, telling us how to live as Christians. Peter, Paul, James, and John wrote some of these letters.

As the last book of the New Testament, the Book of Revelation tells of a prophet named John who talks about the glories of God's kingdom. This book was written to encourage Christians who were suffering from persecution.

The Message of the Bible

Use the secret code to write the important message from the Bible on the lines.

Code

D E G L O S U V

Ø Σ □ Δ Γ Ø ⊥ Δ

Message

___ ___ ___   ___ ___ ___ ___ ___   ___ ___ .

□ Γ Ø   Δ Γ Δ Σ Ø   ⊥ Ø

More Messages from the Bible

Read these four messages that were taken from Scripture. Choose one and circle it. Using your own words, write what you think that message is saying and how you can use it in your life.

God is love, and whoever remains in love remains in God and God in him.

1 John 4:16

But you, our God, are good and true, slow to anger, and governing all with mercy.

Wisdom 15:1

Your kindness should be known to all.

Philippians 4:5

Call on me in time of distress, and I will rescue you.

adapted from Psalm 50:15

_____

_____

_____

_____

_____

A Moment with Jesus

God speaks to us through the Bible and through his Son, Jesus. Let's take some time to thank Jesus for showing us the way to his Father and for giving us the Holy Spirit as our helper.

We Enthrone the Bible

Song and Procession

Enthronement

>**Leader:** Your Word, O Lord, is the joy of my heart!
>
>*(Readings from the Bible; see page 12, opposite)*
>
>**All:** *(After each reading)* Thanks be to God.

Silent Prayer

Intercessions

>**All:** *(Response after each petition)* I will love your Word with all my heart!

Leader: Help us to listen with open hearts to your Word,
Lord God. . . . ℞
Fill our hearts with love for your Word,
Lord God. . . . ℞
Guide us to live according to your Word,
Lord God. . . . ℞
Use us to spread your Word,
Lord God. . . . ℞

All: Your written Word, heavenly Father, has a place of honor in our classroom. May your Word always have first place in our hearts and lives. This we ask through your Son, Jesus, and the Holy Spirit. Amen.

2 Review

Knowing the Bible

Circle the correct word to complete each sentence.

1. Another name for the Bible is

   Acts of the Apostles   Sacred Scripture

2. The part of the Bible that tells what God did for his people before Jesus came is the

   Old Testament   New Testament

3. The part of the Bible that tells about Jesus and the early Church is the

   Old Testament   New Testament

4. The books that contain the life and teachings of Jesus are the

   Gospels   Acts of the Apostles

We Remember

What is the Bible?
The Bible is the written Word of God. It is Sacred Scripture.

What is the message of Scripture?
The message of Scripture is that God loves us.

Words to Know
Hebrews   inspired
prophet

We Respond

Whenever I listen to or read the Bible, I remember that God is speaking to me because he loves me.

Building Family Faith

CHAPTER SUMMARY Sacred Scripture is the written Word of God. Its most important message is love. Christians who grow in love and respect for the Bible reverently listen to and proclaim God's Word.

REFLECT
All scripture is inspired by God and is useful for teaching, for refutation, for correction, and for training in righteousness, so that one who belongs to God may be competent, equipped for every good work.

2 Timothy 3:16–17

DISCUSS AS A FAMILY
• your favorite story in the Bible or a favorite Bible passage.
• how remembering the stories of the Bible can help you during the day.
• how you can best use the Bible.

PRAY
Your Word is spirit and life, O Lord.

DO
• Offer your child the gift of a Bible specific to his or her age range. Inscribe it with a message of encouragement and love.
• After Sunday Mass discuss the readings and ways you can apply them during the week.
• Memorize one passage from the Old Testament and one from the New Testament. Recite one passage as your morning prayer and one as your evening prayer for several weeks. Continue this practice throughout the year.

Visit **www.christourlife.org/family** for more family resources.

God Speaks to Us Through the Church

The Church Spreads the Good News

The Church is the people of God. The baptized members who believe in Jesus and follow the leadership of the pope and the bishops are called Catholics. God speaks to us through the Church, and he sent the Holy Spirit to be with it and to guide it. When we listen to the Catholic Church, we follow Jesus.

The Holy Spirit calls Christians to work together to spread the Good News: *God loves us so much he sent Jesus to be our Savior.*

Everyone in the Church helps to do this. The pope and the bishops teach and govern the Church. They are shepherds who care for God's people and lead them to a holy way of life. Priests celebrate the sacraments with the people. They preach about Jesus' message and about how he died and rose to make us God's children. Deacons preach, baptize, and share in Jesus' work in other ways.

God's People Love and Serve

God's people are united in the celebration of the Eucharist. They receive strength through the sacraments and the presence of the Holy Spirit to spread the Good News and to serve God's kingdom. By loving each other, married men and women show us how Jesus loves the Church. Parents and teachers show children what it means to be a Christian by teaching them to love and help others as Jesus did. Men and women religious show Jesus' love and the holiness of the Church through their special way of life. Single people also serve the Church in many different ways.

Look closely at the photographs on the page. Choose one and explain how it shows someone serving God's kingdom.

_____

_____

_____

_____

Jesus Gave Special Authority to Peter

Narrator: Jesus gave special teaching authority to Peter. One day Jesus asked his apostles a question.

Jesus: Who do people say I am?

Apostles: Some say that you are John the Baptist. Others say you are Elijah or Jeremiah or one of the prophets.

Jesus: But who do you say that I am?

Narrator: Simon Peter answered:

Peter: You are the Messiah, the Son of the living God!

Narrator: Jesus was pleased with Peter's answer.

Jesus: Blessed are you, Simon! No human being has revealed this truth to you. My Father in heaven has made it known to you. And so I say to you, you are Peter, the rock, and on this rock I will build my Church. Nothing, not even the powers of hell, will be able to overcome it. I will give you the keys to the kingdom of heaven. Whatever you bind on earth shall be bound in heaven. Whatever you free on earth shall be freed in heaven.

adapted from Matthew 16:13–19

A Moment with Jesus

Imagine that Jesus asked you the same question he asked Peter, Who do you say that I am? How would you answer him? Ask Jesus to help you learn more and more about him. Then spend a little time thinking about how much you love Jesus.

Francis appears to the public for the first time as pope, at the balcony of St. Peter's Basilica, March 13, 2013.

The Pope Speaks in Jesus' Name

Peter believed that Jesus was truly the Messiah, the Savior that God had promised. Jesus praised Peter's faith. Then Jesus promised to build a Church, to form a new people of God. Jesus is the head of the Church. He chose Peter to be the visible head. Peter would teach and lead the Church in the name of Jesus.

The power to speak in Jesus' name was not given just to Peter, the first pope. Every pope receives the same authority. When the Holy Father, the pope, speaks as the head of the Church, Jesus speaks through him. The Holy Spirit guides the pope and the other bishops who teach and lead.

We love, honor, and obey our Holy Father because he represents Christ on earth. We pray for our Holy Father and our bishops, the shepherds of Christ's Church.

Our pope's name is

_____.

My bishop's name is

_____.

Messages from the Popes

Without prayer, your faith and love will die.

John Paul II

Love is the light—and in the end, the only light—that can always illuminate a world grown dim and give us the courage needed to keep living and working.

Benedict XVI

Every believer in this world of ours must be a spark of light, a center of love.

John XXIII

No more war; war never again.

Paul VI

Another Gospel Story About Peter

One day after Jesus rose from the dead, Peter said, "I'm going fishing." Some of the other apostles went with him. They fished all night but caught nothing.

At dawn Jesus stood on the shore, but the apostles didn't recognize him. Jesus called, "Cast your net over the right side of the boat, and you will find something." When the apostles did so, it was so heavy that they could not pull in the huge catch.

Then one apostle said, "It is the Lord." With that, Peter jumped off the boat and swam ashore. The others came by boat, dragging the net with 153 large fish in it.

Jesus had a charcoal fire going. He served the disciples bread and fish. After breakfast Jesus said to Simon Peter, "Simon, son of John, do you love me more than these?" Peter answered, "Yes, Lord, you know that I love you." Then Jesus said, "Feed my lambs."

Jesus asked a second time, "Simon, son of John, do you love me?" Peter replied, "Yes, Lord, you know that I love you." Jesus said, "Tend my sheep."

He said to Peter a third time, "Simon, son of John, do you love me?" Peter answered, "Lord, you know everything. You know that I love you." Jesus said to him again, "Feed my sheep."

adapted from John 21:1–17

The Church is like an ark, with Peter at the helm. How are all disciples to be fishers of men?

_____

In the story, how did Jesus first help the apostles?

_____

How do the popes "feed" the flock of Jesus just as Peter did?

_____

How do you know from the story that Peter loved Jesus?

_____

_____

How can you tell that Jesus loved Peter?

_____

_____

Check It Out

Complete the following sentences with words from pages 15, 17, and 18.

1. Peter believed that Jesus was the

   _____ .

2. Jesus calls Peter his _____ , on which he will build his Church.

3. Peter and all popes have the power

   to teach and to _____ God's people.

4. When the pope speaks as the visible head of the Church,

   _____ speaks.

5. The Church is always guided by the

   _____ .

6. Everyone in the Church must spread

   the _____ .

We Remember

Why do we believe what the Church teaches?

Jesus gave the leaders of his Church the authority to teach in his name. The Holy Spirit guides the leaders and all the people of the Church

We Respond

O my God, I believe in the Catholic Church and all that it teaches.

Building Family Faith

CHAPTER SUMMARY The Church teaches in Jesus' name, guided by the Holy Spirit. We must pray for and respect the Church and its leaders.

REFLECT
Whoever listens to you listens to me. Whoever rejects you rejects me. And whoever rejects me rejects the one who sent me.

Luke 10:16

DISCUSS AS A FAMILY
- what Jesus wants the Church and its leaders to teach about his life and mission.
- the ways you can help the Church to continue its mission to teach.
- why it is important to belong to the Church.

PRAY
Holy Spirit, inspire and guide our leaders.

DO
- Explore the Vatican Web site, www.vatican.va.
- At mealtime discuss examples of current issues on which the Church has served as a teacher.
- Read Matthew 28:18–20 and then say a prayer for our Church leaders.

Visit **www.christourlife.org/family** for more family resources.

CHAPTER 4

God Offers Us Eternal Life

Knowing God Brings Us to Heaven

God made us for happiness. He knows we can be perfectly happy only when we are with him in heaven. At the Last Supper, Jesus said to his apostles:

> "In my Father's house there are many dwelling places. If there were not, would I have told you that I am going to prepare a place for you? . . . I will come back again and take you to myself, so that where I am you also may be."

John 14:2–3

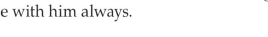

Heaven is our true home. It is more beautiful and wonderful than we can imagine. It is seeing God face to face in all his beauty. It is living in love with God forever. In heaven we will have joy that never ends. Glorified in body and soul, we will reign with Christ forever.

In a parable Jesus told us how precious heaven is. He said:

> "The kingdom of heaven is like a treasure buried in a field, which a person finds and hides again, and out of joy goes and sells all that he has and buys that field."

Matthew 13:44

What did the person give up to get the treasure?

_____

Once we know God, we love him. We long to be with him always.

21

Missing-Letter Game

Look at the pictures that show us ways we come to know God. Use them to help you fill in the missing letters in the puzzle.

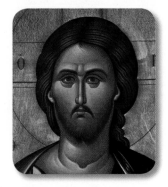

S | | | | | | **N**

C | | | | | **H**

J | | | **S**

Ideas to Remember

How well do you remember the important ideas in this unit? Complete each sentence in the first column with the letter of the ending in the second column. Sentence 1 is done.

1. We celebrate the gift of faith _____ .

2. Faith is the power to believe _____ .

3. Scripture is _____ .

4. The Old Testament tells what _____ .

5. The New Testament tells about _____ .

6. Jesus gave his Church the authority _____ .

7. Those who believe in Jesus will _____ .

8. All members of the Church are to _____ .

9. Jesus said, "Whoever has seen me _____ ."

10. When the pope speaks as the visible

    head of the Church, _____ .

A. **God did for his people before Jesus came**

B. **the written Word of God**

C. **in Baptism**

D. **in God**

E. **have eternal life**

F. **to teach in his name**

G. **Jesus and the early Church**

H. **Jesus speaks through him**

I. **has seen the Father**

J. **spread the Good News**

Names to Remember

Choose a word from the Word Bank to match the descriptions.
Not all choices will be used.

WORD BANK

A. Thomas
B. Peter
C. bishops
D. Jesus
E. Holy Spirit
F. John
G. Philip

_____ **1.** The apostle who asked Jesus to show him the Father

_____ **2.** The one who reveals the Father perfectly

_____ **3.** The apostle who believed only after he had seen Jesus

_____ **4.** The men who teach and govern the Church

_____ **5.** The apostle Jesus gave special authority to teach

_____ **6.** The one sent by Jesus to guide the Church

My Gifts to God

We can work with God to help our life of faith grow. Write in the gift tags
things you can do that will help you grow in your faith. The titles will help
you think of ideas.

1. Praying

I will _____

_____

_____

2. Serving

I will _____

_____

_____

3. Learning

I will _____

_____

_____

We Celebrate Our Faith

Opening Song

Leader: Let us begin our prayer today with the Sign of the Cross.

All: In the name of the Father, and of the Son, and of the Holy Spirit. Amen.

Prayer

Leader: God our Father, we listen to your words of eternal life. Help us be your faithful children forever. We ask this through Jesus Christ our Lord.

All: Amen.

First Reading
Ephesians 1:17–19 adapted

Reader: May the God of our Lord Jesus Christ, the Father of glory, give you a spirit to know and love him. May the eyes of your hearts be enlightened that you may know the rich glories he has promised the holy ones. May you see the greatness of his power in the things he does for us who believe.

The Word of the Lord

All: Thanks be to God.

Intercessions

Leader: Jesus is truly with us. Let us ask him to grant our needs. Our response is "Lord, hear our prayer."

Child 1: That the Holy Father, bishops, priests, deacons, and missionaries may speak God's Word to many people, we pray to the Lord . . . ℟

Child 2: That our parents, brothers, sisters, and all who listen to God's Word may live it in their lives, we pray to the Lord . . . ℟

Child 3: That we may be mindful of God's presence and obey God, we pray to the Lord . . . ℟

Child 4: That we may bring others to God by professing our faith, we pray to the Lord . . . ℟

Child 5: That the sick, the lonely, and the suffering peoples may hear God's words of comfort, we pray to the Lord . . . ℟.

Leader: Father in heaven, hear the prayers of your children and help us to come to know you better. We ask this through Jesus Christ our Lord.

All: Amen.

Second Reading
John 17:3, 7, 8, 11 adapted

Reader: A reading from the holy Gospel according to John.

Jesus said to his Father: This is eternal life: to know you, the only true God, and the one whom you have sent, Jesus Christ. Your people know that everything you gave me is from you. They have believed that it was you who sent me. My Father, keep them true to your name so that they may be one just as we are.

The Gospel of the Lord

All: Praise to you, Lord Jesus Christ.

Prayer

Leader: Jesus, you have given us a share in your life. You promise eternal life to those who believe!

All: Lord, I believe! You have the words of eternal life!

Leader: Jesus, you gave us yourself in the Eucharist so we can have new life.

All: Lord, I believe! I come to you for life.

Leader: Jesus, you promised that you would live in us and we would live in you.

All: Lord, I believe! Live in me and let me live in you.

Leader: Jesus, you promised that we would live forever and be raised up on the last day.

All: Lord, I believe! I hope for eternal life! Amen.

Closing Song

Looking Back at Unit 1

In this unit you have learned that God calls us to faith and eternal life. To help us follow his call, God reveals himself. God shows his might and power in creation and speaks to us in his Word. In the Old Testament God reveals his loving care of his people. In the New Testament God reveals himself through his Son.

Jesus revealed his Father through his words and deeds. He sent his apostles out to spread the Good News. He gave special authority for teaching to Peter and to each pope. He sent the Holy Spirit to guide his Church.

We grow in faith when we pray (especially the Act of Faith), celebrate the sacraments, and do what God tells us. At Mass, we profess our faith in the Nicene Creed, a prayer that lists the chief mysteries of our

faith. With Jesus' help, faith can help us live like true children of God. Then after death, we will live happily with God forever.

Living the Message

Check (✓) each sentence that describes you.

❏ **1.** I can explain what faith is and how to help it grow.

❏ **2.** I can pray the Act of Faith.

❏ **3.** I show respect for Scripture, the Word of God.

❏ **4.** I pray for the leaders of the Church.

❏ **5.** I know what I believe as a Catholic Christian.

Planning to Grow

Calendars help us plan our days by marking events, such as birthdays, dental appointments, or soccer matches. Use the calendar below to plan something to do each day of the week to help your faith grow.

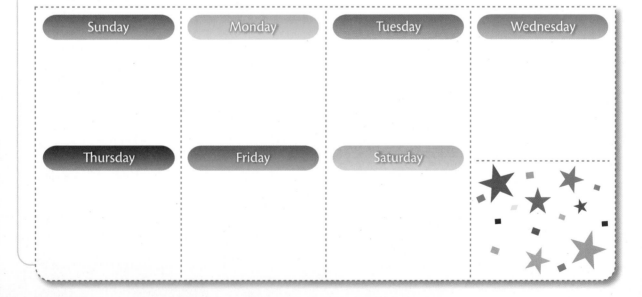

Sunday	Monday	Tuesday	Wednesday
Thursday	Friday	Saturday	

God's Goodness Reflected in Others

God longs to reveal himself to us, and so we are blessed with many ways, large and small, to encounter God in our world and in our daily living. We can meet God through Scripture, the teachings of the Church, and the beauty of creation. For many people, another way to see God more clearly is through the goodness of other people.

We get glimpses of God's saving grace in the compassionate and loving deeds of people who cross our paths each day. Some of these holy people may eventually be recognized and honored by the Church as saints, but most will be remembered by a much smaller circle of family and friends. All who follow the way of Jesus are to be honored for living out the gospel in the times and circumstances of their own lives.

Canonized Saints

The saints are ordinary people who lived extraordinary lives. Some are famous. Some changed the course of history. Many lived quiet lives of humble service. But all the saints are men and women we can learn from. They teach us how to live good lives as we do our work, love our family and friends, and meet life's challenges. The saints prove that God is with us, even when life is most challenging.

Because the saints live with God, all who love God can get to know them. They can be our friends, companions, and teachers. We can ask Saint Jude to pray to God for us in difficult times.

We can learn courage from Saint Joan of Arc and patience from Saint Joseph. Saint Thérèse of Lisieux can teach us how to turn our small and ordinary actions into a prayer.

St. Jude ❯

Some countries are devoted to certain saints and observe their feast days with special rituals.

The Sanchez family's ancestors are from Mexico. Every December 12 this family celebrates the feast of Our Lady of Guadalupe by rising before dawn, joining fellow parishioners to sing hymns to Our Lady, and processing through the neighborhood carrying a banner displaying her image.

The Walshes celebrate the feast of Saint Patrick, patron of Ireland, on March 17 in grand style. They often wear green, attend Mass, and march in a parade.

The Serios from Italy celebrate the feast of Saint Joseph on March 19 by inviting friends and relatives to a feast of specially prepared foods that are also shared with people who are poor.

The Samuelsson family from Sweden observes the feast of Saint Lucy on December 13, eight days before the shortest day of the year. The day is celebrated with bonfires and candles.

The oldest daughter traditionally wears a white dress with a red sash; on her head is a crown of evergreen branches with lit candles. As she brings morning coffee and saffron rolls to her parents, she sings the song "Santa Lucia" and the Christmas season in Sweden officially begins.

St. Lucy Saffron Rolls

2 packages of dry yeast
½ cup warm water
1 cup warm milk
¼ cup honey
1 teaspoon ground cardamom
pinch of saffron or drop
   of yellow food coloring

1 ½ teaspoons salt
½ cup butter
2 eggs
6–7 cups unbleached
   white flour
raisins
1 slightly beaten egg white

Combine the yeast and water. In another bowl combine milk, honey, spices, and salt. Then add butter, eggs, and the yeast mixture. Beat in enough flour to make a stiff dough. Put it onto a lightly floured surface and knead until smooth, about 10 minutes. Place in a greased bowl, cover lightly, and allow to rise for an hour. The dough will double. Knead it for 3 minutes. Return it to the bowl, cover it, and allow to rise for 45 minutes. Punch it down and knead it for 3 more minutes. Cover the dough and let it rest for 15 minutes. Divide the dough into 24 pieces and roll each into a foot-long rope. Form the ropes into an *S* shape on a greased baking sheet. Coil each end of the *S* until it looks like a double snail shell. Put a raisin in the eye of each coil. Brush the buns with egg white and bake at 350° F for 15 to 20 minutes. They will be brown on top. Serve warm.

One Family's Example

Many of us think about our parents when we think of generous and giving people who have helped us know God through their acts of love. But for the Inserra family, the person who also helped them know God was their Aunt Chris. Chris spent several years in a Catholic Worker house, living among the poor and actively promoting peace and justice. She joined thousands of other Catholics and people of faith in an annual request for the closure of the School of the Americas, which has been condemned by U.S. and Latin American Catholic Bishops for training soldiers responsible for atrocities, such as the murder of Archbishop Oscar Romero of El Salvador. She sings in the church choir, sits on the local school board, and puts pressure on local politicians to live up to their campaign promises to serve the community. People who know her have gained insight into what it means to live the faith. When Chris hears the words of Christ we say at Mass: "Peace I leave with you; my peace I give to you" (John 14:27), she feels compelled to share that peace with others.

Faith Word Search

Find and circle words in the puzzle that are related to saints and our own journey in faith.

WORD BANK

Heroes	Holiness
Example	Faith
Hope	Charity
God	Prayer
Saints	Courage
Compassion	Truth
Goodness	Humility
Generous	

```
A C O N E Y R R M T E
G S G A N X U M H O T
A U S R S E A S N G S
N O I S S A P M O C E
P R A Y E R I Y P Y E
E E O G N N T N T L S
S N P I I I D I T S E
T E E G L C R O N S O
R G E I O A P O O H R
U U M P H D S H A G E
T U R C O U R A G E H
H T I A F H S T T E N
```

Family Feature

Activities with Your Family

Read through the suggested family activities below and pick one or more that appeal to you as ways to use the ordinary opportunities of family life to nurture your child's faith.

At dinner some evening soon, tell which saint is your favorite and why. What are the traits that most appeal to you about this saint? Ask everyone gathered around the table to share their favorite saints.

Pick a family saint to inspire, support, and pray for your family. Invite your child to help you research saints online at http://www.catholic.org/saints/ or purchase a book on saints, such as *Loyola Kids Book of Saints* by Amy Welborn (Loyola Press). On your family saint's feast day each year, plan a special meal, light a candle, and say a prayer asking for that saint's guidance. Include that saint in your prayers throughout the year.

Tell about one extended family member, coworker, or friend who exemplified a Christian virtue (for example, honesty, courage, wisdom, holiness, faith, hope, or charity). Ask the children in the family if they can tell about someone who inspires them in the same way.

Impress upon your children the importance of being a good example to others. Because our behavior reflects on God who created us, guide your children in learning to be more like him—kind, inclusive, forgiving, trustworthy, faithful, just, and compassionate.

Visit **www.christourlife.org/family** for more family resources.

God Strengthens Us to Be Holy

Whoever acknowledges that Jesus is the Son of God, God remains in him and he in God.

1 John 4:15

A Letter Home

Dear Parents and Family,

Unit Two of *Christ Our Life* presents children with the ultimate road map to good living: the teachings of Jesus.

At the beginning of this unit, the children are reminded of their responsibility as Christians to live as Jesus did, loving God and others. They are encouraged to follow the path Jesus left for us, making prayer and good works part of their daily lives. The children's study of prayer provides a great opportunity for you to make prayer a bigger part of your family life.

Of course, everyone gets a little lost now and then. In Unit Two, the children will pause and reflect on their need for mercy, as well as on God's readiness to grant it if they are truly sorry for their sins. The children will deepen their understanding of conscience and how to form it in accord with Jesus' teaching. Acknowledging the times when they are lost will foster a greater appreciation for the Sacrament of Reconciliation. You can share your own appreciation of this opportunity for forgiveness by participating in the sacrament in your parish.

Finally in Unit Two, the children will learn the importance of worshiping God. In fact, it's one of the Ten Commandments, a clear set of guidelines to living right, a gift demonstrating God's love for us and his desire to bring us close to him.

At the end of each chapter in this unit, the children will bring home a review of the chapter along with either the Building Family Faith page or the Family Feature section. These features give you a quick review of what your child learned and offer practical ways to reinforce the lesson at home so that the whole family may benefit.

Visit **www.christourlife.org/family** for more family resources.

We Are Called to Follow Jesus

Jesus Teaches Us How to Live

During his lifetime in Palestine, Jesus showed us how to be the best persons we can be. By his words and actions he taught us how to live holy and happy lives. Baptized Christians try to live like Jesus and follow his teachings. We are called to bring his life and love into the world. Jesus said,

> "I came that you might have life—and have it to the full."
>
> adapted from John 10:10

Jesus Showed Love and Concern

A man named Jairus rushed through the crowd to reach Jesus. He knelt before Jesus and said, "My daughter has just died. But come, lay your hand on her, and she will live."

Jesus went with Jairus to his house. He took the little girl by the hand, and she got up. Jesus gave life back to her. Jairus and the girl's mother were filled with joy.

adapted from Matthew 9:18–19,23–2

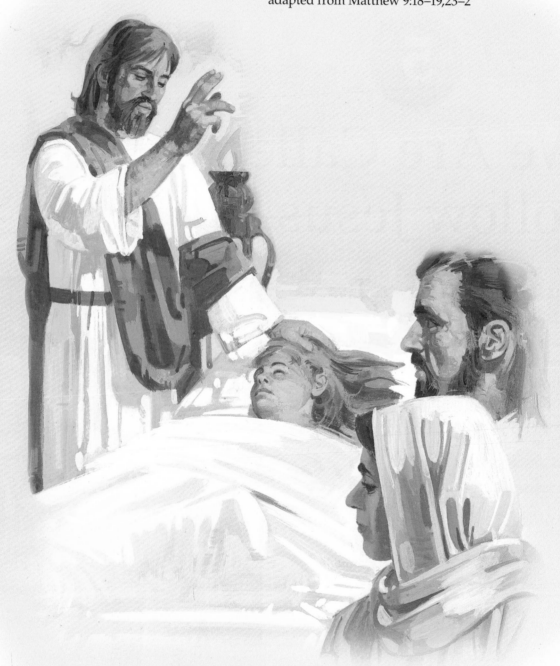

Jesus' Forgiving Love Healed People

One day Jesus was teaching in a house. Many people gathered to hear him speak. They crowded into the house and around the door.

In the crowd was a paralyzed man who wanted to see Jesus. Because the man couldn't get into the house, his friends carried him to the roof. They lifted up part of the roof until they had a large opening. Then they lowered the sick man on his mat.

Jesus stopped teaching. He looked at the sick man and said, "Child, your sins are forgiven."

Then he cured the man's body. The man got up, picked up his mat, and walked out in front of everyone.

adapted from Mark 2:1–5,11–12

Jesus Prayed to His Father

The apostles watched Jesus when he was at prayer. They could see that he knew how to speak to God our Father. Afterward they came to him and said, "Lord, teach us to pray."

Then Jesus taught them the prayer we call the Lord's Prayer. We should try to pray it every day. In this prayer we praise God and ask for all our needs. We ask to be forgiven as we forgive others. We also ask to be saved from evil.

Lord's Prayer

Print the phrase from the Lord's Prayer that matches each sentence. The prayer on the inside cover of your book can help.

God, everyone's loving Father, has given us life.

_____

Heaven is where God lives.

_____

We pray that all people will respect God and God's holy name.

_____

We pray that all people on earth will belong to God's kingdom and do God's will.

_____

_____

We ask for food and for the living bread, the Eucharist. We ask for the things we need every day.

_____

We ask God to forgive us our sins as we forgive others.

_____

We ask God to help us in time of temptation.

_____

We ask God to keep us from all evil, especially sin.

_____

People Who Act Like Jesus

Here are three examples of people who have done what Jesus taught. Read each story and then write the word that matches the deeds described in the story: _pray_, _serve_, or _forgive_.

A young driver made a serious mistake. She drank too much and then drove. This caused an accident that took the lives of a young man and a young woman. While in prison, the driver became very ill. Mrs. Reyes, the mother of the young woman who had been killed, wrote a letter to the state. In it she asked for the release of the driver, who was responsible for the death of her daughter.

Mrs. Reyes knows how to

_____ .

While troops were being sent to the Middle East before the war with Iraq, the fourth graders at Ascension School set aside a special corner in their classroom. There they took turns asking God for peace.

These children know how to

_____ .

When Sister Emmanuelle visited Egypt, she found that thousands of people lived in the garbage dumps. This is where they made their homes. They were bare, with dirt floors and roofs made from palm leaves. Both parents and children survived by collecting garbage, sorting it, and reselling it. Most of these people didn't know how to read or write. Sister moved in with them to give them hope and to teach them that God is love. She has built a school, a clinic, a vocational center, and soccer fields. She says, "I wouldn't want to be anywhere else because here I feel I am giving the life of Jesus Christ to the children."

Sister Emmanuelle knows how to

_____ .

A Moment with Jesus

Is there someone in your family who needs your prayers? Pray to Jesus now for that person, telling him about this family member's needs. Trust that Jesus will bring peace and comfort to him or her. Thank Jesus for his loving care.

Add a Happy Ending

- Tyrone bumped into Carlos in the hall. Carlos' lunchbox opened, and food spilled onto the floor.

- All of Danica's friends brought money to buy a treat, but Danica was unable to bring any money.

- Miguel and Connor were good friends. Both boys tried out for a part in a play. Miguel got a part, but Connor did not.

- Marisol laughed and teased her brother about his new haircut.

- Sophia's friend Molly will not talk to her because Sophia went skating with other friends without inviting Molly.

Can you think of a time when you received kindness? Share this with a partner.

We Remember

What does Jesus say about forgiving others?
Jesus says,

"If you forgive others . . . , your heavenly Father will forgive you."

Matthew 6:14

We Respond

I will forgive those who hurt me.

Building Family Faith

CHAPTER SUMMARY The Gospel shows Jesus curing sick people, forgiving sins, and teaching all how to live in his love. As Jesus' followers, we share his concern for others and forgive those who have hurt us.

REFLECT
When Jesus returned to Capernaum after some days, it became known that he was at home. . . . They came bringing to him a paralytic carried by four men.

Mark 2:1,3

DISCUSS AS A FAMILY
- how loving acceptance and forgiveness are the greatest gifts we have to share with friends and family.

- times that you have forgiven someone who hurt you and how you worked through your anger, sadness, and pain.

PRAY
Jesus, open my eyes to the needs of others.

DO
- Plan a family help day: Volunteer for a parish outreach effort; clean out closets, bookshelves, and toy boxes, and donate these items to a charity.

- Make a pact with your family that together you will work through any arguments or hurt feelings, not simply sweep them under the rug.

- Think globally, act locally by studying as a family the problems of poverty and hunger in the world and learning what you can do in your community to help a family in need.

Visit **www.christourlife.org/family** for more family resources.

Jesus Invites Us to Receive God's Mercy

Our God Is a God of Mercy

The people brought to Jesus a woman who had committed a serious sin. The law said to stone her to death. The people asked Jesus what he thought about that law. Jesus stooped down and began writing on the ground. Then he said, "Let the one among you who has not sinned throw the first stone." He bent down and wrote again.

The people in the crowd were surprised by Jesus' answer, but all of them knew in their hearts that Jesus was right. They too had sinned. Each person walked away. Jesus looked up at the woman and said, "Woman, where are they? Has no one condemned you? Neither will I. Go and from now on do not sin anymore."

adapted from John 8:3–11

The woman had done wrong. She expected a terrible punishment. How surprised she was when Jesus forgave her. Her heart was full of joy!

Jesus loved the other people too. He also wanted to forgive them for their sins, but they had walked away.

Jesus offers forgiveness to all of us. He forgives us in the Sacrament of Penance and Reconciliation.

I Plan My Journey to Jesus in the Sacrament of Reconciliation

Number the stepping stones along Reconciliation Road in the order we do them when we celebrate the Sacrament of Reconciliation.

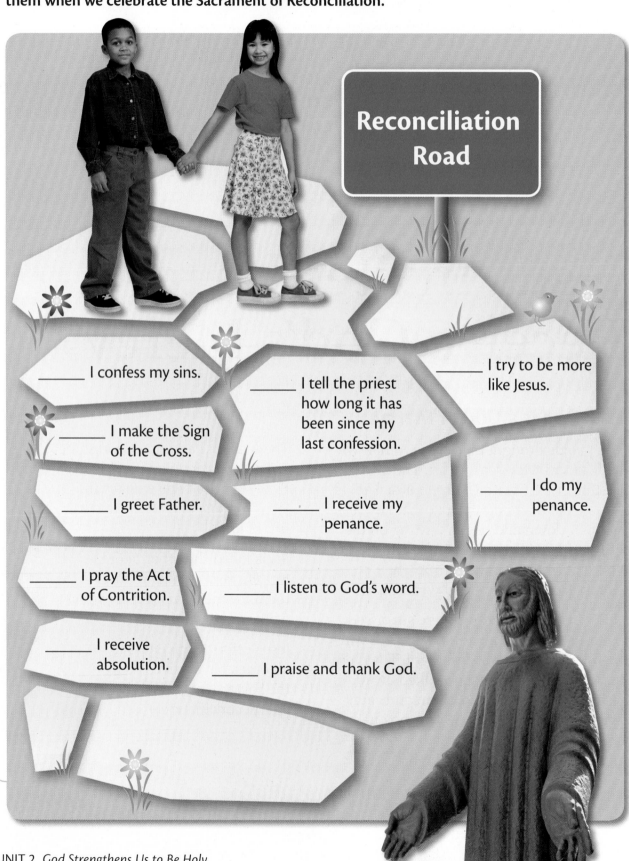

Reconciliation Road

_____ I confess my sins.

_____ I tell the priest how long it has been since my last confession.

_____ I try to be more like Jesus.

_____ I make the Sign of the Cross.

_____ I greet Father.

_____ I receive my penance.

_____ I do my penance.

_____ I pray the Act of Contrition.

_____ I listen to God's word.

_____ I receive absolution.

_____ I praise and thank God.

We Seek Forgiveness

Jesus is waiting for us to come to him in the Sacrament of Reconciliation. He wants to tell us of his love, to forgive our sins, and to make us stronger by following his way. We meet with Jesus through the priest, who acts in Jesus' name and in the name of the Church.

Use the words in the Word Bank to complete the sentences.

WORD BANK

confess   Holy Spirit
conscience   Jesus'
forgiveness   penance
promise   sorry

1. I pray to the _____ to help me.

2. I read what Jesus said of _____ .

3. I examine my _____ .

4. I tell God I am _____ for my sins.

5. I think about how to be more loving and _____ God to try.

6. I _____ my sins to a priest.

7. I receive _____ forgiveness.

8. I do my _____ .

We Use Guides to Make Decisions

We are God's children, and we try to follow his way. We know God is always with us to help us. He has given us the commandments and Beatitudes to guide us. He has also given each of us a conscience that helps us know what is right. From deep in our hearts, our consciences act like judges, deciding what is good and what is evil. Conscience calls us to love and to choose the good, which will take us to God our Father. It calls us to avoid sin and to hate what turns us away from God.

We form good consciences by studying what Christ and his Church teach us. Each of us should always obey his or her conscience. When we do not obey our consciences, we do wrong and sometimes sin.

An important step in preparing to celebrate the Sacrament of Reconciliation is the **examination of conscience.** We examine our consciences by prayerfully thinking about whether our actions have hurt our relationship with God or others.

When we sin, we turn away from God. **Mortal sin** is a very serious wrong. It cuts us off from God's life. **Venial sin** is less serious, but it too should be avoided. All sin hurts our relationship with God, the Church, and others.

Fortunately, even after we have sinned, our consciences help us. Through our consciences, Jesus calls us to his mercy and forgiveness in the Sacrament of Reconciliation.

A Moment with Jesus

Think for a moment about the choices you made today. Were they good choices or could you have made better ones? Thank Jesus for the gift of conscience that helped you make good decisions. Ask for forgiveness for the poor choices you may have made. Now rest quietly in Jesus' love for you.

My Conscience Helps Me Every Day

Read the sentences below and decide whether the actions described are good or bad. Put the numbers of the sentences in the correct box below.

1. I shared my chocolate chip cookies with my friends.

6. I watched a good television program after I had finished my homework.

2. I got a good grade by cheating on my test.

7. I didn't go to Sunday Mass because I wanted to ride my new skateboard.

3. I earned money to get Gabrielle a birthday present.

8. I read a good book to learn about people in China.

4. I lied when the teacher asked whether I had finished my work.

9. I used Kwan's pencil and kept it because I needed one.

5. I gave my snack money to the missions.

10. I did not do my homework last night because I watched television.

These actions are good.

They follow God's Law of Love.

___ ___ ___ ___ ___

These actions are wrong.

They do not follow God's Law of Love.

___ ___ ___ ___ ___

A. absolution
B. Contrition
C. conscience
D. priest
E. forgiveness

Riddles—What Am I?

Write on the lines the letters of the answer choices for these riddles.

1. I help you recognize right from wrong. I am your _____ .

2. Jesus wants to give me to sinners. I am _____ .

3. Your sins are forgiven when I happen in the Sacrament of Reconciliation. I am _____ .

4. God knows you are sorry for your sins when you say me. I am the Act of _____ .

5. I act in Jesus' name when you confess your sins. I am the _____ .

We Remember

How does your conscience help you?

1. It helps me know right from wrong.

2. It leads me to choose what is right.

3. It tells me to be sorry for my sins and ask for forgiveness.

Words to Know

examination of conscience
mortal sin **venial sin**

We Respond

Jesus, help me to follow my conscience and make good choices.

Building Family Faith

CHAPTER SUMMARY Our consciences help us make good choices. Celebrating the Sacrament of Reconciliation regularly helps us form our consciences and grow strong in God's love.

REFLECT

He straightened up and said to them, "Let the one among you who is without sin be the first to throw a stone at her."

Adapted from John 8:7–11

DISCUSS AS A FAMILY

• why Jesus said that the one without sin could throw the first stone.

• what the woman might have been thinking when she was brought to Jesus.

• how you think she may have felt when Jesus said, "Go and . . . do not sin anymore"?

John 8:11

PRAY

Help us, O God, to know and do your will.

DO

• Tell your child about a time you chose to do the right thing in a difficult situation and were glad you did.

• Discuss the choices a character makes in a children's story or television program. Consider the options and reasons for the choices.

• Talk about the great gift God gave us in the Sacrament of Reconciliation. Have the family celebrate the sacrament at church, then afterward share a family treat.

Visit **www.christourlife.org/family** for more family resources.

We Worship God

We Worship God with Love

We see God's greatness and love in the things he has made and in the wonderful things he does for us. We read about God's love for us in the Bible.

Once we know how great and holy God is, we know that he alone deserves all our love. We want to give God the greatest praise and serve him with all our strength.

Our loving response to God is called worship. We worship God by praying and serving him.

Prayer Is Worship

When we pray, we **adore** God as our Creator and Lord. We love God because he is good. We thank God for all his goodness to us, and we tell God we are sorry for sometimes turning away from his love. With trust in God's goodness, we ask him for what we need. When we do these things, we are worshiping God in prayer. The Eucharist is our highest form of worship.

Service Is Worship

We also worship God when we serve him. Serving God is doing the things he wants us to do. It is obeying God's commandments that tell us how to love him and others. Doing good to others is an important part of our worship of God.

Real Worship Comes from the Heart

Our worship is not real unless it comes from our hearts. God had to remind his Chosen People again and again to worship him with love. Many times the people forgot this. They offered prayers and sacrifices in the Temple, but their hearts were far from God. Through the prophets God told them that this empty worship did not please him because it was not worship at all. Worship can only be true when it is offered in love.

"It is love that I desire, not sacrifice. It is not your offerings I want, but that you should know me, your God."

adapted from Hosea 6:6

"These people honor me with their lips alone. Their hearts are far from me."

adapted from Isaiah 29:13

We build upon the love in our hearts when we offer our own sacrifices to God.
Fill in the building blocks with your own ideas of ways to offer your love to God.

We Unite Ourselves with Jesus' Sacrifice

You shall make an altar and upon it shall sacrifice your offerings.

adapted from Exodus 20:24

The Israelites worshiped God by offering him gifts. A gift to God is called a **sacrifice**. God's people brought their best animals, fruit, and grain to the temple priest. The priest placed these gifts on the altar, offering them to God.

The people offered these sacrifices to acknowledge that all the good things they had were gifts from God. Offering some of them in sacrifice to God was a way of saying "You alone, Lord, created these gifts. We offer them back to you in praise."

Write the sacrifices that the Israelites offered to God.

1. _____

2. _____

3. _____

A Moment with Jesus

Share with Jesus one happy thing and one sad thing that happened to you recently. Offer both of them to Jesus. Thank Jesus for the gift of each day and offer all that you do and say to him.

We Offer Ourselves to God

Jesus' whole life was an act of worship. He offered everything he said and did to God his Father. He showed the greatness of his love when he suffered and died on the cross. The sacrifice of Jesus on the cross was the perfect love offering of God's own Son.

In the Mass we gather as God's people to worship him. Jesus has given us his sacrifice to offer to God. Each time we celebrate the Eucharist, we offer Jesus to God under the forms of bread and wine.

We offer all that we think, say, and do to Jesus. We ask him to unite our gift with his own and to give it to our heavenly Father. Then Jesus Christ gives us himself as food and drink to unite and to strengthen us as a holy people.

Our Daily Gift

Although we may not celebrate the Eucharist daily, we can still offer ourselves to God each day. There is a prayer that tells Jesus we offer all our *prayers, works, joys,* and *sufferings* with his holy sacrifice.

Use the secret code to find the name of this prayer.

Code

E F G I M N O R

Prayer

Fill in the puzzle with four things you offer to God in the Morning Offering.

O F F E R I N G

Something to Think About

How are the people in the pictures worshiping God? Find the definition in the Worship Box that fits each picture, and put the number on the line. In the last space draw a way that you will try to worship God a little better and with more love. Write the number for your picture and finish the sentence.

A. The Johnson family celebrates the Sunday Eucharist, taking part in all the prayers and songs.

_____

B. The Janski family rests and enjoys one another's company on Sundays.

_____

C. Olivia's mother asks for help with the cleaning. Olivia helps gladly.

_____

D. Mrs. Cho is old and lives alone. Orlando cares for her yard.

_____

E. Rosa prays each night before going to bed.

_____

F. I will try to

_____

_____

We Remember

What is worship?
Worship is our loving response to God's greatness and holiness.

Word to Know
adore

We Respond

O Jesus, through the Immaculate Heart
    of Mary,
I offer you my prayers, works, joys, and
    sufferings of this day
in union with the holy sacrifice of the
    Mass throughout the world.
I offer them for all the intentions of your
    Sacred Heart. Amen.

Make all your life something beautiful for God.

Blessed Teresa of Calcutta

Building Family Faith

CHAPTER SUMMARY   Worship of God includes prayer and service. We can worship God in all our actions throughout the day.

REFLECT
Oh, that today you would hear his voice: Do not harden your hearts.

adapted from Psalm 95

DISCUSS AS A FAMILY
• some of the ways your family loves and serves God.

• whether we recognize that when we help others or others help us, God is pleased and present in our lives.

PRAY
God, help us love you in all that we do.

DO
• Put a copy of the Morning Offering prayer on the bathroom mirror or the breakfast table so everyone can pray it at the start of each day.

• Have your child tell you the story of Saint Elizabeth Ann Seton or Saint John Bosco at dinner this week.

• Put an empty bowl on the kitchen table with a cup of small candies, such as jelly beans or mints, next to it. Every time a family member makes a sacrifice for another family member, classmate, coworker, or friend, he or she puts a candy in the bowl. At the end of the week, the family can enjoy the treats.

Visit **www.christourlife.org/family** for more family resources.

God Gave Us Laws for Living

God Tells Us How to Live

Narrator: One night Michael dreamed that he was going on a wilderness expedition in the Rocky Mountains. The expedition leader knew that Michael didn't have much hiking experience, so he gave him the book *How to Hike in the Rocky Mountains* to take along on the trip.

Leader: Michael, if you follow the rules in this book, you'll be able to explore the mountains and return safely. Here at base camp we've helped you all we can, but now you're on your own. Follow the directions and you'll enjoy the mountain wilderness.

Michael: Thank you, sir. I'll do everything it says.

Narrator: Then Michael put on his backpack, grabbed the book and a compass, and set off for his hike.

Leader: Have fun on your expedition!

Narrator: The screeching of an eagle startled Michael and woke him up. He realized he had only been dreaming.

God made us and knows what is best for us. God told us how to live well. He gave us laws that tell us how to relate to God, ourselves, other people, and our world. The Church teaches us what God's laws mean.

Moses Receives the Commandments

God led his people out of slavery in Egypt, with Moses as their guide. As they marched through the desert, God protected and cared for them. He made them his special people.

Mount Sinai

One day God told Moses that he would come down on Mount Sinai in three days. The people prepared for the event. On the third day a heavy cloud came down upon the mountain. The people heard thunder and trumpet blasts. They saw lightning. God came down in fire, and Mount Sinai was wrapped in smoke. God called Moses to the top of the mountain and gave him the Ten Commandments. Moses went back to the people and told them God's law. They agreed to do everything God commanded.

The next day Moses sealed the covenant between God and the people, offering a sacrifice to God. Moses sprinkled the blood of the animals he had offered on the altar and on the people. Then God called Moses up to him on the mountain. There God wrote his laws on stone tablets and gave them to Moses.

adapted from Exodus chapters 19 and 24

Complete the sentences with words from the Word Bank.

> **WORD BANK**
>
> Egypt   people
> everything   sacrifice
> Moses   stone

1. God gave the Ten Commandments to

    _____ long ago.

2. God led his people out of _____ and made them his special

    _____ .

3. After the people heard God's laws, they said, "We will do _____
    that the Lord has told us."

4. Moses sealed the covenant by offering a _____ to God.

5. God wrote the commandments on _____ tablets.

God Has a Covenant with His People

God had been faithful to the people. He freed them from slavery, protected and fed them in the desert, and gave them a guide for living—the Ten Commandments. These commandments are our **moral law**. They show us how to live lives that are pleasing to God and respectful of others.

When the people accepted the commandments and agreed to live according to them, they made a choice to belong to God. They made an agreement, a covenant with God. God was their God and they were God's people in a special way.

We too are God's people. We have a special covenant relationship with him. We follow the Ten Commandments and Jesus' example of loving and caring for others, especially those who are in special need of our help.

God's People Love His Commandments

God's people praise and thank him for his laws.

How can a young person be good?
    By keeping to your words.
With all my heart I seek you;
    help me to obey your commands.

Within my heart I treasure your promise,
    that I may not sin against you.
Blessed are you, O LORD;
    teach me your commandments.

With my lips I declare
    the commands of your mouth.
In the way of your laws I rejoice,
    as much as in all riches.

I will think of your teachings
    and study your ways.
In your laws I will delight;
    I will not forget your words.

adapted from Psalm 119:9–16

A Moment with Jesus

Imagine this! When Jesus was a boy, he learned about Moses and God's people. He was expected to obey the commandments. He went to the Temple to worship. His life was very much like yours is now. Share with Jesus whatever is on your mind or in your heart. Jesus listens and understands.

The Commandments Are Laws of Love

God gave us his laws with love to show us how to love him and others. They help us live so that we can be happy on earth and with God in heaven. There we will be forever with Jesus, Mary, the angels, the saints, and those we love.

Finish the Ten Commandments below by writing the missing words from the Word Bank.

WORD BANK

adultery	gods
name	covet
goods	steal
false	holy
father	kill

1. I am the Lord your God:

   you shall not have strange _____ before me.

2. You shall not take the _____ of the Lord your God in vain.

3. Remember to keep _____ the Lord's Day.

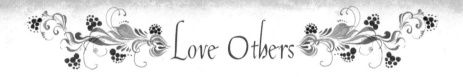

4. Honor your _____ and your mother.

5. You shall not _____ .

6. You shall not commit _____ .

7. You shall not _____ .

8. You shall not bear _____ witness against your neighbor.

9. You shall not _____ your neighbor's wife.

10. You shall not covet your neighbor's _____ .

Decoding God's Message

Use the code to find another name for the Ten Commandments. Print the code letter above each number on the stone tablet.

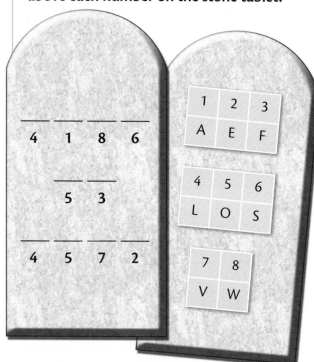

1	2	3
A	E	F

4	5	6
L	O	S

7	8
V	W

___ ___ ___ ___
4   1   8   6

___ ___
5   3

___ ___ ___ ___
4   5   7   2

We Remember

Why did God give us the Ten Commandments?

God gave us the Ten Commandments to show us how to live lives that are pleasing to him and respectful of others.

Word to Know

moral law

We Respond

I will keep all the commands that the Lord has given me.

adapted from Exodus 24:3

Building Family Faith

CHAPTER SUMMARY Because he loves us, God gave the Ten Commandments as a pattern of living that leads to eternal life. The commandments call us to love God and love our neighbor.

REFLECT

I, the LORD, am your God, who brought you out of the land of Egypt, that place of slavery.

Deuteronomy 5:6

DISCUSS AS A FAMILY

• how living according to the commandments is choosing to belong to God.

• the commandments that call us to love God.

• the commandments that tell us how to love our neighbor and ourselves.

PRAY

You have placed your law in our hearts, O God.

DO

• Take turns as a family listing one of the commandments until you have all 10 listed. This is a way to reinforce learning the commandments by heart.

• Rent the movie *The Ten Commandments* and watch it as a family. Discuss any questions you or your child may have after viewing it.

• Make a replica of the two tablets given to Moses and work with your child to decorate them, either with the words of the commandments or with images depicting the ways we love God and others.

Visit **www.christourlife.org/family** for more family resources.

We Honor Mary

Mary Is the Best Disciple

When we pray the Hail Mary, we call God's Mother "holy Mary." After Jesus, the Virgin Mary is the holiest person who ever lived. She loved God and was filled with his life. She did whatever God asked, even when it was puzzling and would bring her much suffering. She always loved and helped others.

Our heavenly mother, Mary, prays for us. She is always ready to help us follow her Son as she did. She wants us to bring Jesus and his love into the world too.

The Annunciation

Narrator: The angel Gabriel was sent by God to a town called Nazareth. He came to a virgin whose name was Mary. The angel said to her:

Angel: Hail, favored one! The Lord is with you.

Narrator: Mary was greatly troubled by these words. She wondered what this greeting could mean. The angel said:

Angel: Do not be afraid, Mary. Behold, you will have a son, and you shall name him Jesus. He will be great and will be called Son of the Most High.

Mary: But how can this come about?

Angel: The Holy Spirit will come upon you, and God's power will overshadow you. And so the Child to be born will be called holy, the Son of God.

Mary: I am the handmaid of the Lord. May it be done to me according to your word.

Narrator: Mary became the Mother of God. Jesus, the Son of God, became Mary's son.

adapted from Luke 1:26–38

We Pray to Mary

Mary's willingness to be the mother of Jesus made her the first and most important follower of Jesus. Through the ages, Catholics have recognized her closeness to Jesus and have prayed to her as Mother of the Church, Queen of all Saints, and Help of Christians. Mary has become the person we most often ask to pray for us. We especially come to her when we are in need.

There are many prayers honoring Mary. The most important is the Hail Mary, which repeats the words of the angel Gabriel. In this prayer we ask Mary to help us, especially at the hour of our death. We pray the Hail Mary 10 times with each decade of the Rosary. We can also pray the Hail Mary morning, noon, and evening when we pray the **Angelus**.

Mary is the Mother of God and our mother. She is the Queen of Heaven because she was taken into heaven when her life on earth was over. From her place next to her Son Jesus, Mary shows her loving concern for our needs and for the needs of the world. Remember her often and never hesitate to ask her to pray for you.

Mary

Comforter of the Afflicted

Queen of Heaven

Cause of Our Joy

Mirror of Justice

House of Gold

Vessel of Honor

Seat of Wisdom

Refuge of Sinners

We Honor Mary in Prayer

When we pray the Angelus, we recall the great mystery of the Incarnation. In this prayer we repeat the words said by the angel and Mary's reply. We honor Mary and give glory to God, who made her and filled her with grace. The Angelus is prayed morning, noon, and evening. In the past church bells rang to remind the people that it was time to pray this prayer. At the ringing of the bells, people would stop whatever they were doing to join together in praying the Angelus.

Jean Francois Millet, *The Angelus*, 1857.

Mary, Full of Grace

Design and color a stained-glass window honoring Mary.

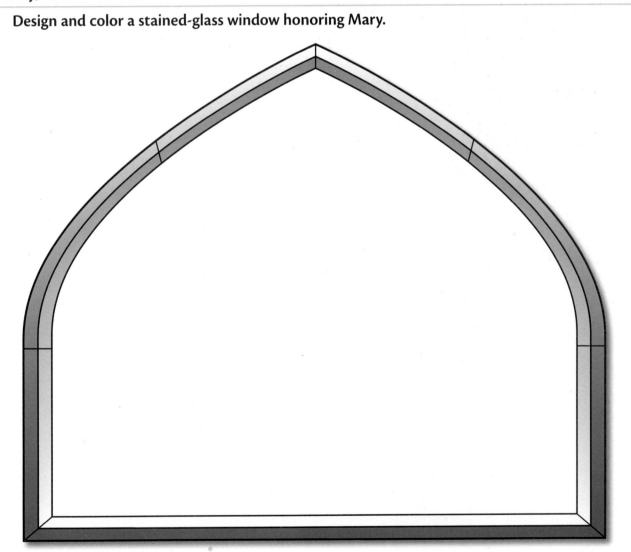

A Puzzle for Experts

Use the clues and the words in the Word Bank to solve the crossword puzzle.

WORD BANK

absolution	hearts
Angelus	Jesus
bread	life
commandments	love
conscience	Reconciliation
contrition	sacrifice
Eucharist	serve

Across

3. What we do if we follow Jesus
7. Sacrament in which God forgives us
11. Sorrow for sin
12. What God's laws show us how to do
13. Our highest form of worship
14. Rules God gave us to be happy

Down

1. What we ask for in the Lord's Prayer
2. Something that helps us know right from wrong
4. Person who taught us the Lord's Prayer
5. What Jesus came to bring us
6. Prayer in which we remember the Incarnation
8. An offering to God
9. Forgiveness of sin
10. What God wants more than sacrifices

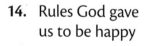

Meet the Needs of Others

We cannot perform miracles to help people as Jesus did, but we can do many thoughtful things for others.

Read each situation below and fill in the box if you can say a prayer asking God to help, if you can make a sacrifice for others, or if you can help by doing something loving. You can fill in one, two, or all three boxes for each situation.

say a prayer · make a sacrifice · offer help

☐ ☐ ☐ Your mother has a bad headache.

☐ ☐ ☐ Your neighbor's home burned down.

☐ ☐ ☐ A flood destroyed a town.

☐ ☐ ☐ A classmate has the flu.

☐ ☐ ☐ Hospitals in India need medicine.

☐ ☐ ☐ Your father has lost his job.

☐ ☐ ☐ A new student joins your class.

☐ ☐ ☐ Your friend did not make the soccer team.

☐ ☐ ☐ Your younger sister cannot read very well yet.

1. Pray

2. Sacrifice

3. Help

We Pray the Angelus

Song

Prayer

Leader: We begin our prayer with the words the angel Gabriel used, "Hail Mary." What joy to speak directly to the Mother of God.

Reader 1: She is full of grace, full of God's life because Jesus has come to dwell in her.

Reader 2: She is blessed among women and shares with us God's greatest blessing, Jesus.

Reader 3: Holy Mary, Mother of God, thank you for being our mother too and for praying for us.

Intercessions

Leader: Mary is the mother of Jesus. She is our mother too. Let us bring our needs and hopes to her. She will bring them to her Son for us.

Our response is "Holy Mary, pray for us.

Child 1: So that we worship God with loving hearts, we ask . . . ℞

Child 2 So that we may be faithful followers of your son Jesus, we ask . . . ℞

Child 3: So that we may be unselfish in serving others, we ask . . . ℞

Child 4: So that we are not afraid to speak to others about God's love and goodness, we ask . . . ℞

Child 5: So that God's will is our will, we ask . . . ℟.

Leader: Loving God, hear the requests of your children and give them what they need to live loving and holy lives. We ask this in the name of Mary and through Jesus Christ, her son and our Lord. Amen.

Introduction to Prayer

Leader: Let us now give thanks for the great mystery of the Incarnation by praying the Angelus.

Prayer

The angel spoke God's message to Mary, and she conceived of the Holy Spirit.

All: Hail Mary. *(Pray the entire prayer.)*

Leader: "I am the lowly servant of the Lord: let it be done to me according to your word."

All: Hail Mary. *(Pray the entire prayer.)*

Leader: And the Word became flesh and lived among us.

All: Hail Mary. *(Pray the entire prayer.)*

Leader: Pray for us, holy Mother of God, that we may become worthy of the promises of Christ.

Let us pray together.

All: Lord, fill our hearts with your grace: once, through the message of an angel you revealed to us the Incarnation of your Son; now, through his suffering and death lead us to the glory of his Resurrection. We ask this through Christ our Lord. Amen.

Closing Song

Looking Back at Unit 2

In this unit you have learned that Jesus revealed the greatness and goodness of God perfectly. God wants us to become holy. We can do this by acting more like Jesus. We can show loving concern for others and worship the Father. In Reconciliation and the Eucharist, Jesus helps us become like him.

God made a covenant of love with us at Baptism. We respond to God by adoring and serving him. We offer our worship together with the worship that Jesus offered his Father. We show our love by trying to do what God asks. When we live by God's laws, we become holy and happy.

Word to Know
Angelus

Spreading the Word Around Town

Design a bumper sticker encouraging people to be with God or to follow his laws.

Living the Message

Check (✓) each sentence that describes you.

❏ 1. I know the meaning of the Lord's Prayer and pray it with love.

❏ 2. I can explain how my conscience can help me become like Jesus.

❏ 3. I try to be aware of what is happening at Mass.

❏ 4. I know many ways God has shown his greatness and goodness.

❏ 5. I can explain ways to be like Jesus.

Planning to Grow

Fill in the blanks.

I can worship God by _____ and _____ him.

Family Feature

Give Thanks to God

The Ledet family has passed on African folklore and traditional African-American recipes for generations. One story they like to tell explains why people have to work for food.

Long ago the sky was close to the earth and was a source of food for the people. Anyone who was hungry could just reach up and break off a piece. Soon they began to waste their food. They would take a bite or two and throw the rest away. The sky warned that if people were not more careful with its gift of food, it would move far away. For a while the people changed, but then they again became greedy and careless. Finally the sky moved up so high that it could not be reached. At first the people waited for the sky to come down again, but as they grew hungry and the sky stayed out of reach, they began to make tools to plant and harvest their own food. To this day people must work for their food.

From generation to generation, these stories pass on important values, such as caring for the gifts of the earth and sharing them with one another. Were stories passed on in your family that helped shape your values? What stories are you telling your child?

Visit **www.christourlife.org/family** for more family resources.

Family Feature

Storytelling and mealtimes go together.

You can make a meal special by including a dish from your family's heritage or from another culture that interests you, and sharing stories as you enjoy the dish. Here's a delicious recipe for bread pudding, a popular dessert in Great Britain and in the southeastern United States that you can make with your child. You can add your favorite ingredients to make this your family's dessert tradition.

Bread pudding

2 cups milk
3 eggs, beaten
⅓ cup sugar
½ teaspoon salt
½ teaspoon vanilla extract
12–14 slices white bread, without crust
1 teaspoon cinnamon
dash nutmeg
½ cup raisins, optional
1 can of fruit-pie filling, optional

Heat the milk over low heat until it is hot but not boiling. In a bowl, combine eggs, sugar, and salt; stir well. Gradually stir about 1/4 of the hot milk into the egg mixture. Add remaining milk, stirring constantly. Stir in vanilla.

Place bread slices in a buttered, two-quart baking dish. Raisins or other dried fruit can be sprinkled over the bread. Pour the milk mixture over the bread. Combine cinnamon and nutmeg and sprinkle over the pudding mixture. Leave uncovered and bake at 300° for about 50 minutes. Serve warm with vanilla ice cream or other dessert topping, if desired. (serves 6)

The Gift of Family

Let the gingerbread people shown here represent different members of your family. (You can trace over these to make as many gingerbread people as you need. You can include grandparents and other close relatives as well.) Have everyone present write his or her name on his or her own gingerbread person. Then, on the lines provided, every member of the family can take a turn writing down traits of that person for which they are thankful.

When all the spaces are filled, your child can cut out the gingerbread people and give each person the one with his or her name and traits. You might want to post them all on the refrigerator as a reminder of the benefits of being a family.

Thanking God as a Family

Gratitude is an essential building block of all spirituality. When our hearts are thankful, we are more likely to care for the many gifts God offers in our lives. You can nurture the virtue of gratitude in your child and in your family. Here are two ways you can foster gratitude at home.

Draw Out Your Gratitude

Get an oversized sheet of paper or poster board and crayons, markers, or finger paints. Begin by writing a brief prayer of gratitude on the paper. Have every member of the family take a turn creating a work of art. Let your child begin by drawing one thing he or she is grateful for. Then, one by one, each takes a turn. Keep filling in the piece of art until the entire work is finished. Then have everyone explains the parts of the picture he or she contributed, telling what it means to him or her. Let everyone sign the masterpiece and display it in a prominent place in your home for the coming week.

Decorate Your Thanksgiving Day Tablecloth

Get a light-colored tablecloth and some permanent markers. Spread out the tablecloth on a table that has been protected by a piece of cardboard or similar material. After Thanksgiving dinner, or whenever you have the extended family over, have everyone present write a message of thanks and gratitude on the tablecloth. Encourage people to decorate the section of tablecloth in front of them in any way that expresses their thanks to God. You might even include the names of deceased family members who shared your table in years past.

You can use this tablecloth year after year on Thanksgiving and for other family gatherings. Every year people can add more decorations as well as the names of new family members to the tablecloth showing that it, like life and family and faith, is a work in progress.

We Love God

Let us love not in word and speech but in deed and truth.

1 John 3:18

A Letter Home

Dear Parents and Family,

Your child has studied the Ten Commandments over the years and, in Unit Two, learned that these instructions for living a good life are a sign of God's love. In Unit Three, the focus of the children's study will be the first three commandments—those that tell us how we should worship God.

The children will begin by recognizing the other gods in their lives, the people and things that claim their attention. They will learn to put God first by worshiping him with faith, hope, and love. Consider the ways you demonstrate in your home that God is first above all things.

As they continue in this unit with the Second Commandment, the children will learn that people who seek to honor God show reverence for his name and for the people, places, and objects related to his service and worship. The children will learn to become aware of their casual language as well as their attitudes and behavior in church.

Studying the Third Commandment, the children will explore ways to keep the Lord's Day holy, including worshiping at Mass and receiving Communion, as well as putting aside those things that interfere with the rest and prayer for which the Lord's Day was intended. This can be a tall order in our busy society, but it can become a welcome custom and respite in your family.

The primary message your child will carry from Unit Three is that by keeping these three commandments, we show our love for God.

At the end of each chapter in this unit, the children will bring home a review of the chapter along with either the Building Family Faith page or the Family Feature section. These features give you a quick review of what your child learned and offer practical ways to reinforce the lesson at home so that the whole family may benefit.

Visit **www.christourlife.org/family** for more family resources.

We Show Our Love for God

God Gives Us Gifts

God our Father made us and gives us life. He gives us all the beautiful things in the world. Every good thing we have is a gift from God.

God wants us to love his good gifts because he made them. They show us God's glory and tell us of his love. God's gifts lead us to worship him.

> I will praise the Lord with all my heart. . . .
>
> Great are the works of the Lord.
>
> Psalm 111:1–2

God Asks for Our Love

God is good and much greater than all his gifts. God wants us to love him more than everything else. He knows all things and tells us what is true. He wants us to believe in him. As our loving Father, God always cares for us. He wants us to hope in him.

In the First Commandment God says to worship only him.

> I, the Lord, am your God. . . . You shall not have other gods besides me.
>
> Exodus 20:2–3

God says, "Give me your love." He wants to be first in our lives.

Jesus is God's best gift to us. He shows us how to love God our Father above everything else. He shows us how to adore God. He shows us how to love God by loving and serving others.

My God and My All

Read the sentences and add the missing words.

WORD BANK

adore	hope
love	believe
goodness	pray

1. God's gifts show us his _____ .

2. God calls us to _____ him.

3. God tells us what is true, so we can _____ in him.

4. God cares for us. He wants us to have _____ in him.

5. God wants us to _____ him more than his gifts.

6. We show our love when we _____ to God.

We Give God Our Love in Prayer

When we pray, we lift up our minds and hearts to God. We think of him and love him. God listens to us and speaks to us too. He loves us and wants us to pray.

Jesus teaches us how to pray. He often went off by himself to pray. Sometimes he prayed all night. Can you think of a time when Jesus prayed? Write it here.

_____

_____

_____

Jesus said,

> "Go to your inner room, close the door, and pray to your Father in secret."

> Matthew 6:6

He also said,

> "Ask and it will be given to you."

> Matthew 7:7

We ask God to give us all we need. A prayer in which we ask for something is called a **prayer of petition**, but there are three other kinds of prayer besides prayers of petition. In prayer we can praise God, thank God, and tell God we are sorry for our sins. A long time ago, God's people prayed all these ways. The prayers they wrote are called the psalms. We still pray them today.

A Moment with Jesus

Speak to Jesus in the quiet of your heart. Knowing that Jesus said that the Father will take care of all your needs, tell him what it is that you need most now. It could be a job for your dad or help with your math homework or good health for a friend who is sick. Jesus will take your need to the Father. Know that God will hear your prayer.

We Honor Mary, the Angels, and the Saints in Prayer

God wants us to love and to honor those who are in heaven with him. Mary, Jesus' mother and ours, lives there. Heaven is also home for the angels who bring us God's messages. God's special friends and ours, the saints, live there too. They pray for us and ask God to bless us. One day we will live with them in heaven.

We show our love for Mary, the angels, and the saints by asking them to pray for us and by imitating them. When we honor them, we honor God, who made them.

Mary, pray for us.

St. Michael, pray for us.

St. Julie, pray for us.

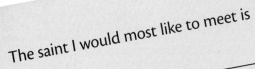

The saint I would most like to meet is

_____

_____

I would like to meet this saint because

_____

_____

_____

_____

I would like to ask this saint

_____

_____

_____

_____

We Pray the Psalms

Print on each blank the word that tells the kind of prayer each psalm verse is. The Word Bank will help you.

Psalm of _____

Give thanks to the Lord, who
is good,
whose kindness lasts forever.

adapted from Psalm 106:1

Psalm of _____

Shout joyfully to God, all you
on earth;
sing of his glorious name.

Psalm 66:1–2

Psalm of _____

Have mercy on me, O God, . . .
wipe out my sin.

adapted from Psalm 51:3

Psalm of _____

Come quickly to help me,
my Lord and my salvation!

Psalm 38:23

CHAPTER 10 Review

We Remember

What is prayer?
Prayer is the lifting up of our minds and hearts to God.

What is the First Commandment?
The First Commandment is

"I am the Lord your God: you shall not have strange gods before me."

Word to Know
prayer of petition

We Respond

Come, Holy Spirit, fill the
hearts of your faithful.
And kindle in them the
fire of your love.
Send forth your Spirit
and they shall be created.
And you will renew the
face of the earth.

Building Family Faith

CHAPTER SUMMARY God is revealed as a loving father. Sometimes we let that which is not God take the place of God in our lives. God calls us into a right relationship with him, the one true God.

REFLECT
Everything the Lord has said, we will do.
Exodus 19:8

DISCUSS AS A FAMILY
- some of the other gods that might lead us away from the true God.
- what happens when people put that which is not God into the place that only God can fill.
- what God promises to those who keep his commandments.

PRAY
My God, I love and adore you above all things.

DO
- Review the four kinds of prayer—praise, contrition (sorrow), thanks, and petition (request). At dinner this week, have each member of the family mention one thing he or she praises God for, one thing he or she is sorry for, one thing he or she is grateful for, and one thing he or she is asking God for.
- Plan time for a cookie bake. Make cookies in the shape of the symbols for faith ✝, hope ⚓, and love ❤. Decorate them as you wish. Remind family members to ask God to help them grow in these virtues.

Visit **www.christourlife.org/family** for more family resources.

We Love All That Is Holy

We Praise the Name of the Lord

We give our love to God when we keep the Second Commandment.

> You shall not take the name of the LORD, your God, in vain.
>
> Exodus 20:7

In vain means "for no good reason."

Our names are important because they stand for us. We do not like it when others make fun of our names. We are pleased and happy when our names are said with love. God's name is holy because God is holy. Because of their great respect for God, Jewish people would never say God's name.

Jesus taught us to call God our Father and to pray: "Hallowed be thy name."

We honor God's name as "hallowed," or holy, when we use it with love and respect. We do not say God's name carelessly in everyday speech. We do not use God's name in anger or to curse. Cursing is using God's name to wish harm to someone or something. If we love God, we say his name only in prayer or for another good reason. For instance, in court people are sometimes asked to swear. In this case swearing means calling on God to witness that what they say is true.

> O LORD, our Lord,
>   how awesome is your name through all
>   the earth!
>
> Psalm 8:2

God Has Many Names

When we sing and pray, we use many of the names of God. Each name that we call God tells how good or powerful he is.

Unscramble the letters and write the name of God that belongs on each blank.

1. _____

   SUJES

   means "God saves."

2. Another name for Jesus is

   _____ .

   HCRSTI

3. The Third Person of the Blessed Trinity is the

   _____

   YHOL

   _____ .

   TRISPI

4. We call God

   _____

   DLOR
   because he rules heaven and earth.

5. Jesus told us to call God our

   _____ .

   HAFTRE

When you pray, what holy name for God do you use the most?

_____

Use that name now to tell God that you love him.

The Name of Jesus Is Holy

The name of Jesus is powerful. When Jesus walked the earth, blind men who called his name with faith were given sight. Later Peter and John healed a crippled man in the name of Jesus. Other disciples did many marvels in his holy name.

The Bible says that God gave to his Son the name

> that is above every name,
> that at the name of Jesus
> every knee should bend,
> of those in heaven and on earth and
> under the earth.
>
> Philippians 2:9–10

Because the name of Jesus is so holy and powerful, repeating it is itself one of the oldest and best prayers. When praying the name of Jesus, people come to feel his love and presence.

A Moment with Jesus

Imagine that you are in a quiet place and that Jesus is with you. You are so happy to be with him that you just say his name over and over softly and reverently. Close your eyes and let the word "Jesus" be your prayer. Then just sit quietly in the presence of Jesus. When you are ready, open your eyes and pray "Amen."

We Respect All That Is Holy

One day when Jesus went to the **Temple** to worship, he saw people buying and selling for their own profit. Jesus was angry when he saw that people were not honoring God in that holy place. He knocked over tables with piles of money on them and ordered people who were selling things to leave the Temple.

Then Jesus said, "My Father's house shall be a house of prayer. You are making it a den of thieves."

adapted from Matthew 21:12–13

Jesus wanted the people to respect the Temple as a holy place. Today, he wants us to respect all holy, or sacred, people, places, and things. In the Second Commandment, God our Father taught us the same thing. Holy people, places, and things help us think of God. When we honor what is holy, we praise and honor God.

All people are called to holiness. Some are called to give themselves entirely to God and to his work.

Complete the help wanted ad below. Fill in some qualities you think would be found in a person seeking holiness.

HELP WANTED

Needed: Holy People

Job: To do God's work and help make our world a better place

Qualities:

_____

_____

_____

_____

_____

Reward: Happiness on earth and in heaven

Our Homes Are Holy

Certain places are called holy because they are special places where people pray and worship. Our homes are holy too because we often pray together there as a family.

Certain things are called holy because they remind us of God or because they are used when we pray.

Think about your own home. On the line, write the name of a fourth room in your house. Then draw a picture of some holy things that can be found in each of the rooms.

Bedroom

_____

Kitchen

Living Room

Living the Second Commandment

Circle the names of the children who are showing reverence for what is holy.

1. Winston laughed and said Jesus' name when his friend struck out.

2. Labelle played with her rosary by swinging it around and making designs with it.

3. Before taking a test, Claire prayed for help.

4. When a friend said God's name in anger, Brigitte said in her heart, "Praised be Jesus Christ."

5. Emma bowed her head whenever she heard the name of Jesus.

6. During Mass, Christopher kept kicking the kneeler, disturbing people nearby.

We Remember

What is the Second Commandment?
The Second Commandment is "You shall not take the name of the Lord your God in vain."

Word to Know
Temple

We Respond

I will honor God's name and respect all that is holy.

Western Wall of the Temple in Jerusalem, built by King Herod the Great.

Building Family Faith

CHAPTER SUMMARY Christians are called to give special respect to people, places, and things related to God. We should especially revere God's name and not use it carelessly or in anger.

REFLECT
"You shall not take the name of the LORD, your God, in vain."

Exodus 20:7

DISCUSS AS A FAMILY
- some ways you misuse God's name.
- how to handle anger and frustration constructively.
- how to give proper respect to holy things at home, school, and church.

PRAY
You are holy, Lord. Blessed be your holy name.

DO
Talk about the importance of names, the reasons you reverence God's name, and what you can do when you hear God's name being misused or abused.

Name the holy things you have in your house. Talk about how you show respect for them.

Sing "Holy God We Praise Thy Name" or another song that shows reverence for God.

Visit **www.christourlife.org/family** for more family resources.

We Keep the Lord's Day Holy

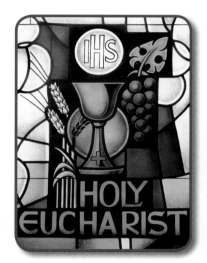

God Tells Us to Keep His Day Holy

When God created the world, he worked for six days and rested on the seventh. God blessed the seventh day and made it holy.

> So God blessed the seventh day and made it holy, because on it he rested from all the work he had done in creation.
>
> Genesis 2:3

In his Third Commandment God told his people to do as he had done.

> Remember to keep holy the sabbath day.
>
> Exodus 20:8

God explained, "You may work for six days, but the seventh day is the Sabbath of the Lord." God's people loved him and were careful to keep Saturday, the **Sabbath** day, holy. They went to the temple or the synagogue to worship together. They rejoiced with others. They rested from work. They did all their work before the day of rest.

The early Christians kept Sunday as the Lord's Day because Jesus rose from the dead on Easter Sunday. Christians celebrated Sunday to show they believed in Jesus. They came together for the Breaking of the Bread, the Eucharist. At this celebration the risen Christ offered himself to the Father for them, united them, and nourished them with himself.

We Celebrate Sundays and Holy Days

In his Third Commandment God tells us that he wants us to keep his day holy. The Church tells us to keep Sunday holy by celebrating Mass and resting from our work. As Catholics, we praise and thank God together at the Eucharist on Saturday evening or on Sunday. We celebrate the new life Jesus won by his dying and rising. We make Sunday a day of rest and celebration by enjoying ourselves and being with others. Celebrating each Sunday reminds us of the big celebration we will enjoy in heaven one day.

Here are three good reasons for celebrating Sunday with the Eucharist, making time to rest, and having fun with others.

- God tells us to keep the Lord's Day holy.
- Rest, prayer, and fun are good for our physical and mental health.
- Celebrating the Eucharist and spending fun time with others build up the community.

As Catholic Christians, we also come together for Mass to celebrate special feasts in honor of Jesus, Mary, and the saints. These feasts are called holy days. There are certain laws of the Church that are called **Precepts of the Church**. One of these laws requires Catholics to go to Mass on specific holy days.

Name some holy days that we celebrate in our country.

_____

_____

_____

Keeping the Lord's Day Holy

Answer the questions, using the words in the Word Bank.

WORD BANK

resting
Sunday
praying
rejoicing

Jesus' rising
the Eucharist
the Sabbath

1. What was the Lord's Day first called?

_____

2. How did God's people keep the Sabbath holy?

a. _____

b. _____

c. _____

3. What day do Christians keep as the Lord's Day?

_____

4. What happened on that day?

_____

5. What do Christians share?

_____

A Moment with Jesus

Quiet your body and your mind. Think of some special gifts that you have been given. Have you ever thought of Sunday as a gift? On Sunday, God gives you the opportunity to spend extra time with him, to rest, and to do fun things with your family. Share with Jesus how you spend your Sundays. Ask him to help you use your day of prayer and rest well.

The Eucharist Is Our Greatest Prayer

As we celebrate the Eucharist, we pray prayers of praise, thanks, sorrow, and petition. Beside each numbered part of the Mass, write the letter identifying the kind of prayer it is.

KINDS OF PRAYER

A. Praise   B. Thanks
C. Sorrow   D. Petition

_____ 1. "Give us this day our daily bread."

_____ 2. Lamb of God

_____ 3. Holy, Holy, Holy

_____ 4. Prayer of the Faithful

_____ 5. *Gloria*

_____ 6. "Let us give thanks to the Lord our God."

_____ 7. ". . . And graciously grant [the Church] peace and unity in accordance with your will."

_____ 8. "Lord, have mercy."

_____ 9. "Through him, and with him, and in him, O God, almighty Father, in the unity of the Holy Spirit, all glory and honor is yours, for ever and ever."

_____ 10. "The Word of the Lord." "Thanks be to God."

May the Lord accept the sacrifice at your hands for the praise and glory of his name, for our good, and the good of all his holy Church.

Make the Sun Shine on the Lord's Day

On each sun ray, print one way in which you can celebrate Sunday with your family. Print *Celebrate the Eucharist* in the center of the sun.

Saint Margaret Valued the Eucharist

Long ago in England and Wales, it was a crime to be a Catholic. Many people risked being sentenced to a cruel death if they celebrated the Eucharist. Hundreds of priests and laypeople were killed for their faith. Margaret Clitherow was one of these laypeople.

Margaret became a Catholic shortly after she married. She hid priests in her house, where they would celebrate Mass in secret. She hired a Catholic to tutor her children in the faith. This too was against the law.

One day officers came to search the house while the children were being tutored. Margaret was imprisoned, but she refused to give up her Catholic faith to save her life. In 1586 she was put to death. Saint Margaret Clitherow was canonized by Pope Paul VI in 1970.

We Remember

What is the Third Commandment?
The Third Commandment is "Remember to keep holy the Lord's Day."

Words to Know
Precepts of the Church   Sabbath

We Respond

I will keep the Lord's Day holy by celebrating the Eucharist on Sundays or Saturday evenings and on holy days.

Building Family Faith

CHAPTER SUMMARY Christians set aside Sunday as a special day to worship God, to receive the Eucharist, and to rest and relax. We do this to celebrate Jesus' Resurrection and to build up our community of faith.

REFLECT
"Remember to keep holy the sabbath day. Six days you may labor and do all your work, but the seventh day is the Sabbath of the Lord, your God."
Exodus 20:8–10

DISCUSS AS A FAMILY
- why it is important to take time to rest and relax with family and friends.
- how your family observes Sunday.
- the ways you celebrate other holy days of the Church.

PRAY
Thank you, Lord, for the great gift of your Sabbath.

DO
Plan something special for the family to do together on Sundays.

Prepare for Sunday Mass by reading the Gospel together the night before. Talk about the reading as a family.

Spend some time on Sunday with fellow parishioners. Mingle with them after Mass. Invite another family for Sunday brunch.

Visit **www.christourlife.org/family** for more family resources.

We Grow in Holiness

We Receive the Word of the Kingdom

Jesus told the parable of the sower.

"Hear this! A sower went out to sow seed. As he sowed, some seed fell on the path and the birds came and ate it up. Other seed fell on rocky ground where it had little soil. It sprang up at once because the soil was not deep. And when the sun rose, it scorched the little plants. Not having roots, they withered and died. Some seed fell among thorns, and the thorns choked the plants so they produced no grain. And some seed fell on rich soil and produced fruit—thirty, sixty, and a hundredfold. Whoever has ears to hear ought to hear!"

adapted from Mark 4:3–9

Then Jesus explained the parable.

"The sower is anyone who spreads God's word. The seed is God's word. The people on the path hear the word, but Satan comes and takes it from them. The people who receive the word on rocky ground are those who listen with joy at first. But it does not stay with them. When it is hard to keep God's word, they give up. The people who receive the word among thorns listen to the word, but it is choked by the worries of this world and the desire for riches. But the people who receive the word on rich soil are those who hear the word, accept it, and bear fruit.

adapted from Mark 4:14–20

How Well Do You Understand?

Match the sentences with the pictures of Jesus' parable. Write the number of your choice in the small box.

1. This person spreads God's word.

2. Satan steals the seed from some people as soon as they hear it.

3. Some people listen to God's word at first with joy. But when it becomes hard to keep God's word, they give up.

4. Some people worry about money and what people think of them. The word of God is choked.

5. Some people hear the word and accept it. It produces a harvest of good works.

The sower went out to sow.

Some seed fell on rocky ground. It started to grow, but the plants soon withered.

Some seed fell on the path. The birds took it away.

Some seed fell on good soil. It grew and produced fruit.

Some seed fell among thorns. It grew, but thorns choked the plants.

Is God's Word Growing?

Read these stories and tell what these children will do if God's word is growing in them.

1. When Eduardo plays with friends, he uses words that are not respectful of God or others. He says the boys will tease him if he doesn't do what they do.

   Eduardo should

   _____

   _____

   _____

2. An elderly man on Sam's street lives alone. Sam often stops in to visit or to run errands for him rather than playing with his friends.

   Sam should

   _____

   _____

   _____

3. All during Mass, Su Lin is thinking about the fun she will have at the pool with her friend that afternoon.

   Su Lin should

   _____

   _____

4. Madeline likes to watch television. When her mother calls, she doesn't even hear her. She hardly notices all the work her mother has to do.

   Madeline should

   _____

   _____

   _____

Word Search

Find and circle the words from the Word Bank that refer to the first three commandments.

WORD BANK

believe	Easter	God	holy
honor	hope	Jesus	love
Mary	Mass	name	petition
praise	pray	rest	saints
sorrow	thanks	worship	

```
L C N O P R A I S E Q U A D
P R A Y O E L Z S A I N T S
B I M O A S T W U L H C F O
E P E T I T I O N H O N O R
L L J G O D M R D I P S I R
I O E H M A S S A L E T P O
E V S I V B C H Y U S I C W
V E U H O L Y I T H A N K S
E A S T E R Q P N A M A R Y
```

Jigsaw Puzzle

Print a motto on one side of a card and decorate it. Draw lines on the other side to divide the card into 10 pieces. Cut apart the card on the lines and put the pieces in an envelope. Exchange your envelope with that of a classmate and work each other's puzzle.

Some Mottos You Could Use

Love God with all your heart.　　Lift up your hearts.

Trust in the Lord.　　Pray to the Lord.

Love the Eucharist.

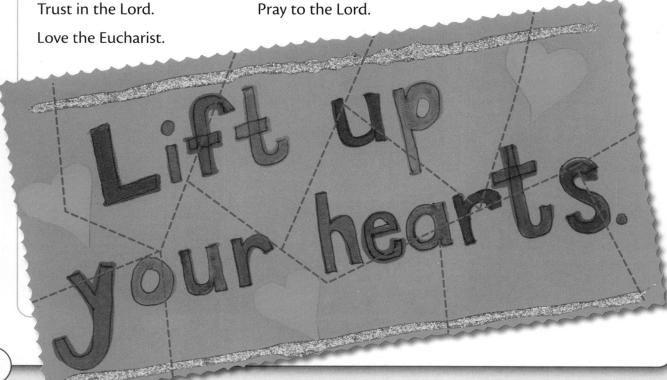

Follow the Footsteps

Use the words in the footsteps to complete the sentences.

1. God gave us the Ten Commandments to help us reach _____ .

2. The first three commandments tell us to love _____ .

3. In the First Commandment God said, "I am the _____ your God."

4. "You shall not have strange _____ besides me."

5. Prayer is lifting our minds and _____ to God.

6. When we honor Mary, the angels, or the _____ , we honor God, who made them.

7. In the Second Commandment God tells us not to use his name in _____ .

8. We respect holy _____ , places, and things.

9. In the Third Commandment God tells us to keep holy the _____ Day.

10. Catholics celebrate the Eucharist on Saturday evenings or Sundays and on _____ days.

A Prayer Puzzle

Complete the puzzle, using the words in the Word Bank to name the kinds of prayer.

WORD BANK

petition   praise
sorrow   thanks

P __ __ __ __ __

__ __ R __ __ __

__ __ A __ __ __

Y

__ E __ __ __ __ __

R

From Tiny Seeds the Kingdom Grows

Procession and Song

Leader: In the name of the Father, and of the Son, and of the Holy Spirit.

All: Amen.

Leader: Praise be to God who gives such abundant growth.

All: Now and forever.

Leader: Loving God, we want to serve your kingdom with joy in all we think, say, and do. Help us be fruitful soil so that the kingdom Jesus preached might continue to grow. We ask this in Jesus' name.

All: Amen.

Reading from Mark 4:1–9

Reader: A reading from the holy Gospel according to Mark.

All: Glory to you, O Lord.

Reader: On another occasion he [Jesus] began to teach by the sea. A very large crowd gathered around him so that he got into a boat on the sea and sat down. And the whole crowd was beside the sea on land. And he taught them at length in parables, and in the course of his instruction he said to them, "Hear this! A sower went out to sow. And as he sowed, some seed fell on the path, and the birds came and ate it up. Other seed fell on rocky ground where it had little soil. It sprang up at once because the soil was not deep. And when the sun rose, it was scorched and it withered for lack of roots. Some seed fell among thorns, and the thorns grew up and choked it and it produced no grain. And some seed fell on rich soil and produced fruit. It came up and grew and yielded thirty, sixty, and a hundredfold." He added, "Whoever has ears to hear ought to hear."

The Gospel of the Lord

All: Praise to you, Lord Jesus Christ.

All: I will share the stories of my faith, sharing lessons from of old.

Side A: We have heard them, we know them; our ancestors have recited them to us.

All: I will share the stories of my faith, sharing lessons from of old.

Side B: We do not keep the stories to ourselves; we tell them over and over.

All: I will share the stories of my faith, sharing lessons from of old.

Side A: We tell others the wondrous deeds of Jesus, the miracles he performed.

All: I will share the stories of my faith, sharing lessons from of old.

Side B: So that children still to be born know these stories.

All: I will share the stories of my faith, sharing lessons from of old.

[adapted from Psalm 78:2–6]

Intercessions

Leader: Let us pray that we continue to serve God's kingdom.

That your Word will grow in our hearts, we pray to the Lord.

Response: Lord, we love and serve in your kingdom.

Leader: That bishops, priests, deacons, missionaries, and all of us may spread your Word, we pray to the Lord . . . ℟

That we may continue to make sacrifices for others, we pray to the Lord . . . ℟

That we may love and serve with joy in your kingdom, we pray to the Lord . . . ℟

That we may grow and produce a harvest of good works, we pray to the Lord . . . ℟

Leader: As members of the kingdom, we pray to the Father in the words our Savior taught us:

All: Our Father, . . . Amen.

Closing Song

Looking Back at Unit 3

You have studied the first three commandments in this unit. They tell us to respond to God's love by putting God first in our lives. This means praying to God to express praise, thanksgiving, and sorrow for sin—as well as to ask for things for ourselves and others. Loving God means using his name with reverence and showing respect for sacred persons, places, and things. It also means making the Lord's day holy through rest, recreation, and the celebration of the Eucharist.

Living the Message

Check (✓) each sentence to which you can say yes.

❏ **1.** I pray each day.

❏ **2.** I try not to take God's name in vain.

❏ **3.** I make my Sundays special in different ways.

❏ **4.** I pray to Mary and the saints.

❏ **5.** I join in the prayers and songs at Sunday Mass.

Planning Ahead

When in the morning is a good time for you to pray?

_____

What prayers will you say?

_____

When in the evening is a good time for you to pray?

_____

What prayers will you say?

_____

Which weekend Mass at your parish is best for you to attend?

_____

How can you better take part in this celebration?

_____

_____

_____

Family Feature

God's Care Shines Through the Darkness

Each year the Sher family celebrates Hanukkah. This is an eight-day feast of lights that takes place in December when Jewish people remember a marvelous deed God worked for them in a time of great peril. It happened more than a hundred years before Jesus was born.

A pagan king was persecuting the Jews and had offered sacrifices to Zeus in the Jewish temple. Led by the Maccabees (Mattathias and his five sons), the Jewish people rebelled, held fast to their faith, and defeated the enemy. The Maccabees wanted to relight the lamps in the Temple and hold a rededication ceremony, but only enough oil to light the lamps for one day could be found. Miraculously, the lamps burned for eight days. In remembrance of this miracle, on each day during Hanukkah another candle is lit on a multibranched candleholder called a menorah.

Family Feature

At Hanukkah the Sher children play a game with a spinning top called a dreidel. The dreidel has four sides, each marked with a Hebrew letter. Taken together, the letters refer to the miracle celebrated at Hanukkah and stand for the phrase, "a great miracle happened there." Players take turns spinning the top. When it stops, the letter at the top of the dreidel tells the spinner what to do.

You can make a dreidel out of a four-inch square of heavy paper or cardboard. On each of the four sides write one of the following letters: N, G, H, S. The code for these is below. Insert a pencil or other stick in the center of the sheet with the point down.

Each player starts with the same amount of tokens (which can be chips, raisins, nuts, pennies, or chocolate coins) and places one in a central pot. Then each player takes a turn spinning the dreidel and doing what it says at the top of the dreidel when it falls to its side. If during play the pot goes down to one token, everyone adds another one. The player who ends up with all the tokens wins. Then redistribute the tokens and play again.

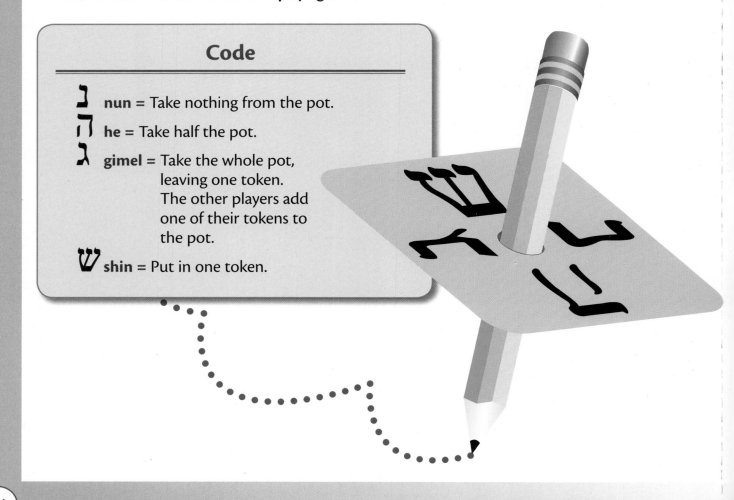

Code

נ **nun** = Take nothing from the pot.

ה **he** = Take half the pot.

ג **gimel** = Take the whole pot, leaving one token. The other players add one of their tokens to the pot.

ש **shin** = Put in one token.

Let It Glow, Let It Glow, Let It Glow

The symbol of light in the darkness is a central part of the Christian faith. Jesus said, "I am the light of the world." During Advent, when the days grow shorter and the nights longer, the Church waits in confident hope for the coming of Jesus, our Lord and our light.

Visit **www.christourlife.org/family** for more family resources.

Here's a family activity that you can do to experience the power of light shining in the darkness. Gather some candles, two or three times the number of people in your family. The easiest to use are tea lights or vigil lights, but other candles, including birthday candles, will do. Make sure the candles are securely placed for safety. Have matches or a lighter on hand.

Get everyone in the family settled in a comfortable place with the candles situated close by. Ask everyone to think about reasons he or she is thankful for being part of this family. Tell them you're going to give them a minute to think about it and then turn down the lights. After a short time sitting in the dark, have each person tell a reason why he or she is thankful. When the person is finished, he or she lights a candle. (Be ready to help younger family members light their candles safely.) Keep taking turns until all the candles are lit. As each person describes why he or she is thankful, the light grows and grows.

Finish by having a favorite family treat together.

Family Feature

Decisions

Unscramble the words in each step to help you in making good decisions.

1. _____ for a moment.
   psot

2. _____ Why do I want to do what I feel is wrong?
   ktnih   What will happen if I choose to do it? How will I feel?
                  What would my parents and best friends think?

3. _____ to the Holy Spirit to help you make a good choice.
   aryp

4. _____ someone you trust to tell you what he or she thinks is the
   sak   right choice.

5. _____ to do what you think is the right thing.
   ohoesc

(Answers: Stop; Think; Pray; Ask; Choose)

We Love God's People

Beloved, if God so loved us, we must also love one another.

1 John 4:11

A Letter Home

Dear Parents and Family,

Unit Four brings your child to a discussion of the remaining commandments. In Unit Three, the children studied the first three commandments, which give us direction in how to show love for God. Now the children will learn about how to show love for others.

In addition to loving and obeying our parents, the Fourth Commandment calls for us to be considerate of and to respect people in authority. In reviewing the Fifth Commandment, the children will be guided to show appreciation for the gift of life by showing kindness and concern for others. When studying the Sixth and Ninth Commandments, the children will learn to respect themselves and others and to be faithful in their personal relationships.

The Seventh and Tenth Commandments ensure the right to own property, to receive just compensation for work, and to share in the world's natural resources. The children will learn to respect others' property, to care for the gifts of the earth, and to share their own gifts freely. The children will learn that the Eighth Commandment charges us to speak the truth in all things and to keep our promises.

The activities and the closing celebration encourage the children to appreciate the Ten Commandments and to show their love for God by keeping them.

At the end of each chapter in this unit, the children will bring home a review of the chapter along with either the Building Family Faith page or the Family Feature section. These features give you a quick review of what your child learned and offer practical ways to reinforce the lesson at home so that the whole family may benefit.

Visit **www.christourlife.org/family** for more family resources.

We Honor and Obey

We Bring Happiness to Our Families

We belong to God's large family. God wants us to help make his family happy by loving everyone in it. The last seven commandments help us do this. The Fourth Commandment helps us bring happiness to our own family.

Families are different in many ways, but they should all have one thing in common: members of a family should love and care about one another. Children should honor and respect their parents.

Jesus belonged to a family. Mary was his mother, and Joseph was his foster father. Jesus loved the parents his heavenly Father had given him. He showed his love for them through his **obedience**. He kept the Fourth Commandment.

> Honor your father and your mother.
>
> Exodus 20:12

Jesus respected and obeyed his parents, although he was greater than they were because he was God's Son.

God shows us how precious the gift of life is by giving us this commandment. God wants us to honor our mothers and fathers. Through our parents' marriage and their love for each other, they created our family. They helped give us life. God promises special blessings if we honor them.

God asks our parents to love and care for us. They are to give us what we need to grow as God's children. Our parents make many sacrifices for us. When we honor and respect them, we please God. When we obey them, we obey God and bring happiness to our families and ourselves.

Wheel of Happiness

The words on the Wheel of Happiness tell how we honor our parents. We love, respect, help, and obey them. We also pray for our parents.

Match the words in the wheel with the sentences below. On the line after each sentence, print the word that tells best how we honor our parents when we do what the sentence says.

1. We do what our parents tell us.

   _____

2. We talk politely to our parents.

   _____

3. We do the dishes.

   _____

4. We do kind things for our parents.

   _____

5. We listen politely to our parents.

   _____

6. We ask God to bless our parents.

   _____

7. We carry out the trash.

   _____

8. We say nice things about our parents.

   _____

9. We clean our rooms and pick up our things.

   _____

10. We come when our parents call us.

   _____

A Moment with Jesus

Imagine that you can see Jesus at home with Mary and Joseph. He is your age. What is he doing? Is he helping around the house? Is he talking with Mary and Joseph, or are they playing a game together? Tell Jesus how things are at your home. He is always interested in what is going on in your life. Ask Jesus to bless your home and all who live there.

We Respect Our Leaders

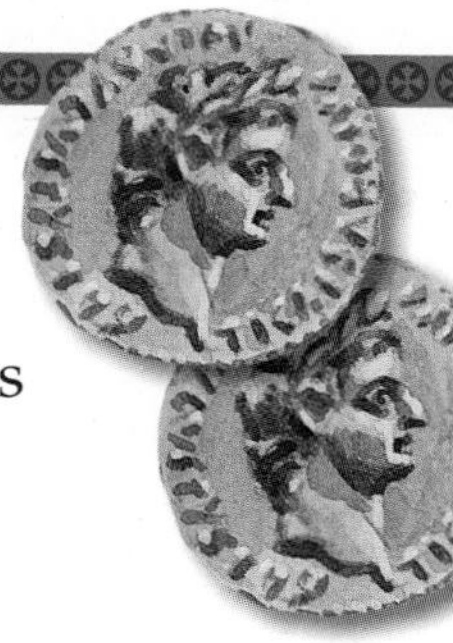

There are other people besides our parents who guide and protect us. We also keep the Fourth Commandment when we respect and obey those in authority, such as our teachers or crossing guards. Jesus taught us to honor our leaders. The Holy Spirit helps us honor and obey them.

One day some men asked Jesus whether they should pay taxes to Caesar, the leader of their country.

Jesus said to them, "Bring me a coin to look at." When they brought one to him, he asked, "Whose image and inscription is this?"

They replied, "Caesar's."

So Jesus said to them, "Repay to Caesar what belongs to Caesar and to God what belongs to God."

adapted from Mark 12:13–17

Jesus wants us to respect and obey the leaders in our country and our Church. God guides us through these leaders.

Leaders Have Duties

Our leaders must show respect to us too. They must always love and respect those whom they lead and never ask others to do something that is wrong. They must do their jobs the best way they can, and they must be honest and trustworthy.

A good leader will try to be like Jesus and help others follow him more closely. Leaders should pray for their people, and we should pray for our leaders.

Write in each blue-ribbon award a word that tells what a good leader is like. Use the words you chose to write a prayer for someone who is your leader.

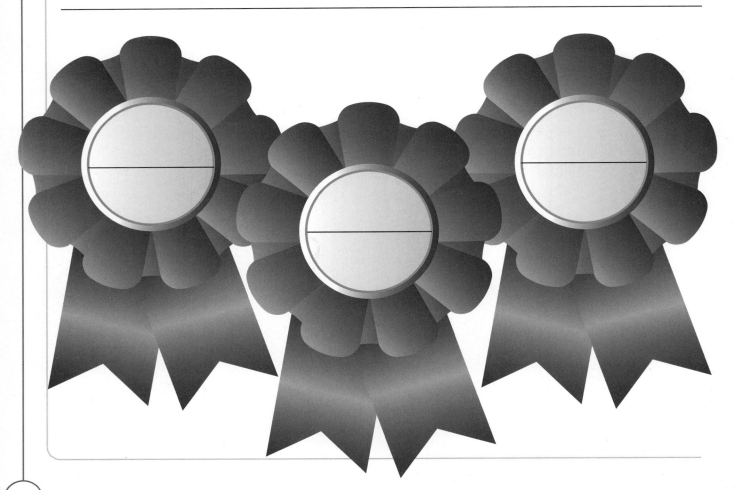

We Respect and Obey Those Who Guide Us

Teacher: Today we are going to talk about leaders. Has anyone here ever been chosen to be a leader in a game?

Jack: *(Smiling proudly, raises his hand)* Me! I'm always team captain!

Teacher: I can see that you like being a leader, Jack. Can you tell the class why?

Jack: I enjoy telling others how to play a good game. It's fun when everybody plays hard to win. I like everybody to listen and do as I say.

Teacher: *(Laughing)* I also like everyone to listen and do as I say! Does that make me a leader too?

Megan: Yes, but you're not like *him!*

Teacher: Jack and I guide you in different ways. There are many different leaders who try to guide us to do what is right. Can you think of some others?

Ethan: People such as the mayor.

Olivia: And the pope!

Teacher: That's right, we have leaders in our Church and government— and there are even more. All leaders need the help of those they lead in order to do a good job. For instance, how can you help Jack lead well during a game?

Owen: Watch for his signals and try to work well with each other as a team.

Ethan: Always listen to what Jack says.

Olivia: What if someone who is our captain asked us to cheat to win a game?

Jack: I would never do that!

Teacher: I know you wouldn't, Jack, but we must always remember never to obey *anyone* who tells us to do something we know is wrong.

Fourth Commandment Word Scramble

Complete the sentences by writing the correct word next to the scrambled letters.

1. The [ortufh] _____ commandment tells us how to honor our fathers and mothers.

2. [nohro] _____ means to love, respect, and obey.

3. The Fourth Commandment helps us bring [piespahsn] _____ to our families.

4. Besides our parents, [daeresl] _____ guide and protect us.

5. We should never do [rgnow] _____ even if a leader says we should.

We Remember

What is the Fourth Commandment?

The Fourth Commandment is "Honor your father and your mother."

Word to Know
obedience

We Respond

I will love, respect, and obey my parents and others who guide and protect me.

Building Family Faith

CHAPTER SUMMARY Christians respect and obey those in authority. Children owe respect and obedience to their parents. Everyone honors those who lead our country and our Church.

REFLECT

"Honor your father and your mother, as the LORD, your God, has commanded you, that you may have a long life and prosperity in the land which the LORD, your God, is giving you."

Deuteronomy 5:16

DISCUSS AS A FAMILY

- how everyone in the family respects and obeys those in authority.
- the ways children honor their parents.
- the reasons why respect for authority is important for your whole family.

Visit **www.christourlife.org/family** for more family resources.

PRAY

Father, bless our family. Show us how to love and honor each other.

DO

Discuss your family's history. Draw a family tree. View pictures of your ancestors and tell stories about them. Find out how your ancestors came to America.

Ask each person to share an experience that made him or her happy to be a member of the family.

Draw names. In the coming week, do something special for the person whose name you drew.

CHAPTER 15

We Respect the Gift of Life

Life Is God's Precious Gift

God said, "Let us make man in our image, after our likeness."

Genesis 1:26

Life is not a gift we keep for ourselves. It always belongs to God. He created all life out of love. The life of every person belongs to God.

All life is precious to God: tiny babies still inside their mothers, men and women who are too sick to move, people in other countries, people you do not like, and even dogs and whales. God wants us to take care of our own lives and those of others.

God tells us in the Fifth Commandment to respect life and to protect it.

You shall not kill.

Exodus 20:13

How can you tell that the people in these pictures love life?

We Take Care of Ourselves

Do you know how wonderful you are? Think of some amazing facts about your body. It changes food into skin and bones. When it is cut or bruised, it heals itself. It has parts like eyes and ears that are cleverly designed to put you in touch with the world and other people. Think of some of the amazing things you can do. You can speak and sing. You can create new and beautiful things. You can experience the joy that comes from loving and being loved.

God wants us to be healthy, happy people and to love ourselves. We are to take care of our bodies. We are to use our minds and our talents, and we are to grow. Then we will be able to enrich the world, help others, and give glory to God, our Maker.

Prescription for Healthy Living

Write a prescription for a long, healthy life, as though you are a doctor. Under Do's, list ways to care for your life. Under Don'ts, list things to avoid. (Hint: Recall things that your parents often tell you.)

For _____

Address _____

Date _____

℞

Do's

Don'ts

SUBSTITUTION PERMITTED

REFILL _____ TIMES

DISPENSE AS WRITTEN

DEA No. _____

MO

God Wants Us to Take Care of Others

People who really love Jesus do nothing to harm others or to hurt others' feelings. Instead they protect others and help them enjoy life. They are kind to others.

Peter Claver was a Spanish priest who spent his life helping Africans in the West Indies. Many had been brought there to be slaves. Father Claver saw how cruel slavery was. He met the slave ships as they arrived from Africa. Sometimes the slaves were starving. Father Claver gave them fresh fruit. He gave medicine to the sick and helped the dying.

After Father Claver helped these people, he told them about Jesus. He taught them to offer their sufferings to God and told them that one day they could join God in heaven. God wants all people to be saved. Many slaves asked to be baptized. Father Claver baptized more than 40 thousand slaves. Now he is in heaven, and we call him Saint Peter Claver.

The terms in the jar are like poison. They harm and destroy life. Choose two of these terms. Circle them and write how you would act instead. Use examples.

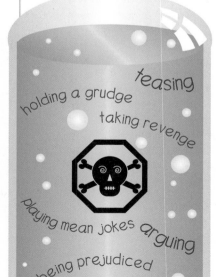

teasing
holding a grudge
taking revenge
playing mean jokes
arguing
being prejudiced
fighting
refusing to speak to someone

1. _____

_____

_____

_____

2. _____

_____

_____

_____

Christians Are Kind and Merciful

A lawyer asked Jesus what to do in order to win eternal life. Jesus told him to love God and his neighbor. Then the lawyer asked Jesus, "Who is my neighbor?" Jesus answered by telling this story:

A man going down the road was attacked by robbers. They took the man's money and clothes and left him half dead. Soon a religious man came by. He saw the man but went right on. Another traveler saw the dying man, but he passed by too.

Then a man from Samaria came along and felt sorry for the man. He cleaned and bandaged the man's wounds. The Samaritan put the man on a donkey and rode to an inn, where he cared for the wounded man. The next day the Samaritan gave two silver coins to the innkeeper and said, "Take care of this man. If you need more money, I will repay you on my way back."

Jesus then asked, "Which of these three was a good neighbor to the wounded man?"

The lawyer replied, "The man who treated him with kindness and mercy."

Jesus said, "Go and do the same."

adapted from Luke 10:25–37

A Moment with Jesus

Did you find an opportunity to be a Good Samaritan today? Did you pick up something someone else dropped? Did you share with someone who needed a pencil? Were you helpful at home? Jesus wants you to know that you don't have to do big things to be a Good Samaritan. Little things count too. Ask Jesus to help you do caring things for others. Thank him for always being there for you.

How Are These People Like the Good Samaritan?

1. Mr. and Mrs. Ortiz, an elderly couple, lived next door to Peter. One night it snowed very hard. Peter and his friend Julius shoveled the Ortizes' deck. When Mr. Ortiz offered to reward them, Peter and Julius refused to take any money.

2. Sarah and Bo Yun met Mrs. Reynolds in the store. Mrs. Reynolds was trying to watch her three small children and shop too. The two girls took care of the children so that Mrs. Reynolds could do her shopping.

3. Mara's brother had prepared supper for the family. When Mara sat down to eat, she noticed some food she did not like. Mara ate it anyway, without complaining, and thanked her brother for the meal.

A Puzzle About Life

Work the puzzle on the globe, using the Word Bank.

WORD BANK

God	respect
mercy	life
kindness	

Down

1. All life belongs to _____ .

2. The Fifth Commandment tells us to care for _____ .

3. When we forgive others, we show_____ .

Across

4. When we say or do loving things, we show _____ .

5. We are to show _____ for all forms of life.

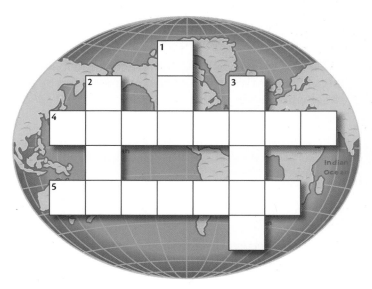

Award for Bravery

Awarded to

for

Life Givers Are Heroes

Ten-year-old Betty Ruth Hood awoke in the middle of the night to see her bed on fire. She woke up her mother. She took her sister out of her crib and carried her to safety. Then she returned to the house to rescue her brother.

In 1996 Betty was awarded one of the Young American Medals for Bravery by the president. That same year, Shivon Kershaw received the Young American Medal for Service. She organized teenagers to collect and ship relief packages to orphanages across the United States.

Not all life givers receive rewards in this life. Do you know someone who has done something brave or special to help others live a better life?

Write the person's name on the award and the reason he or she deserves it.

We Remember

What is the Fifth Commandment?
The Fifth Commandment is "You shall not kill."

We Respond

I thank God for the gift of life. I will respect life and show kindness toward others.

Building Family Faith

CHAPTER SUMMARY All life is sacred and belongs to God. We show our appreciation for the gift of life by taking good care of ourselves and by protecting and cherishing others, especially those who are vulnerable and weak.

REFLECT
When the Samaritan traveler came upon the injured man in the road, he "was moved with compassion at the sight."
Luke 10:33

DISCUSS AS A FAMILY
- how we care for each other when someone is sick or in need in other ways.
- the people in our family or in our neighborhood whom we know need help and how we can help them.
- ways we can take good care of ourselves.

PRAY
Lord Jesus, thank you for giving us life. Keep us safe and strong. Show us how to care for others.

DO
Determine ways to avoid things that endanger us, such as smoking, taking drugs, poor eating habits, and risky behavior.

Prepare healthy meals and snacks for the family.

Identify someone who is in need, such as an older person who has trouble getting around or a parishioner or neighbor who is ill. Give aid to that person.

Visit **www.christourlife.org/family** for more family resources.

We Are Faithful to Ourselves and Others

Our Bodies Are Good

Have you ever watched the Olympics? The beauty and grace of the gymnasts, divers, ice skaters, and other athletes amaze and inspire us. They make us realize just how wonderful our human bodies are.

God gave us the gift of our bodies when he made us. Scripture tells us:

> God created man in his image;
> . . . male and female he created them.
>
> Genesis 1:27

God wants us to be happy with who we are. Each of us can be proud to be a boy or a girl and be happy with the wonderful body God has given us. We can thank God by treating our bodies with respect. This way we can live and grow as human beings.

Another great gift we have is the ability to form friendships. We let others know who we are, and we come to know and love others. In our friendships God asks us to be true to ourselves and others. We are true to ourselves and to others when we treat our bodies with respect.

We Are True to Ourselves

Long ago Saint Paul wrote a letter to some people who had been Christians for only a short time. He wanted them to know that they were holy. He gives three good reasons for respecting their bodies. This letter in the Bible is meant for us too. Saint Paul tells us how to be true to ourselves.

Dear Friends in Christ,

God raised the Lord and will also raise us by his power. Do you not know that your bodies are members of Christ? . . . Keep yourselves holy and pure. . . . Your body is a temple of the Holy Spirit. You do not belong to yourselves but to God. He bought you at a great price. So use your body to give glory to God. My love to all of you in Christ Jesus.

Paul the Apostle

adapted from 1 Corinthians 6:14,15,18–20

How Can We Keep Ourselves Holy?

Draw a line to connect the beginning of each sentence with the right ending.

1. Look at •   • to the Holy Spirit for guidance.

2. Make •   • movies, TV shows, books, and pictures with good values.

3. Pray •   • sacrifices to show love for God and others.

4. Receive •   • your body and those of others.

5. Respect •   • the Eucharist and the Sacrament of Penance often.

We Are Faithful to Others

Friends are people who care about each other. They like to be together and to do things together. They also help each other in times of need. Good friends can always count on each other. They are faithful. They help each other to love God and to do what is right.

God wants us to have many good friends. He is pleased when we are true to them.

Scripture says,

A faithful friend is beyond price.

Sirach 6:15

The Sixth and Ninth Commandments help us be faithful.

You shall not commit adultery.
You shall not covet your neighbor's wife.

Exodus 20:14 and 17

A Moment with Jesus

Speak to Jesus in your heart, naming all your friends for him. Does a friend need help because of something going on in school or in his or her family? Is there something special you need? If so, tell Jesus about it. He always listens; he always understands. Let Jesus know how glad you are to be his friend.

Marriage Is a Special Friendship

Sometimes a man and a woman have a special kind of friendship. They want to share their lives and start a new family. They get married in order to do this.

At their wedding a husband and wife make special promises to each other before God. They promise to love and care for each other always. Through the Sacrament of Matrimony, the Holy Spirit helps the husband and wife keep their promises.

Marriage Vows

Read the sentences and fill in the missing words from the Word Bank.

WORD BANK

love	promises
care	other
God	

At their wedding a man and woman

make special _____

to each _____

before _____ .

They promise to _____

and _____ for

each other always.

A Heartfelt Discovery

To discover what is at the heart of every marriage, follow the strings of the heart-shaped balloons. Only four strings will find their way to the spaces below.

___ ___ ___ ___

We Are Temples of the Holy Spirit

Mia: Hi, Mom. We're home!

Alex: Hi! We had a great class today. Try to guess what I learned. I'll give you some hints. It's about something that is like a temple or a church. It belongs to God because he made it. He came to live in it at Baptism. Do you know what it is?

Mom: Could it be your body or the body of anyone who is baptized?

Alex: Right, Mom. Think about it: I'm a temple of the Holy Spirit.

Mia: Am I a temple too?

Mom: Yes, Mia. It's so wonderful that I hope you'll always remember it.

Alex: That's just what Saint Paul told us to do. Do you know what else he said?

Mia: No. What else?

Alex: He said we respect our bodies when we act in ways that give glory to God. We should care for our bodies because they are a gift from God. *(Suddenly smiling)* Mom, do you think I would be caring for my body if I ate some of your great pizza?

Mia: Yeah, me too, Mom!

Mom: *(Laughing)* I think it would be good if you both changed your clothes first, washed your hands, and then ate some of my pizza.

Alex: Awesome!

Mia: Okay, Mom!

Respecting Our Bodies

Finish this sentence that is based on Saint Paul's letter on page 104.

We do not want to use our bodies the wrong way because one day they will

_____ . Our bodies are

parts, or members, of _____

and _____ of the Holy Spirit.

We Remember

What is the Sixth Commandment?
The Sixth Commandment is "You shall not commit adultery."

What is the Ninth Commandment?
The Ninth Commandment is "You shall not covet your neighbor's wife."

We Respond

I will respect myself and others and be faithful to my friends.

Building Family Faith

CHAPTER SUMMARY We have a special dignity because we are made in the image and likeness of God. We honor God and ourselves when we take good care of ourselves, when we are faithful, and when married people are true to their marriage promises.

REFLECT
"Do you not know that your body is a temple of the holy Spirit within you . . . ? Therefore, glorify God in your body."
1 Corinthians 6:19–20

DISCUSS AS A FAMILY
- the ways we give honor to God by the way we use and care for our bodies.
- how we have been faithful to friends through hard times and troubles.
- what it means to be a good friend.

PRAY
Jesus, help me be true to myself, to others, and to you.

DO
Take a careful look at the television programs and movies your family watches. Choose to watch those that show proper respect and reverence for people.

Write letters to television station managers encouraging them to offer more appropriate programming.

Visit **www.christourlife.org/family** for more family resources.

CHAPTER 17

We Respect What God Has Given Us

God Gives Us the Things We Need

God loves all the people he made. God put into the world everything we need to lead good lives. All of us have a right to what we need, but God wants us to use his gifts in the proper way. We should take care of our belongings and those of others. We should share with others.

How can we take care of what we have?

When can we share with others?

We show love for others when we respect what they own. It is wrong to take what belongs to them. In the Seventh Commandment God tells us this.

> You shall not steal.
>
> Exodus 20:15

How do others feel when we respect their things?

If we are living good, healthy lives, we should be satisfied with what we have. We should not envy others for things or talents they have that we do not. We also should not envy them because they have more things than we do. God tells us this in the Tenth Commandment.

> You shall not covet your neighbor's goods.
>
> adapted from Exodus 20:17

We Respect the Property of Others

Everyone has a right to own things. God wants us to respect others' rights. He wants us to respect other people's belongings and to be honest and fair in all we do.

We show respect for other people's belongings by using them the right way. We should be careful not to damage, ruin, or lose what belongs to others. If we damage anything, we must repair it or pay for it.

It is wrong to steal from people or to cheat them. A person who takes anything that belongs to someone else must always return it to the owner or pay for it.

We ask others before using their things. We return what we borrow. When we find things that are not ours, we try to return them to their owner.

When we take tests, we do not cheat. When we play games, we are fair and follow the rules.

Signs of Respect

Read the sentences and fill in the letters to complete the missing words.

1. We respect others and share because we c ___ ___ ___ .

2. We respect the b ___ ___ ___ ___ ___ ___ ___ ___ ___ of others.

3. When we take a test, we are h ___ ___ ___ ___ ___ ; we do not cheat.

4. We make up to others for d ___ ___ ___ ___ ___ to their property.

5. We are satisfied with all we have and t ___ ___ ___ ___ God for his gifts.

Choosing to Do Right or Wrong

The decision to do right or wrong, to sin or not, is a **moral choice**. God gave us the commandments as guides for living holy lives. God also gave us **free will,** which allows us to choose to do right or wrong. The Holy Spirit will help us make good decisions.

Put a check (✓) on the blank if the sentence is about someone who is following either the Seventh or Tenth Commandment. If the sentence is about someone not keeping either commandment, write the letter of the answer that tells what wrong is being done.

A. stealing
B. cheating
C. envy
D. damaging property

_____ 1. Tawanda told the librarian that she had accidentally torn a page in a book.

_____ 2. Joe took a CD from the store, hid it under his coat, and left without paying for it.

_____ 3. After accidentally breaking Mr. Joyce's window, some boys offered to pay for it.

_____ 4. Nathan took money from his dad's dresser to buy an ice-cream cone.

_____ 5. Catherine was angry because she could not have Gerald's new CD.

_____ 6. To get a higher grade, Claire copied an answer from Brigitte's test paper.

_____ 7. Rosalita shared her new jewelry-making kit with her friends.

_____ 8. Emma left her friend's new bike out in the rain.

_____ 9. Aida returned the pencil she had borrowed.

_____ 10. With his skateboard, Max rolled over the flowers in his neighbor's garden.

Dorothy Becomes a Hero for Justice

Dorothy Day was born in New York City in 1897. Her family moved around a lot. They were living in California when a terrible earthquake occurred. The quake left many families homeless and without food. Dorothy remembers her mother jumping in to help them. This memory stayed with young Dorothy.

As she grew older, Dorothy came to realize that taking care of the poor was the most important thing anyone could do. Later, when she became a Catholic, she decided to be a worker for justice. She wanted to follow the example Jesus gave.

Dorothy and a friend created a newspaper called the *Catholic Worker*. This newspaper told what life was like for the poor and how to make their lives better.

Dorothy believed that it wasn't enough just to give money to people in need. You should take them in and treat them as you would treat Jesus. So she created hospitality houses where the poor could live and get help.

Dorothy Day died in 1980. During her life, she didn't just talk about justice. She worked for justice. She became one of the poor herself. She lived with them and became their friend.

A Moment with Jesus

Share with Jesus what you think about Dorothy Day. Ask him to help you find ways to make things easier for the people in your life. Jesus knows you try to be good. Maybe he wants you to try a little harder. Talk this over with Jesus. Then share with him anything else that's on your mind.

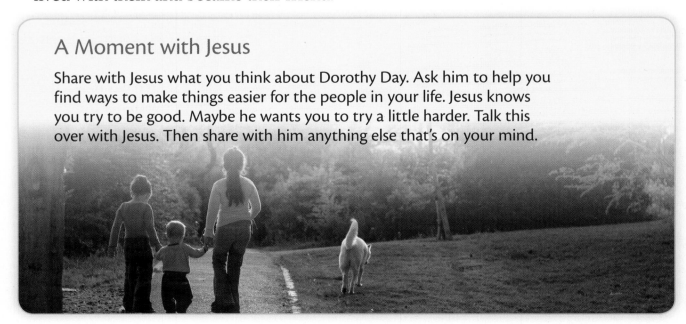

Unjust Acts Cause Harm

Respecting people's rights is just. Acts against the Seventh and Tenth Commandments are unjust. They cause harm and make us sad and fearful. They break down peace in the world and in our hearts.

Read each unjust act in the first column. Find each one's unhappy result in the second column. Write the letter of the answer on the line.

_____ 1. Houses on a block are broken into.

_____ 2. People shoplift.

_____ 3. Gangs cover public walls with words and pictures.

_____ 4. A company cheats its customers.

_____ 5. Items are stolen at school.

_____ 6. Someone does not play fair.

A. People do not trust salespeople.

B. The game is ruined.

C. Prices are raised to cover the cost.

D. Rooms and lockers must be locked.

E. People live in fear.

F. Neighborhoods are no longer beautiful.

Peace Walk

Find your way to peace by keeping the commandments and avoiding unjust acts.

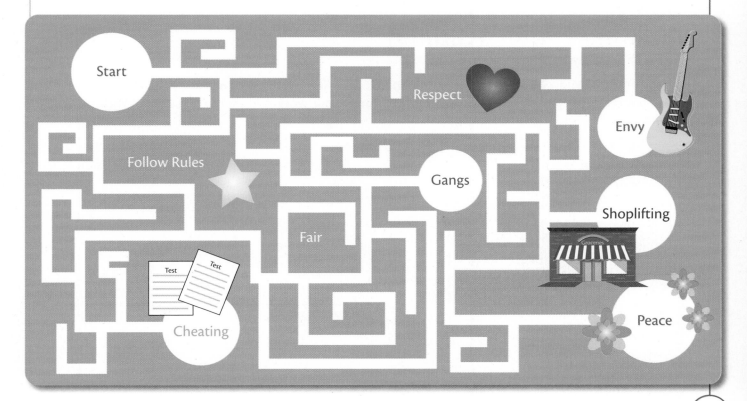

My Own Book

Imagine you are writing a book about the Seventh and Tenth Commandments. What would be a good title? Write it on the book cover.

We Remember

What is the Seventh Commandment?
The Seventh Commandment is "You shall not steal."

What is the Tenth Commandment?
The Tenth Commandment is "You shall not covet your neighbor's goods."

Words to Know
free will   moral choice

We Respond

I will be honest and fair. I will be satisfied with what I have.

Building Family Faith

CHAPTER SUMMARY All of us have the right to share in the goodness of the earth's resources, to own property, and to receive just compensation for our work. We should be satisfied with what we have and respect the property and rights of others.

REFLECT
"You shall not steal."
Exodus 20:15

DISCUSS AS A FAMILY
- the possessions we have that are most important to us. Why are they important?
- how we take care of the things we have.
- the ways we show respect for the possessions of others—in our family, at school, among our friends.

PRAY
"The LORD will surely grant abundance;
   our land will yield its increase."
Psalm 85:13

DO
Work through a charity supported by your parish, if possible, and have the children get personally involved in making the donation.

Participate as a family in a community beautification or conservation project.

At dinner or bedtime, pray prayers of thanks for God's generosity to your family.

Visit **www.christourlife.org/family** for more family resources.

We Respect the Gifts of the Earth

We Care for Our Earth Home

God made all things on earth. In the Bible we read about it.

> God looked at everything he had made, and he found it very good.
>
> Genesis 1:31

God put all the wonderful gifts of the earth in our care. He wants us to respect them and use them the right way. At the end of time they will be changed and share in God's glory too.

We use God's gifts the right way when we are not wasteful and when we take good care of them. It is right to share them with other people. If we use God's gifts properly, earth will be a pleasant place to live, and we will reach heaven.

The Poor Man Gets His Reward

Jesus told a story about a rich man and Lazarus. The rich man had fancy clothes and fine feasts with his friends. Lazarus, a poor and sick man, begged at the door for scraps of food from the rich man's table. He was given nothing.

Both the rich man and Lazarus died. Lazarus was taken to a place of happiness for all eternity. The rich man was taken to a place of suffering.

The rich man begged, "Send Lazarus down with a drop of water to cool my tongue and relieve my suffering."

The answer came, "You received what was good during your life. Lazarus received what was bad. Now he is comforted and you are suffering."

adapted from Luke 16:19–31

God gives the gifts of creation to everyone. He wants those who have more to share with those who have less. By not sharing even the smallest portion of what he owned with Lazarus, the rich man was keeping for himself the gifts God had given him. He did not show real gratitude.

A Moment with Jesus

Close your eyes and relax. Tell Jesus about some of your favorite things. He might ask if you are willing to share what you have with someone who has little. What is your answer? Jesus knows that it can be hard to give up the things you like. He promises to help. Jesus loves you.

Operation Rice Bowl Helps People Live Better Lives

Every day on the news we see stories about children who need help. God has given us our world to share, but what can we do to help other people?

In 1975, Catholics in the Diocese of Allentown, Pennsylvania, decided to do something about helping others during the season of Lent. They began a program that became known as Operation Rice Bowl. It gives families the opportunity to pray with one another. The families are also asked to make small sacrifices and donate the money saved to help meet the needs of others.

The money that is collected by Operation Rice Bowl helps people live better lives.

Farmers are given the opportunity to produce better crops. Mothers and children are given health and dental care. It also helps people create a better water supply, a serious need in some parts of the world.

Operation Rice Bowl has been very successful in helping others. More than 15,000 parishes, schools, and faith communities participate every year. About eight million dollars a year is collected to help people locally and worldwide.

Participating in Operation Rice Bowl is a great way to be part of the big picture in answering God's call to share with people in need.

Alphabet Soup

Fill in the word from the steaming bowl of soup that best completes each sentence.

1. We treat the gifts God has given us with _____ .

2. We _____ God's gifts with others.

3. We do not _____ things.

4. We take good _____ of them.

5. God found all he had made _____ .

care   respect   waste   good   share

We Share God's Gifts with Others

We call the earth our planet, but the earth and everything on it really belong to God. He has given the earth to his creatures to use in order to live and grow. There are some people in our world, however, who have no homes. Others have no clothing, no food, no medicine, no education.

Some people are in need because they have been treated unfairly. Others are very lonely. They are not loved or cared for by anyone.

Many people in the world have not heard the Good News. They need someone to teach them about Jesus.

We belong to God's big family of people with the earth as our home. God wants all his people to be happy. All of us, including future generations, have a right to the world's gifts. So we must use the riches of the earth carefully and wisely. Those of us who have more should share with people in need. When we do this, we show that we are all brothers and sisters in God's family.

Words of Wisdom

Print in the boxes the message from Saint Paul that will help you share God's gifts with others. Use the code to help you.

Code

A	C	D	E	F	G	H	I	L	O	R	S	U	V
1	2	3	4	5	6	7	8	9	10	11	12	13	14

| 6 | 10 | 3 | | 9 | 10 | 14 | 4 | | 12 |

| 1 | 2 | 7 | 4 | 4 | 11 | 5 | 13 | 9 |

| 6 | 8 | 14 | 4 | 11 | .

2 Corinthians 9:7

You Are Never Too Young

People may stare at Michael Munds. Sometimes kids tease him. That's because Michael has a disease that causes the bones in his face to not fit together like other people's do. He looks different. Since being born in 1989, he has had many operations on his face, and he has more to go. That doesn't stop Michael from helping others.

Michael raises and donates money for people who need it. He started when he was very young. At age five, he donated all his stuffed animals to children who had lost theirs in a flood. Then when he was six years old, there was a bombing in Oklahoma City. He organized a bowling game, and he asked people to donate money for every pin knocked down. He raised $37,649. He has raised money for the Children's Miracle Network and for the victims of 9/11. In all, he has raised and donated close to $200,000 for different people and organizations. And he doesn't plan to stop.

When people ask Michael why he does all this, he answers, "If we all make a difference—even a little bit—one person at a time, then maybe when I grow up the world will be a better place to live."

It's Your Turn Now

**Is there a person or a group of people that you could help?
Write down whom you can help and describe what you would do.**

_____

_____

_____

_____

_____

_____

Reminder Notes

Fill in what you will respect in each place.
Choose from the words listed on the right.

water	walls	clothes	dishes
toys	animals	books	trees
birds	lawn	desks	paper

At school

_____

_____

_____

_____

At home

_____

_____

_____

_____

Outside

_____

_____

_____

_____

_____

We Remember

How do we use the gifts of the earth in the right way?

We use the gifts of the earth in the right way by sharing them, not wasting them, and taking care of them.

We Respond

Lord, our world is full of your goodness. Help me use the gifts of the earth in the right way.

Building Family Faith

CHAPTER SUMMARY God created a world rich in beauty, resources, and wealth. He expects us to use these resources wisely and to care for them responsibly.

REFLECT
"The land will yield its fruit and you will have food in abundance, so that you may live there without worry."

Leviticus 25:19

DISCUSS AS A FAMILY
• how our family benefits from the natural abundance of the earth.
• how the labor of others serves us.
• the ways we waste things—at home and in our community.
• the ways we can conserve and care for the good things of the earth.

PRAY
"Give us this day our daily bread."

DO
Organize a family beautification day. Clean up the house or the yard.

Find old or damaged household items. Whenever possible, fix them up and use them again instead of throwing them out.

Learn about recycling. Take old items to the recycling center and ask for a quick tour.

Visit **www.christourlife.org/family** for more family resources.

We Speak the Truth with Love

God Wants Us to Speak the Truth

God is always true. He loves the truth and God is truth. We trust God because everything he says is true. God is always faithful to his promises.

God wants us to tell the truth and to keep our promises. He tells us this in the Eighth Commandment.

> You shall not bear false witness against your neighbor.
>
> Exodus 20:16

To bear false witness means to tell a lie. God tells us to be always truthful. It is especially important to tell the truth when we are talking about others.

When we tell the truth and keep our promises, we show love for God and for others. Our trust in one another grows. We trust those who tell the truth.

Jesus, Sermon on the Mount, ❯ Church of the Annunciation, Nazareth, Israel.

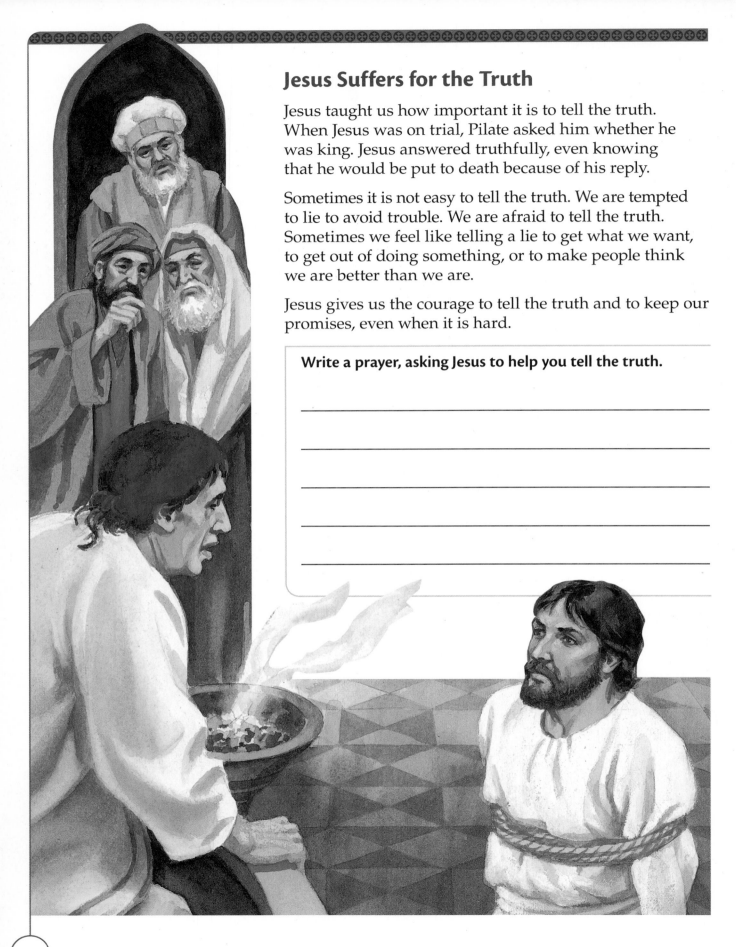

Jesus Suffers for the Truth

Jesus taught us how important it is to tell the truth. When Jesus was on trial, Pilate asked him whether he was king. Jesus answered truthfully, even knowing that he would be put to death because of his reply.

Sometimes it is not easy to tell the truth. We are tempted to lie to avoid trouble. We are afraid to tell the truth. Sometimes we feel like telling a lie to get what we want, to get out of doing something, or to make people think we are better than we are.

Jesus gives us the courage to tell the truth and to keep our promises, even when it is hard.

Write a prayer, asking Jesus to help you tell the truth.

_____

_____

_____

_____

_____

Sometimes We Suffer for the Truth

Thomas More was a lawyer and a helper to the king of England. The people loved him because he was fair to all and good to the poor. Thomas prayed at Mass every day and asked God to help him do what was right. He wanted to never offend God.

Henry VIII was king when Thomas lived. The king liked Thomas. He knew that Thomas would do whatever he could to help him.

Then King Henry made himself the head of the Church in England. When Thomas heard this, he would no longer work for the king. King Henry was very angry at Thomas and had him put into prison. Thomas still would not say that the king was the head of the Church, because it was not true. When the judges could not make Thomas say what was not true, they said he must die. Thomas's last words were, "I die the king's good servant, but God's first."

A Man of Truth

Work the puzzle about Saint Thomas More. Find the answers in the story above.

M Every day Thomas prayed for

God's help at _____ .

O Thomas loved God and would

not _____ him.

R Thomas prayed that God would help him

do what was _____ .

E Thomas More lived in _____ .

God Wants Us to Speak with Love

God gave us the wonderful gift of speech. With it we can help others learn, speak to them with love, and bring them good news and happiness.

Saint Paul wrote a letter that tells how to speak with love. This is what he said:

> Love is patient, love is kind. It is not jealous; it is not boastful. It is not rude, selfish, or quick-tempered. Love is never happy with evil but is happy with the truth.
>
> adapted from 1 Corinthians 13:1,4–6

Our words are *true* when we are honest. Our words are *patient* when we speak calmly and hold back anger. Our words are *unselfish* when we praise others or share their joy. Our words are *kind* when we say polite and thoughtful things to others.

God wants us to say only what is true and good. He wants us to protect others' good names. Sometimes we show love just by being quiet. When someone does something wrong, we show love by not talking about it, except to protect that person or someone else. God wants us to say only what will bring happiness and peace to others.

Look at the two scenes below. Fill in the bubbles with what you think the children are talking about. Write some kind words in the bubbles.

A Moment with Jesus

Listen to Jesus as he speaks to you in your heart about what it means to tell the truth. Did he remind you to write only what is true as well? Whether we are speaking or writing, Jesus wants us to be truthful, kind, and encouraging. Sometimes that is hard to do, especially if we are angry with someone or have hurt feelings. Ask Jesus to send his Holy Spirit to help you. He never refuses a call for help. He loves you so much!

We Have Fun with Words

We like to hear tall tales. We listen to people say the strangest things, such as "I didn't sleep a wink."

Sometimes people say what is not true just to tease. Make-believe stories are not wrong, because everyone knows that they are not really true.

Color the clouds around the sentences that tease or that are make-believe.

Ernesto said that it was raining cats and dogs.

Luke told his little brother that there is a pot of gold at the end of the rainbow.

The bell rang to announce the end of the school day.

Josh liked carrots. His father said, "One day you'll turn into a rabbit."

Mother told Alexis that elves must have made her doll's new clothes.

Helena said that she has a pet dinosaur on her farm.

The horse spread its wings and flew over the steep mountain.

Nicole's mother is a police officer.

True or False?

Check (✓) the box under T if the sentence is true. Check the box under F if the sentence is false.

T F

☐ ☐ **1.** The truth makes trust grow.

☐ ☐ **2.** We do wrong when we pretend or play make-believe.

☐ ☐ **3.** Jesus told the truth at his trial.

☐ ☐ **4.** It is all right to talk about what others did wrong.

☐ ☐ **5.** We keep the secrets of others.

We Remember

What is the Eighth Commandment?
The Eighth Commandment is "You shall not bear false witness against your neighbor."

We Respond

I will speak the truth with love, saying only things that are kind and true.

Building Family Faith

CHAPTER SUMMARY It is important to speak the truth and to keep our promises. We do this in imitation of God, who loves truth and who commands us to always say what is true, good, and loving.

REFLECT
"Speak the truth to one another; let there be honesty and peace in the judgments at your gates."

Zechariah 8:16

DISCUSS AS A FAMILY
• the negative consequences of lying.
• how you felt when someone told a lie about you.
• how keeping a promise is a way of speaking the truth.

PRAY
Jesus, you are the way, the truth, and the life. Give me the strength to always be truthful.

DO
Think of people who had the courage to tell the truth, such as Abraham Lincoln or Dominic Savio. Who are some current examples?

As a family, adopt and live by the motto of the knights of King Arthur: "Live pure, speak true, right wrong, follow the King!"

Visit **www.christourlife.org/family** for more family resources.

We Live God's Laws

God's Laws Bring Happiness

The Ten Commandments show us how to love. The first three tell us how to love God, and the rest spell out how to love others.

A Song About God's Laws
(To the melody of "If You're Happy")

O be prayerful and give honor to God's name.
O be prayerful and give honor to God's name.
You'll be happy and will know it,
And your life will surely show it.
O be prayerful and give honor to God's name.

Go to Mass and celebrate the Sabbath day.
Go to Mass and celebrate the Sabbath day.
You'll be happy and will know it,
And your life will surely show it.
Go to Mass and celebrate the Sabbath day.

Be obedient, kind, and truthful every day.
Be obedient, kind, and truthful every day.
You'll be happy and will know it,
And your life will surely show it.
Be obedient, kind, and truthful every day.

O be faithful and respectful every day.
O be faithful and respectful every day.
You'll be happy and will know it.
And your life will surely show it.
O be faithful and respectful every day.

O be honest and be careful with all things.
O be honest and be careful with all things.
You'll be happy and will know it,
And your life will surely show it.
O be honest and be careful with all things.

Climb the Mountain

How to Play

- Roll the die and move your marker the number of spaces it shows.

- Read what is on the space and name the commandment it matches.

- A person acting as Moses checks the answers against the commandments listed on page 197 If you are correct, keep your marker on the space. If you are incorrect, move back one space. Read what is on that space and name the commandment it matches.

- If you are incorrect again, move back one more space; your turn is now over.

- The player who reaches the top of the mountain first wins.

What You Need

Marker for each player

Die

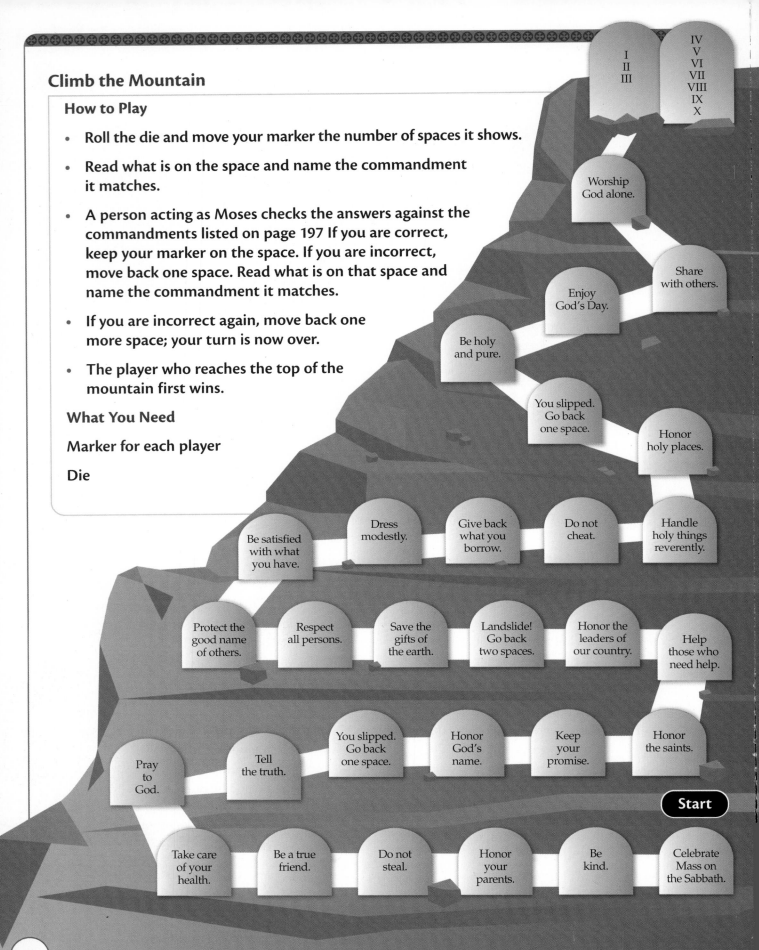

I II III

IV V VI VII VIII IX X

Worship God alone.

Share with others.

Enjoy God's Day.

Be holy and pure.

You slipped. Go back one space.

Honor holy places.

Be satisfied with what you have.

Dress modestly.

Give back what you borrow.

Do not cheat.

Handle holy things reverently.

Protect the good name of others.

Respect all persons.

Save the gifts of the earth.

Landslide! Go back two spaces.

Honor the leaders of our country.

Help those who need help.

Pray to God.

Tell the truth.

You slipped. Go back one space.

Honor God's name.

Keep your promise.

Honor the saints.

Start

Take care of your health.

Be a true friend.

Do not steal.

Honor your parents.

Be kind.

Celebrate Mass on the Sabbath.

An E-Mail Message

Write the message on the lines, using the code.

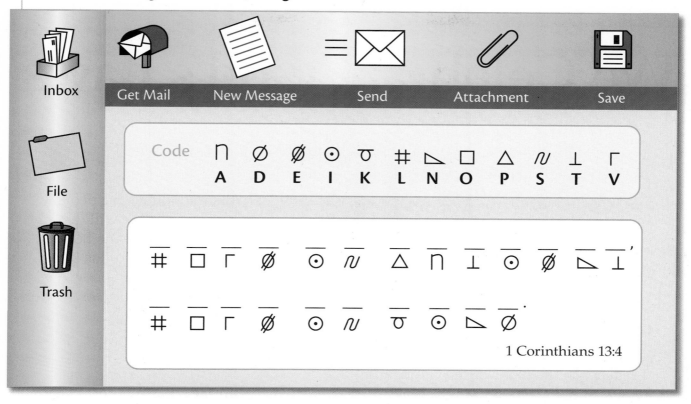

Code											
∩	∅	∅	⊙	σ	#	▷	□	△	ℳ	⊥	Γ
A	D	E	I	K	L	N	O	P	S	T	V

□ Γ ∅ ⊙ ℳ △ ∩ ⊥ ⊙ ∅ ▷ ⊥ ,

□ Γ ∅ ⊙ ℳ σ ⊙ ▷ ∅ .

1 Corinthians 13:4

A Path for Life

Find the words on the sidewalk and write them on the lines.

1. The First Commandment is to _____ .

2. The Second Commandment is to honor God's _____ .

3. The Third Commandment is to keep the Lord's Day _____ .

4. The Fourth Commandment is to _____ our parents.

5. The Fifth Commandment is to be _____ to others.

6. The Sixth and Ninth Commandments are to be _____ .

7. The Seventh and Tenth Commandments are to be _____ .

8. The Eighth Commandment is to speak the _____ .

honest
pray
holy
kind
truth
name
faithful
obey

We Celebrate God's Laws

Song

> ("A Song About God's Laws," page 127)
>
> *The children process with, and then put in place, the Bible, the Ten Commandments tablets, and candles.*

Prayer

Leader: In the name of the Father and of the Son and of the Holy Spirit. Amen.

Let us join together as we pray:

All: Lord God, we raise our hearts to you with joy. We want to live as you have told us. Put your love into our hearts today. Keep us faithful to your laws. We ask this through Jesus our Lord. Amen.

Leader: When God gave the people of Israel the laws he wanted them to follow, the people responded, "We will do everything that the LORD has told us." (Exodus 24:3) God asks you to follow his commandments. How do you respond?

All: We will do everything God has told us.

Leader: In the letter we are about to hear, Saint Paul tells us that when we keep the commandments, we are like runners in a race trying to win a prize. But the prize we win will last forever, because it is heaven.

**Reading adapted from
1 Corinthians 9:24–25**

Leader: A reading from the first letter of Saint Paul to the Corinthians

All the runners in a race are trying to win, but only one gets the prize. They do many difficult things to train for the race. They run fast to win a prize that will not last long. But we run for a prize that will last forever. Run so as to win.

The Word of the Lord

All: Thanks be to God.

Homily *(in dialogue with the children)*

Silent Prayer

Awards

Leader: Accept this medal as a sign that you will live God's laws with joy.

Each child (upon receiving the medal):

Child: I want to keep God's laws.

Prayer with Commandments

All: Your Word, O Lord, is the joy of my heart. I sing your praises and walk with gladness.

For each commandment, a child prays and holds up a picture. Response to each prayer:

All: Lord, teach us to love your laws.

Final Prayer

Leader: Let us now pray together with joyful voices.

All: Lord, we rejoice because we have your laws. They are better than great riches. We will follow them closely. Help us obey them, O Lord. Amen.

Closing Song

Looking Back at Unit 4

Jesus reminded us that love for God is shown in love for our neighbor. The last seven commandments tell us how to love others in our daily lives. Keeping them brings us happiness and also helps bring God's kingdom of peace, justice, and joy to others.

In the Ten Commandments, God tells us to care for the gifts of the earth, to use them the right way, and to share them. God tells us to value life in all forms as a precious gift. God tells us to be faithful to ourselves and to others and to respect others' rights. We ask God's help in following these laws with love.

Living the Message

Check (✓) each sentence that describes you.

❏ **1.** I can explain what the last seven commandments tell me to do and not to do.

❏ **2.** I show that I value God's earthly gifts and my own life by the way I treat them.

❏ **3.** I treat others with respect and kindness.

❏ **4.** I try to be honest and truthful.

❏ **5.** I can recite the Ten Commandments by heart.

Planning Ahead

Fill in the Don't Forget list with ways you can show Jesus' love in words or deeds.

Don't Forget . . .

Sunday: At Mass, I'll remember to_____

Monday: At school, I'll_____

Tuesday: At home, I'll_____

Wednesday: I'll help my neighbor by_____

Thursday: On the playground, I'll_____

Friday: With my friends, I'll_____

Saturday: Around the house, I'll_____

The Ten Commandments Are Gifts from God

Your first thought about the commandments might be that they are obligations. Though we are obliged to understand, accept, and obey them to the best of our ability, we do so because following them is the way to our truest happiness. That's the real gift of the commandments. Here is a look at the commandments along with some of the wisdom they hold for our lives.

1. I am the Lord your God: you shall not have strange gods before me.

There's good news and even better news. The good news is that there is a God, and the better news is that it's not me. It's a human temptation to want to make ourselves gods. Instead, we have a Creator who loves us, cares for us, and calls us to be one with him.

2. You shall not take the name of the Lord your God in vain.

When we are careless in our use of God's name, we demean the truth about him.

3. Remember to keep holy the Lord's Day.

With our culture's frantic workaholic tendencies, we need the Sabbath as a spiritual antidote. We need to stop, rest, and get in tune with the reality that we are at our core deeply spiritual beings.

4. Honor your father and your mother.

A culture grows shallow when it fails to honor its elders. When life becomes all about "me, me, me," we fail to become the human beings we were created to be—people for others.

5. You shall not kill.

There are many ways to do mortal damage to others. We can kill people's spirits, their reputations, their hopes, and their dreams. God calls us to choose life.

6. You shall not commit adultery.
and
9. You shall not covet your neighbor's wife.

These are commandments about respect for other people, their inherent dignity, and their relationships.

7. You shall not steal.
and
10. You shall not covet your neighbor's goods.

These are commandments about respect for other people and for what belongs to them.

8. You shall not bear false witness against your neighbor.

Ours is a God of truth. Telling lies about others is unjust and unfair. Lies harm not only the person we lie about, but they also undermine society as a whole.

Respect for Material Gifts

"You'd be surprised what people throw away," says John Havlicek, a man who sells rescued treasures at a local flea market. "People in our society have just so much stuff that they fail to appreciate what they're tossing in the alley. They throw things out just to make room for their next round of purchases."

Saint Benedict

God's laws tell us to love God, other people, and ourselves. In their great wisdom, these laws tell us to take care of and to share the gifts of the earth so that there is enough for everyone. We are to treat the gifts that God gives us with care. Saint Benedict (480–547) was the founder of many monasteries. He taught his monks to treat the everyday objects in the monastery, such as forks and spoons, clothing, and furniture, as though they were the vessels (chalice, paten, and ciborium) used on the altar. He wanted the monks to be able to recognize the inherent worth and sacredness of such common household items. This is a lesson we ought to model and teach to our children.

Visit **www.christourlife.org/family** for more family resources.

Gifts on Loan

Catholic wisdom tells us that the material items in our possession are gifts on loan from God. We are told to care for them. We must not hoard them but share them with others. We must realize they are given to us to serve the common good. Saint Basil (329–379) said, "The extra cloak that hangs in the closet belongs to the one who has none."

Steps your family can take to show greater care for the gifts God has given:

Participate in your area's recycling efforts. Some common objects in your home that you might not realize can be recycled or refurbished are old cell phones, used printer cartridges, prescription eyeglasses, batteries, and even running shoes.

Treat the possessions in your home with respect. Gently remind one another to turn off the lights when you leave a room or to pick up clothes that are crumpled on the bedroom floor.

Teach your child the importance of sharing with others. When your family bakes cookies, put some on a plate for your neighbor.

Have your child help you gather and deliver donations of used and well-cared-for items to charities that help families in need. Your children can take a few minutes to look in their closets and pick a few toys that they don't play with anymore. They can pass them along for another child to enjoy (even if it's only one toy).

Thank God regularly for all that you've been given in life. Ask for help in using these gifts for the greater honor and glory of God.

Family Feature

Love of Others

For each saying write the number of the commandment it matches.

1. _____ Don't let your parents down. They brought you up.

2. _____ He who lives by the sword dies by the sword.

3. _____ Don't let Sunday pass without going to Mass.

Saint Thomas More

4. _____ "I die the king's good servant, but God's first." (St. Thomas More)

5. _____ If friends are true, they don't envy what belongs to you.

6. _____ _____ Honesty is the best policy.

7. _____ Never in anger, only in love, do we say the name of God.

8. _____ _____ The greatest gift parents can give a child is to love each other.

9. _____ O what a tangled web we weave, When first we practice to deceive! (Sir Walter Scott)

10. _____ _____ The measure of life is not length, but honesty. (John Lyly)

1. I am the Lord your God: you shall not have strange gods before me.
2. You shall not take the name of the Lord your God in vain.
3. Remember to keep holy the Lord's Day.
4. Honor your father and your mother.
5. You shall not kill.
6. You shall not commit adultery.
7. You shall not steal.
8. You shall not bear false witness against your neighbor.
9. You shall not covet your neighbor's wife.
10. You shall not covet your neighbor's goods.

(Answers: **1.** 4, **2.** 5, **3.** 3, **4.** 1, **5.** 10, **6.** 7 and 8, **7.** 2, **8.** 6 and 9, **9.** 8, **10.** 7 and 8)

Jesus Leads Us to Happiness

Jesus said to him, "I am the way and the truth and the life."

John 14:6

A Letter Home

Dear Parents and Family,

In this final unit, the children will study the Beatitudes, Jesus' lessons for happiness. They will learn that by following in the footsteps of Jesus, Mary, and the saints, they can achieve happiness.

The first beatitude advises us to be detached from material things and to feel satisfied with what we have. The children will be encouraged to share with others and to trust in God for all their needs.

Suffering is part of daily life. In the second and third beatitudes, Jesus calls blessed those who mourn and the meek. By imitating Jesus, who is gentle and humble of heart, they can learn to meet life's challenges with patience and to comfort others who are suffering.

In the fourth and fifth beatitudes, Christ calls us to purity and holiness so that we can share in his happiness. The children will learn just what it means to seek God alone: doing what God wants, aligning their intentions with him, and following the example of the Blessed Virgin Mary and the saints.

The following two beatitudes share the ways in which the children can express mercy, through love and compassion. Jesus' word and example encourage them to become peacemakers in their schools, their homes, and the world around them.

The last beatitude tells us that God can bring good from evil and happiness from suffering. The children are encouraged to trust in God's grace for the strength to bear suffering with love, keeping in mind the example of the martyrs and Jesus' promise of happiness.

The children end this unit with a celebration, motivating them to live the Beatitudes and thus achieve the happiness promised to the faithful.

At the end of each chapter in this unit, the children will bring home a review of the chapter along with either the Building Family Faith page or the Family Feature section. These features give you a quick review of what your child learned and offer practical ways to reinforce the lesson at home so that the whole family may benefit.

Visit **www.christourlife.org/family** for more family resources.

Happy Are the Poor in Spirit

Jesus Showed Us the Way to Happiness

While he was on earth, Jesus showed us what it means to be happy. He showed us that true happiness comes from being willing to love God as our Father.

Jesus worked for low wages as a carpenter. He faced suffering in his life. He showed us that happiness is not found in owning many things or in having only pleasant things happen to us. The true source of Jesus' happiness was his Father's love.

Jesus wants us all to share his happiness. While teaching on a mountainside, he gave us the eight **Beatitudes** to help us live in hope and love. They lead us to God's kingdom, where we will share God's life forever. Jesus' teaching of the Beatitudes is part of his **Sermon on the Mount.**

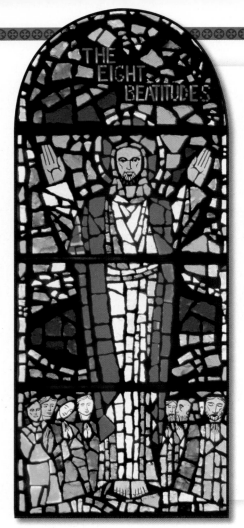

The Beatitudes

Happy are the poor in spirit,
    for theirs is the kingdom of heaven.
Happy are they who mourn,
    for they will be comforted.
Happy are the meek,
    for they will inherit the land.
Happy are they who hunger and thirst
       for righteousness,
    for they will be satisfied.
Happy are the merciful,
    for they will be shown mercy.
Happy are the clean of heart,
    for they will see God.
Happy are the peacemakers,
    for they will be called children of God.
Happy are they who are persecuted
       for the sake of righteousness,
    for theirs is the kingdom of heaven.

          adapted from Matthew 5:3–10

Saint Francis Was "God's Little Poor Man"

"Happy are the poor in spirit,
for theirs is the kingdom of heaven."
adapted from Matthew 5:3

Francis was a very rich young man who lived in the Italian town of Assisi. His father, who had a good business, wanted Francis to follow in his footsteps. But God had other plans; he called Francis to follow the example of his Son, Jesus.

One time, Francis met a poor man who was dressed in rags. He felt so sorry for the man that he exchanged clothes with him. The poor man walked away wearing Francis' fine coat, belt, and sandals. When Francis put on the poor man's ragged clothes, he felt the happiness promised to those who are poor in spirit.

The Holy Spirit led Francis to understand that he could show his love for Jesus by giving up his riches. So Francis left behind all that he owned to live as a poor man.

Francis did not miss his worldly riches, because he loved God above all things. He saw God's love and care in everything around him. Saint Francis wanted to share God's love with others. Most of all, he wanted to share it with the people in the world who were hungry, poor, and sad. He wanted to bring them happiness by sharing his food, clothing, and joy with them. God wants us to do the same.

Fill in the word that tells what we will want to do if we are poor in spirit.

If we are poor in spirit, we will

_____ with others.

Jesus Promises Happiness

People are foolish to think that riches can bring them happiness. If we remember that Jesus told us to love God above everything, we can be poor in spirit. To be "poor in spirit" means to realize that we always need God's help. It is to be satisfied having what we need, to be grateful for God's gifts, and to share with others. When we do these things, we will have the happiness that Jesus promised.

Write the word on each line that tells how the people in these stories are poor in spirit. Use the Word Bank to help you.

> **WORD BANK**
>
> generous   grateful
> content   God

1. Samantha received a new bike for Christmas. She took it over to show Angela. Angela was happy for Samantha, but Angela was just as happy with her own gift, a puzzle. Angela was poor in spirit because she was

    _____ .

2. Andrew planned to buy a new baseball with the money he had earned. At Sunday Mass, Andrew gave part of his money to help hungry people in the missions. Andrew was poor in spirit because he was

    _____ .

3. Mr. and Mrs. Marino own a large department store and a beautiful house. Each day before going to their store, they ask God to help them be honest and fair to their customers. They are poor in spirit because they show they need

    _____ .

4. Hannah lives alone with her mother, who works hard to support them. Hannah always has clean clothes, enough food, and people who love her, but not many extras. At night Hannah thanks God for caring for her mother and herself. She is poor in spirit because she shows she is

    _____ .

A Moment with Jesus

Spend this special time with Jesus. Ask him to help you find ways to be poor in spirit. Jesus wants you to know that it is all right to have things. After all, God gave you the gifts of creation. He wants you to enjoy what you have while still being generous to those who have less. Talk this over with Jesus and then just rest in his love.

Saint Francis realized that God had given him all the wonders of the universe. He was rich! With a grateful heart, he prayed a beautiful prayer.

Canticle of the Sun

Be praised, my Lord,
For all your creatures,
For Brother Sun,
Who is beautiful and radiant in all
    his splendor.
Be praised for Sisters Moon and Stars.

Be praised for Brothers Wind and Air,
For the clouds, and for all kinds
    of weather.

Be praised for Sister Water,
Who is so useful and precious and
    pure.

Be praised for Brother Fire,
Who is so beautiful, bright, and strong.

Be praised for Sister Earth, our
    mother,
Who gives us fruit and plants
    and flowers.

Be praised for those
Who forgive others for love of you,
And who endure sickness and trial.

Praise and bless the Lord,
All you children.
Serve him and give him thanks.

Word Jumble

Unscramble the letters to discover Jesus' promise to those who live the Beatitudes.

The _____
gtihe

Beatitudes lead us to God's

_____ where
idognkm

we will live _____
rrefvoe

in _____ .
ppinhaess

We Remember

What do we call the way to happiness that Jesus gave us?

We call Jesus' way to happiness the Beatitudes.

What did Jesus say about the poor in spirit?

Jesus said, "Happy are the poor in spirit, for theirs is the kingdom of heaven."

Words to Know
Beatitudes
Sermon on the Mount

We Respond

Happy are they who . . . seek the Lord with all their heart.

adapted from Psalm 119:2

Building Family Faith

CHAPTER SUMMARY Much of Jesus' teaching about happiness is summarized in the Beatitudes. The first beatitude, "happy are the poor in spirit," speaks to the importance of being detached from material things.

REFLECT
"Do not worry about your life, what you will eat [or drink], or about your body, what you will wear. Is not life more than food and the body more than clothing?"

Matthew 6:25

DISCUSS AS A FAMILY
• the ways God provides for our family's needs, as he promises he will. Read Matthew 6:25–34.
• the ways we take care of one another's needs in our family.
• how we can avoid worrying about how our needs will be met.

PRAY
Father, you care for us. Show us how to care for others.

DO
Ask each family member to complete the sentence, "Happiness is . . . ." Discuss the answers.

Have family members name as many blessings from God as they can in two minutes. Write them down and discuss the list when finished.

Regularly pray prayers of thanksgiving to God for the resources your family has.

Visit **www.christourlife.org/family** for more family resources.

God's Sorrowing and Meek People Receive a Special Promise

Sorrowing People Will Be Comforted

By his life, Jesus taught us to trust that God our Father will comfort us in times of sorrow. In one of the Beatitudes, he promised a special peace to sorrowing or suffering people.

> "Happy are they who mourn,
> for they will be comforted."

> adapted from Matthew 5:4

Jesus had sorrows and sufferings just as we do, but he put his trust in his Father. When he suffered in the garden on the night before he died, he prayed:

> "My Father, if it is possible, take this suffering away from me! Yet, let it be not as I will, but as you will."

> adapted from Matthew 26:39

Jesus faced death with courage. The Father accepted his sacrifice for our **salvation.** Jesus' suffering saved us from our sin. In heaven his sorrows are turned into joy.

Mary has the title Mother of Sorrows because she suffered so much when she stood at the foot of the cross. But her sorrow was changed into joy when Jesus rose from the dead.

Jesus let us know that his followers would have to suffer too. He said,

> "Take up your cross and follow me."

> adapted from Mark 8:34

In the Beatitudes, however, Jesus promises that in the midst of our suffering we will be comforted.

Jesus Helps Suffering People

Jesus felt sorry for people who were suffering. Once he looked out over the city of Jerusalem and saw that many people suffered because they did not believe in him. Jesus did all he could to help them. He prayed for them, taught them, and forgave them. He even gave his life to save them from sin and death.

God's people feel sorry when they see others suffer. They feel sad when they see that others are unhappy because they do not know or love Jesus. They pray and offer sacrifices to bring these people to him.

A Moment with Jesus

Think about all that Jesus suffered because of his love for you. Do you want to thank him? You can do it now. Then ask Jesus to help you through the hard times in your life. Jesus reminds you that he will always be at your side to help and to comfort you. Rest now in the love of Jesus and your heavenly Father.

Veronica Mourned for Jesus

In the Stations of the Cross we hear about a woman named Veronica who felt sorry for Jesus when she saw him carrying the heavy cross. She comforted him by wiping his face with her veil. Later she found the face of Jesus imprinted on the veil.

Jesus calls us to help those who suffer. Even though it may be difficult for us, he wants us to help those who need our kindness, prayers, and sacrifices. By showing love and concern for others, we show our love for Jesus. This is one way we show that we belong to God's people.

When we help those who suffer, Jesus gives us a greater share in his life and love. In heaven, we will find that he has changed all our sorrows into joy!

Words for Those Who Mourn

It is not easy to be one of God's sorrowing people. Jesus tells us what to do when we have sorrow.

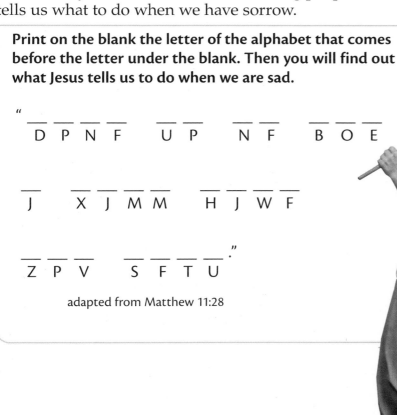

Print on the blank the letter of the alphabet that comes before the letter under the blank. Then you will find out what Jesus tells us to do when we are sad.

" _ _ _ _   _ _   _ _ _   _ _ _
  D P N F   U P   N F   B O E

_   _ _ _ _   _ _ _ _
J   X J M M   H J W F

_ _ _   _ _ _ _ ."
Z P V   S F T U

adapted from Matthew 11:28

Meek People Are Humble and Gentle

In one of the Beatitudes, Jesus spoke about people who are meek.

"Happy are the meek,
    for they will inherit the land."

adapted from Matthew 5:5

Jesus also said,

"Learn from me, for I am meek
    and humble of heart."

Matthew 11:29

Francis de Sales Was a Gentleman Saint

Francis was born into a noble Catholic family in France in 1567. Francis' father thought his son should be a soldier, so he was trained to use a sword. Francis had other ideas about his life; he wanted to be a priest. Yet he didn't want to give up his fancy clothes for the humble clothes of a priest. Finally he decided that, no matter what, it was time to answer God's call.

Some people thought that Francis was too proud to be a priest. Others thought he had too hot a temper. But Francis was serious. He really wanted to follow God's calling. He decided to ask Jesus for help whenever he felt himself getting angry or upset. He began to make up for hurting someone by doing something kind for that person. Over the years, Francis became so kind and gentle that people could hardly believe he once had a bad temper.

Francis lived during hard times for the Church. Many people were opposed to the Catholic faith and had left the Church. Francis left his own country and went to Switzerland to teach and preach. There he walked the countryside speaking to anyone who would listen. People threw rocks at him as he passed. So he wrote pamphlets and slid them under the doors of the homes.

Francis knew that in these troubled times, he needed to be meek and gentle. He began teaching the children. Soon their parents were also drawn to his gentle manner. When he became a bishop, Francis continued to work in his gentle way, and many more people were drawn to his writings and teachings. His manner won over their hearts. Because of him, more than 70,000 people returned to the Catholic faith. Francis was not always meek and humble, but with God's help, he changed his ways. That is why today we know him as Saint Francis de Sales.

Learning to Be Gentle

When we are gentle and humble like Jesus, Mary, and the saints, we show that we understand what Jesus said about meek people.

Fill in the blanks in these sentences with words from the Gentle Savings Bank to find out how you can become more gentle and humble.

GENTLE SAVINGS BANK

pray   patient   quiet   praise   serve

forgive

1. If you are upset, be _____ until you can speak kindly.

2. Be _____ when people do not understand you.

3. Be willing to _____ those who are unkind.

4. Be ready to _____ those who need help.

5. When others play well and win, _____ them.

6. To control hurtful feelings, _____ for grace.

Draw a 🙂 if the sentence describes a way to be gentle or humble.
If it does not, draw a ☹.

○ 1. Say "I'm sorry. Please forgive me."

○ 2. Say "You really did a good job."

○ 3. Push yourself ahead of someone in line.

○ 4. Share something you like.

○ 5. Pout when someone else wins a game.

○ 6. Offer to do a chore for someone.

○ 7. Pray for someone who has been unkind to you.

○ 8. Let someone have the first turn doing something you like.

We Remember

What did Jesus say about the sorrowing?
"Happy are they who mourn, for they will be comforted."

What did Jesus say about the meek?
"Happy are the meek, for they will inherit the land."

Word to Know
salvation

We Respond

Jesus, meek and humble of heart, make my heart like yours.

Building Family Faith

CHAPTER SUMMARY Suffering is part of our daily life. We accept it and look to God for the strength to bear it and learn from it.

REFLECT
"Blessed are they who mourn,
　　for they will be comforted.
Blessed are the meek,
　　for they will inherit the land."
　　　　　　　　Matthew 5:4–5

DISCUSS AS A FAMILY
• a recent difficulty, frustration, or failure in the family and the positive results of these experiences.
• how God uses us and other people we know to bring comfort to sorrowing people.

PRAY
Our hearts are open to you, Jesus. Fill them with your love.

DO
Help alleviate pressures and difficulties people in your family have right now.

Comfort someone who is suffering physically, in your extended family, your neighborhood, or elsewhere.

Pray regularly for the suffering people you have talked about.

Visit **www.christourlife.org/family** for more family resources.

CHAPTER 23

Holy Trinity, Dominican Church, Krakow, Poland.

God's People Long to Be Clean of Heart and Holy

The Clean of Heart Will See God

The pure of heart are God's happy people. Jesus spoke of them.

> "Happy are the clean of heart, for they will see God."
>
> adapted from Matthew 5:8

Jesus' heart was filled with love for his Father. He saw God our Father in everything, and everyone saw the Father's love in Jesus. Jesus gave glory to the Father by his life and his death on the cross.

Mary's heart was free from sin too. From the moment God made her, she belonged entirely to him. Her heart was full of love, so Mary pleased God in everything she did. She thought of others and made them happy. Now Mary is with God in heaven, where she sees him in all his beauty and glory. Mary will help us be clean of heart. We can say to her, "Mother most pure, pray for us."

147

Saint Aloysius Was Clean of Heart

In the 16th century, a boy named Aloysius lived in Italy. His family was rich, and he had everything he wanted. One summer, when he was seven, his father took him to a camp where soldiers trained. Aloysius heard some bad words from these men. After he returned home, he repeated these words in school. When his teacher scolded him for speaking this way, Aloysius learned how wrong it was to offend God, even in a small way. From that time on, he was careful not to say or do anything that would offend God or hurt others. He tried to please God and to keep his heart pure.

Aloysius grew in love for God by praying to him often during the day. He especially loved to pray the psalms, and he prayed special prayers to Mary each day. Once he went to a shrine of Mary in the city of Florence. When he knelt before her beautiful statue, he was filled with a great desire to be pure and holy. He wanted to serve God always and to please our Blessed Mother. Aloysius promised God that he would never sin and asked Mary to help him. He often went to church to pray and was happy when he could receive Jesus in Holy Communion.

Aloysius loved Jesus so much that he decided to give himself to Jesus in a special way by becoming a priest. He left his rich home and gave up his money to become a member of the Society of Jesus, also known as the Jesuits.

While Aloysius was studying in Rome to be a priest, a terrible disease broke out. Aloysius helped care for the sick until he became sick himself. After suffering for three months, he died at the age of 23. Now Aloysius is with God in heaven, where he sees him in all his glory. He has received the wonderful reward Jesus promised the pure of heart.

Color the medal of Mary. Make a design around the frame of the medal. Print the words *Mary, pray for us* on the lines.

We too can become pure of heart like Jesus, Mary, and the saints. When our hearts are pure, we are able to see God in the beautiful world around us, in ourselves, and in other people. One day we will see God in heaven. Until then, we can ask Mary and Saint Aloysius to pray for us.

Finish the beatitude by naming the reward of the pure of heart.

"Happy are the clean of heart, for they will

_____ _____ ."

A Moment with Jesus

Share with Jesus the story you just read about Saint Aloysius. Now imagine Jesus asked you if you would like to be holy as this saint was. What would you answer? Jesus reminds you that wanting to be holy is the first step. The other steps will be harder, but Jesus promises to walk with you. Thank him and then share with him anything else you would like.

We Hunger and Thirst for Righteousness

Jesus told us about people who desire to be holy.

> "Happy are they who hunger and thirst for righteousness, for they will be satisfied."
>
> adapted from Matthew 5:6

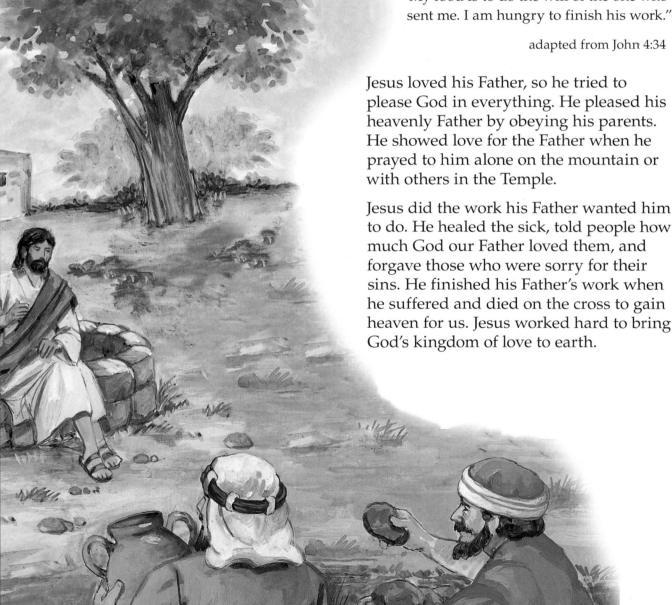

We show our desire to be holy when we try to love God with all our hearts, please God in all things, and work to spread peace and justice in the world.

Once Jesus sat down at a well to rest. His disciples knew that he was hungry and said, "Master, have something to eat." But Jesus told them:

> "My food is to do the will of the one who sent me. I am hungry to finish his work."
>
> adapted from John 4:34

Jesus loved his Father, so he tried to please God in everything. He pleased his heavenly Father by obeying his parents. He showed love for the Father when he prayed to him alone on the mountain or with others in the Temple.

Jesus did the work his Father wanted him to do. He healed the sick, told people how much God our Father loved them, and forgave those who were sorry for their sins. He finished his Father's work when he suffered and died on the cross to gain heaven for us. Jesus worked hard to bring God's kingdom of love to earth.

Mary Desired to Be Holy

Mary was holy. Because she loved God so much, her greatest desire was to do his will. When the angel told her that God wanted her to be the mother of Jesus, she said,

> "May it be done to me according to your word."
>
> Luke 1:38

Mary was happy because she always did what God wished. Now she is happy with God in heaven. We pray to her, "Holy Mary, Mother of God, pray for us."

Mary's joy in the risen Lord was greater than anyone else's because she loved and believed more deeply than anyone else. The glorious risen Jesus, the Son of God, was and always will be her son. She now shares his glory.

Thérèse Desired to Be Holy

In 1873, a girl named Thérèse Martin was born in France. Even as a child, Thérèse wanted to be holy. She knew that, to become a saint, one had to love God and to suffer like Jesus.

Thérèse also understood that she was free to sacrifice much or little for Jesus, but she loved Jesus so much that she told him: "I choose everything you want me to do. I am not afraid to suffer for you."

All her life Thérèse made sacrifices for Jesus. She always tried to be like him. Once Thérèse said, "My heart does not wish for riches or glory. What I ask for is love. Only one thing, my Jesus, to love you."

When Thérèse was 24 years old, she died from tuberculosis. Now Saint Thérèse is with God in heaven.

Ponder This

Using the words in the Word Bank, complete the sentences below. Then circle those words in the puzzle.

WORD BANK

wish	Word	will
hunger	love	thirsty

God's _____ tells us how to be holy.

A desire to be holy is like a _____ for food.

A desire is a strong _____ .

We want to do God's _____ .

We can be _____ for holiness.

To become holy, we must give God our _____ .

```
L R S H U N G E R A
O D W M G W O R D L
V S I T H I R S T Y
E K L U D S Q E Q Z
G B L U P H J N U E
D I H Z Q U N I L O
```

We Remember

What did Jesus say about the pure of heart?

"Happy are the clean of heart, for they will see God."

What did Jesus say about those who hunger and thirst for righteousness?

"Happy are they who hunger and thirst for righteousness, for they will be satisfied."

We Respond

Those who seek the LORD want for no good thing.

adapted from Psalm 34:11

Building Family Faith

CHAPTER SUMMARY We are called to be pure and holy so that we may share in the joy God intends for us. This means putting God first. We follow Jesus, and we imitate him, Mary, and the saints.

REFLECT
"Blessed are the clean of heart, for they will see God."
Matthew 5:8

DISCUSS AS A FAMILY
- the story of Saint Aloysius from pages 148–149, after reading it together as a family. What kind of person was Aloysius? How can we be like him?
- the quality of Jesus you would most like to imitate.

PRAY
Holy Mary, Mother of God, pray for us sinners.

DO
What person living today would you call holy? Discuss why.

Review the television programs the family watches. Do they reflect the values that promote purity of heart? Should we do something else for entertainment?

Visit **www.ChristOurLife.org/family** for more family resources.

God's People Bring Mercy and Peace to Others

Jesus tells us to show mercy.

> "Happy are the merciful,
> for they will be shown mercy."

adapted from Matthew 5:7

Jesus was merciful like his Father. When he was dying on the cross, he said,

> "Father, forgive them, they know not what they do."

Luke 23:34

Jesus had mercy on people who were sick and suffering. List two people who were helped by Jesus.

_____

_____

Jesus told us how to show mercy. He said:

> "Love your enemies. Do good to those who hate you and pray for those who mistreat you. Give to those who are in need. Do not wish for anything in return. Be merciful as your heavenly Father is merciful. Forgive, and you will be forgiven. Give, and gifts will be given to you."

adapted from Luke 6:27–38

Mother Cabrini Was Merciful

Frances Cabrini wanted to help everyone. She left her home in Italy to be a missionary sister in the United States. Some people from her country had moved to America hoping to find a better life, but many of them could not find jobs. They lived in very poor places and went without the food and clothes they needed. Many became weak and ill.

Mother Cabrini and her sisters begged for food and clothing for these people. They started hospitals, homes for children, and schools.

Before Mother Cabrini died, she became an American citizen in 1909. Now she is Saint Frances Cabrini, the first United States citizen to be named a saint.

We Are Called to Be Merciful

The **Corporal Works of Mercy** are ways we can meet the material needs of people. We do what we can to help feed, clothe, and find homes for those who have none. We also visit and comfort people who are sick.

The **Spiritual Works of Mercy** include teaching, consoling, comforting, forgiving, and being patient when others do wrong to us. The Church has been doing these acts of mercy following the example of Jesus.

Work the puzzle. The clues below will help you.

Down

1. Merciful people _____ those who hurt them.

3. They _____ their enemies.

4. They do _____ to those who hate them.

Across

2. Merciful people _____ for those who mistreat them.

4. They _____ to everyone in need.

God's Children Are Peacemakers

"Happy are the peacemakers,
 for they will be called children of God."

Matthew 5:9

In this beatitude, Jesus speaks of the peace that comes from loving God and others, and from doing what is right.

God sent Jesus into the world to give us his peace. Jesus often greeted his apostles by saying "Peace be with you."

Isaac Jogues Was a Missionary of Peace

All God's saints were peacemakers. Isaac Jogues, a 17th-century French priest of the Society of Jesus, left France to bring God's peace to the North American tribes. Father Jogues lived as the American Indians lived. He ate the kinds of food they ate and slept on a bed of bark chips. He helped those who were sick, and he shared his food with those who were hungry.

Father Jogues and other missionaries often smoked the ceremonial peace pipe with their American Indian friends as a sign that they could trust one another. One Iroquois tribe would not smoke the peace pipe with the French. They captured Father Jogues, but while their prisoner, Father Jogues prayed for them, taught them about God's love, and offered his sufferings to God for them.

One day Father Jogues escaped and returned to France. He was so thin and sick that his friends did not know him. As soon as he was well, he went back to work with the American Indians again. He tried to help enemy tribes make peace with one another. Father Jogues even went to help the Iroquois who had taken him prisoner. He had forgiven them.

One night someone in the camp invited Father Jogues to his home for supper. As Father Jogues entered the tent, another Iroquois Indian struck him with a tomahawk and killed him. Isaac Jogues, God's peacemaker, died a martyr for Jesus.

Doing Things to Make Peace

Read each story and underline the choice that shows what each child could do to bring God's peace to others.

1. At supper Dylan told the family that his sister, Emily, had been in trouble for playing after the school bell had rung. Emily felt embarrassed and angry. Their father told Dylan that he didn't have to tell on Emily. Dylan said he was sorry, but Emily's anger could make the evening meal unpleasant. What should Emily do?

   • Tell something mean about Dylan.

   • Forgive Dylan.

   • Keep being angry.

2. Maribel's little sister Jasmine took off the best dress from Maribel's doll to put on her teddy bear. She tore the dress. When Maribel came home, Jasmine was in tears about the accident. What should Maribel do?

   • Say she will mend it if she can.

   • Scold Jasmine.

   • Take something away from Jasmine.

3. Abigail saw that her baby brother's toys were all over the floor. She knew her mother would not like such a mess. What should Abigail do?

   • Leave the toys on the floor.

   • Tell her mother.

   • Help pick up the toys.

4. Patrick went out to play at recess. He wanted to play a game of Keep Away. The other boys wanted to play basketball. What should Patrick do?

   • Quarrel with the boys.

   • Play basketball.

   • Refuse to play.

A Moment with Jesus

Think of the example of peacemaking Jesus gave us. He was silent when people made fun of him, forgiving when they hurt him. Can you be a peacemaker in your home? in school? on the playground? What would you have to do? Talk about this with Jesus. Then ask him to send the Holy Spirit to help you.

Bringing-Mercy-and-Peace Game

Throw a die and move a marker as many spaces as the die tells you. Write on the scorecard the number of spaces moved. If you land on a space that names a good act, add the number given there to your score. Each player gets six turns; the one with the highest score wins.

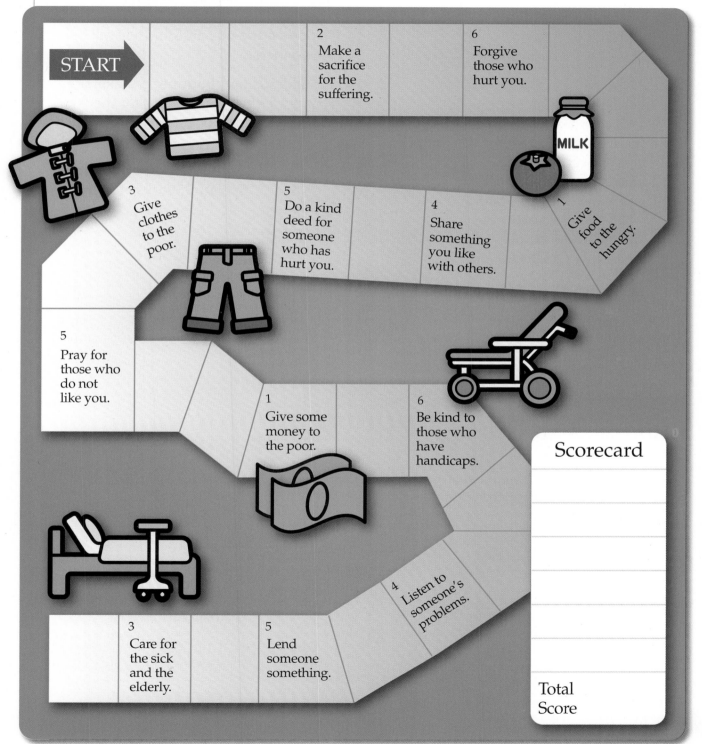

START

2
Make a sacrifice for the suffering.

6
Forgive those who hurt you.

1
Give food to the hungry.

3
Give clothes to the poor.

5
Do a kind deed for someone who has hurt you.

4
Share something you like with others.

5
Pray for those who do not like you.

1
Give some money to the poor.

6
Be kind to those who have handicaps.

Scorecard

4
Listen to someone's problems.

3
Care for the sick and the elderly.

5
Lend someone something.

Total Score

Prayer for Peace

Here is part of a prayer said to have been written by Saint Francis of Assisi. Pray it often.

Lord, make me an instrument
  of your peace.
where there is hatred, let me
  sow love;
where there is injury, pardon;
where there is doubt, faith;
where there is despair, hope;
where there is darkness, light;
where there is sadness, joy.

We Remember

What did Jesus say about people who are merciful?

"Happy are the merciful, for they will be shown mercy."

What did Jesus say about peacemakers?

"Happy are the peacemakers, for they will be called children of God."

Words to Know
Corporal Works of Mercy
Spiritual Works of Mercy

We Respond

Lord, make me an instrument of your peace.

Building Family Faith

CHAPTER SUMMARY Our relationship with God causes us to bring love, peace, and mercy to others. We do this through the gifts of the Holy Spirit and by striving to be like Jesus.

REFLECT
"Blessed are the peacemakers,
  for they will be called children of God."
                              Matthew 5:9

DISCUSS AS A FAMILY
• how Jesus showed mercy to others. Refer to his parables, such as the Good Samaritan, and to the miracles he performed.
• how we have seen disputes and disagreements settled peacefully. What made the difference?
• disagreements we presently have at home or in school that need to be resolved.

PRAY
Lord, make me an instrument of your peace.

DO
Make the prayer of Saint Francis your family's prayer. Take advantage of opportunities to bring peace to others, to bring hope to those in despair, and to bring joy to those who are sad.

Decide as a family which television shows are too violent to watch.

Visit **www.christourlife.org/family** for more family resources.

God's People Are Happy

Jesus Shows Us the Way

Jesus loved us so much that he suffered and died for us. He told his followers to love others as he did and not to be afraid:

> "People will hate you because of my name. They will make you suffer. They may put some of you to death."
>
> adapted from Luke 21:16–17

In one of the Beatitudes, Jesus spoke about those who would suffer for him.

> "Happy are they who are persecuted for the sake of righteousness,
> for theirs is the kingdom of heaven."
>
> adapted from Matthew 5:10

Our Blessed Mother loved and suffered as Jesus did. We call her the Queen of Martyrs. The saints loved God as Jesus did. Those who suffered and died for Jesus are **martyrs.**

Fill in the puzzle. Use the clues in the sentences to help you.

M _____ is the Queen of Martyrs.

A We _____ Jesus to help us face suffering bravely.

R The Kingdom of Heaven will be our _____ .

T We must _____ others kindly.

Y We should say _____ to what God wants us to do.

R We must be willing to suffer for what is _____ .

M | | | |
A | | | |
R | | | | |
T | | | |
Y | | |
R | | | |

Saint Joan of Arc Was God's Soldier

Joan of Arc was a brave girl who lived in a village in France during the 1400s. At the time she lived, her country was at war with England. The king of France was weak and afraid that his armies could not save France. Joan began hearing the voices of saints, urging her to save her country. She said that Saint Michael the Archangel had told her, "Daughter of God, go and save France."

Although Joan was afraid, she did what God wanted. Carrying a banner, she led the French army into battle. On the banner were written the names of Jesus and Mary. Joan won battles that helped save France.

Many people did not believe that God had spoken to Joan in a special way. They called her a witch and other wicked names. But Joan kept on doing what she thought was right.

Soon she was captured by the enemy and put in prison. Although she was treated unfairly, she forgave and prayed for her enemies. When she was put to death by fire, her last word was "Jesus." Joan suffered bravely for God and for her country. Today we call her Saint Joan of Arc.

Print the names that appeared on Saint Joan's banner, and then decorate it.

A Happy-Heart Puzzle

Work this puzzle. Use the clues and the Word Bank.

WORD BANK

merciful	peace	comfort	meek	suffer
clean	right	happy	poor	Mary
holy	Arc	children		

Across

4. Jesus said, "_____ be with you."

6. We should be _____ like our heavenly Father.

8. The Beatitudes help us be _____ .

11. We please God when we do what is _____ .

12. Peacemakers will be called _____ of God.

Down

1. Sometimes Christians must _____ for the name of Jesus.

2. We become _____ by doing God's will.

3. _____ people are gentle.

4. The _____ of heart will see God.

6. _____ is the holiest woman.

7. God's sorrowing people will receive _____ .

9. The Kingdom of Heaven belongs to the _____ in spirit.

10. The saint who fought for France was Saint Joan of _____ .

Beatitudes Review in Code

A	B	C	D	E	F	H	I	L
1	2	3	4	5	6	7	8	9

M	N	O	P	R	S	T	U	Y
10	11	12	13	14	15	16	17	18

Print in the boxes the letters that match the numbers.

1. Jesus gave us the Beatitudes to help us share

   his __ __ __ __ __ __ __ __ __ .
      7 1 13 13 8 11 5 15 15

2. People are __ __ __ __ __ __ __ to think that riches will make them happy.
      6 12 12 9 8 15 7

3. Sorrowing people will be __ __ __ __ __ __ __ __ __ .
      3 12 10 6 12 14 16 5 4

4. Meek people are gentle and __ __ __ __ __ __ of heart.
      7 17 10 2 9 5

5. People who hunger and thirst to be holy __ __ __ __ __ __ to please God.
      4 5 15 8 14 5

6. Jesus said, "Be __ __ __ __ __ __ __ __ as your heavenly Father is merciful."
      10 5 14 3 8 6 17 9

7. Peacemakers will be called __ __ __ __ __ __ __ __ of God.
      3 7 8 9 4 14 5 11

8. Jesus said, "They will make you __ __ __ __ __ __ for my name."
      15 17 6 6 5 14

We Are Glad in the Lord

Leader: In the eight Beatitudes, Jesus calls us to the greatest happiness—joy in the Lord. He and his blessed Mother have shown us the way. The saints who followed their example found happiness both in this life and in heaven. Jesus wants us to be happy now and always.

Procession and Song

(The child carrying the Bible leads the children who are carrying flowers.)

Leader: Saint Paul was happy like Jesus. He taught the early Christians what they must do to have joy in the Lord.

First Reading from Philippians 4:4–7

Reader 1: A reading from a letter of Saint Paul

Rejoice in the Lord always. I shall say it again: rejoice! Your kindness should be known to all. The Lord is near. Have no anxiety at all, but in everything, by prayer and petition, with thanksgiving, make your requests known to God. Then the peace of God that surpasses all understanding will guard your hearts and minds in Christ Jesus.

The Word of the Lord

All: Thanks be to God.

Intercessions

(After each petition is read, the children will put a flower, one for the beatitude mentioned, into the vase.)

All: *(Response to each petition)* Stay with us, Lord, and be our joy.

Leaders of Prayer: That we may become poor in spirit and be happy to share with others . . . ℟.

That we may try to help those who are sorrowing . . . ℟.

That we may become gentle and more willing to serve others . . . ℟.

That we may become holy by loving God with all our hearts . . . ℟.

That we may be forgiving and show mercy to those in need . . . ℟.

That we may be clean of heart by loving God and others . . . ℟.

That we may become peacemakers for God and for others . . . ℟.

That we may be strong enough to suffer for what is right . . . ℟.

Leader: In the Beatitudes, Jesus teaches us that we can have joy if we love and serve God and others. Paul tells us about having a glad heart.

Second Reading adapted from 2 Corinthians 9:6–7

Reader 2: A reading from a letter of Saint Paul

Whoever plants a few seeds will have a small crop. Whoever plants many seeds will have a large crop. Be generous, then, when you give. Do not give sadly or grudgingly. Give with a glad heart, because God loves a cheerful giver.

The Word of the Lord

All: Thanks be to God.

Silent Prayer

What makes you happy? What does Jesus say will make you happy? Ask Jesus to help you be a cheerful and generous giver.

Leader: Jesus tells us about the happiness of heaven. Let us listen.

Third Reading adapted from Revelation 22: 4–14

Reader 3: A reading from the Book of Revelation

Jesus says, "I am coming soon. Happy are they who keep my words. I will reward each one for what he or she has done. Happy are they who have the life of grace. To them, the Holy Spirit will say, 'Come.' They will be able to come through the city gates."

The Word of the Lord

All: Thanks be to God.

Psalm Prayer

Side A: All you people, clap your hands, shout to God with cries of gladness,

Side B: For the LORD, the Most High, is the great king over all the earth.

Side A: For king of all the earth is God; let the trumpets blast with joy,

Side B: Sing praise to God, sing praise; sing praise to our king.

adapted from
Psalm 47:2,3,8,6,7

Leader: Jesus showed us in the eight Beatitudes how to live in hope and in love. He has blessed us with happiness in this celebration. Let us thank Jesus and tell him we will try to live lives pleasing to him.

All: We offer our prayer in the name of the Father and of the Son and of the Holy Spirit. Amen.

Closing Song

Looking Back at Unit 5

You learned in this unit that Jesus gave us the Beatitudes as a guide to Christian living and as a means to reach happiness, both in this life and in the one to come. Living the Beatitudes with courage and love, we follow the example of Jesus, Mary, and the saints.

When we are poor in spirit, sorrowing, meek, merciful, and clean of heart—when we hunger and thirst for righteousness, try to be peacemakers, and are persecuted for what is right—we are living the fullness of the Christian life.

Living the Message

Check (✓) each sentence that describes you.

❏ 1. I know the meaning of the Beatitudes.

❏ 2. I am not selfish but try to share what I have.

❏ 3. I try to do what is right even when it is hard.

❏ 4. I try to be kind and gentle.

❏ 5. I pray to become a good, loving Christian.

Word to Know
martyr

Planning Ahead

Draw a picture of something you will do for someone at home and in your neighborhood to show your love for Jesus. Write on the lines what you will do.

At Home

I will _____ .

In My Neighborhood

I will _____ .

Family Feature

Let There Be Peace

The paper crane has become an international symbol for peace. It started with a young girl from Japan who died as a result of the effects of war. Sadako Sasaki was just two years old at the end of World War II when an atomic bomb was dropped on Hiroshima, a town near her home. At the age of 11 she was diagnosed with leukemia as a result of exposure to radiation from the bomb nine years earlier.

Sadako's best friend told her of the Japanese legend that said that anyone who makes a thousand paper cranes would be granted a wish. Sadako began the intricate work of folding the cranes, and she created hundreds of them before she died. Inspired by her courage, Sadako's friends committed to make the rest of the cranes so that she could be buried with the thousand cranes. Her story spread among the children of Japan, who donated money for a statue to honor Sadako and all the children who died as a result of the war. The inscription at the monument in Hiroshima's Peace Park reads

Children's Peace Monument, Hiroshima, Japan.

"This is our cry. This is our prayer. Peace in the world."

Even today, the story of the paper cranes continues to spread, giving children a way to express their hopes for peace in the world. To learn how to make a paper crane, go to **www.christourlife.org/peacecrane**.

166a

Raise a Toast to Peace

Origami is the traditional Japanese art of paper folding. With patience, attention, and skill, those who practice origami can make many beautiful objects. Here is a simple origami exercise you can try at home. When you are finished folding your paper drinking cups, you can decorate them with signs of peace. Then use the cups to toast peace and harmony in your home and in the world.

Visit **www.ChristOurLife.org/family** for more family resources.

How to Make a Paper Drinking Cup

1. Take an eight-inch square of paper and fold it diagonally into a triangle.

2. Next fold the left corner up to meet the right edge of the paper.

3. Fold the right corner up to meet the left edge of the paper.

4. Fold down the front flap toward you and the back flap away from you.

5. Squeeze the sides of the bottom, and the cup will open.

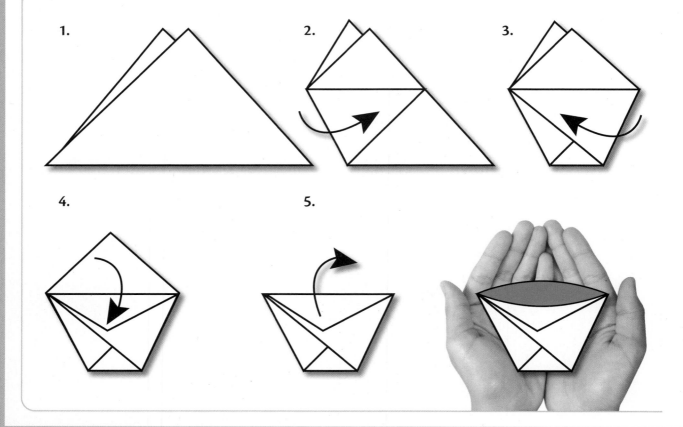

Prescription for Peace and Happiness

The Beatitudes (Matthew 5:1–10) are Jesus' prescription for true happiness and peace. Like all profound religious concepts, they involve paradoxes—the meek will inherit, those who hunger will be satisfied. The Beatitudes present a challenge that all serious believers must grow into over the course of their lives. Read them often and be open to the truths they contain.

Spelling Fun

On the lines below see how many words you can make out of the letters in the word *beatitude*.

_____   _____

_____   _____

_____   _____

_____   _____

_____   _____

_____   _____

_____   _____

_____   _____

_____   _____

_____   _____

Ten words is good. Fifteen words is great. Twenty or more, you're a real champ!

From Sorrow to Joy

Follow the directions and you will find out what "Beatitude people" receive.

HARDSHIP

Remove the third and fourth letters.

Add an *N* to the end.

Change the *S* to a *V*.

Change the *HIP* to an *E*.

Insert an E between the *H* and *A*.

_____

Family Feature

Bee-attitudes

In the Sermon on the Mount, Jesus gave us the Beatitudes (Matthew 5:1–10) as ways that we can find peace and happiness in life. What are some of the "bee-attitudes" (the attitudes that shape the way you are) that you need to have peace and happiness in your home? In each of the bees below, join with family members to write down the attitudes that make for peace and joy.

Possible answers: honesty, forgiveness, respectfulness, understanding, sense of humor, prayer time, kindness

Special Seasons and Lessons

The Year in Our Church

Ordinary Time
Lent
Christmas
Holy Week
Epiphany
Advent
Christmas
Ash Wednesday
Easter Sunday
Easter
First Sunday of Advent
Feast of All Saints
Winter
Spring
Fall
Summer
Pentecost
Ordinary Time

Liturgical Calendar

The liturgical calendar highlights the feast days and seasons of the Church year. Various colors symbolize the different seasons.

1|Feast of All Saints

Jesus taught us what it means to be happy in the Kingdom of God. We call this teaching the Beatitudes. *Beatitudes* means "deep happiness or blessing."

This is what Jesus taught.

Happy are the poor in spirit,
    for theirs is the kingdom of heaven.
Happy are they who mourn,
    for they will be comforted.
Happy are the meek,
    for they will inherit the land.
Happy are they who hunger and thirst for
      righteousness,
    for they will be satisfied.
Happy are the merciful,
    for they will be shown mercy.
Happy are the clean of heart,
    for they will see God.
Happy are the peacemakers,
    for they will be called children of God.
Happy are they who are persecuted for
      the sake of righteousness,
    for theirs is the kingdom of heaven.

adapted from Matthew 5:3–10

The saints are those who have lived the Beatitudes and who now enjoy eternal happiness. They are now with God in heaven.

169

On Feast of All Saints, November 1st, we hear the Beatitudes proclaimed in the Gospel. Jesus' words describe God's promise of eternal happiness. They also describe the path to holiness. The Beatitudes explain what it means to live as a disciple of Christ.

Saints Living Beatitudes

Choose one of the Beatitudes and identify a saint who has lived this Beatitude. Then write how you can also live this Beatitude today. An example is provided.

Beatitude: Happy are the poor in spirit, for theirs is the kingdom of heaven.

Saint: St. Francis of Assisi, who lived simply and shared all that he had with the poor.

Living this Beatitude today: We can share with others. We can be thankful for the things that we have and not desire things we do not need. We can live simply.

Beatitude: _____

_____

_____

_____

Saint: _____

Living this Beatitude today: _____

_____

_____

_____

_____

_____

2 | Advent

During Advent, we prepare a straight highway for the Lord. We ask God to help us make low the mountains created by our sin and selfishness. We try to raise the valleys by filling them with our love, prayer, and good deeds. How will you prepare a straight highway for the Lord?

Preparing the Way

Write some things that you want to change during Advent so that you can make low the mountains of sin and selfishness.

Write some good deeds that you will do for Jesus to raise the valleys.

Advent is a time when we can tear down what keeps us from sharing with others. We can put love, prayers, and good deeds in the empty spaces of our hearts.

Time for Advent

Complete the words in the sentences below.

Advent is a time when we l __ __ __ for Jesus' coming.

Advent is a time when we p __ __ __ __ __ __ for Jesus' coming into our hearts.

3 | Christmas

We Celebrate Christmas as a Season

Christmas is the day we remember the Nativity of the Lord, December 25th. And, like Advent, Christmas is also a season. The Christmas Season begins on Christmas Eve and ends on the Feast of the Baptism of the Lord. Within the Season of Christmas are several important feasts, including the Feast of Epiphany. On Epiphany, we remember the Magi who followed the light of a new star that led them to Jesus, the Light of the World, a Light to all the Nations.

Match the Season

> **How is the season of Advent different from the season of Christmas? Match the season in the space provided. Write the letter C for Christmas or A for Advent.**
>
> _____ white (feast)
>
> _____ waiting and preparing
>
> _____ Christmas tree
>
> _____ star
>
> _____ preparation for the Messiah
>
> _____ Nativity
>
> _____ purple
>
> _____ welcoming
>
> _____ Advent Wreath
>
> _____ stories about Jesus' birth

We Welcome Christ

**Opening Song
(O Come, All Ye Faithful)**

Opening Prayer

Leader: Christ our Light, open our hearts to welcome you with love during this Christmas Season.

All: Amen.

Gospel (John 1:1–14):

A reading from the holy Gospel according to John.

In the beginning was the Word,
     and the Word was with God,
and the Word was God.
He was in the beginning with God.

All things came to be
          through him,
     and without him
          nothing came to be.

What came to be through
          him was life,
     and this life was the
          light of the human
          race;

the light shines in the
          darkness,
     and the darkness has
          not overcome it.

And the Word became flesh
     and made his dwelling
          among us,
     and we saw his glory,
     the glory as of the
          Father's only Son,
     full of grace and truth.

The Gospel of the Lord.

All: Praise to you, Lord Jesus Christ.

Quiet Prayer Response

In the quiet of your heart, tell Jesus how you will welcome him into your heart this Christmas Season.

Closing Prayer

May the light of Christ continue to enlighten our hearts that we will see and serve Christ in others. Amen.

4 | Lent

At the Easter Vigil, we bless and light the Paschal Candle (also called the Easter Candle). We place the Alpha and the Omega on the candle. Alpha and Omega are symbols for Christ. The Alpha symbol tells us that Christ is the beginning of all things, and the Omega symbol tells us that he is the end of all things.

At Easter we celebrate Jesus' passing over from death to new life. We call this the Paschal Mystery. Our Baptism is a participation in Jesus' dying and rising to new life.

During Lent, we prepare to live more faithfully the Paschal Mystery. We do this through prayer, fasting, and almsgiving. Through these Lenten practices we find ways to move away from selfishness and sin so that we can share in the new life Jesus gives to us.

Write ways you will participate in these Lenten practices:

Prayer: _____

_____

Fasting: _____

_____

Almsgiving: _____

_____

_____

Complete the Words

Fill in the missing letters to show what you have learned.

The mystery of Christ's suffering, death, and Resurrection:

__ __ S __ __ __ L   __ Y __ __ __ __ Y

We participate in the Paschal Mystery through our

__ __ P __ __ __ M

The great feast on which we celebrate Christ's Paschal Mystery:

__ __ S __ __ R

The season during which we prepare to live the Paschal Mystery more faithfully:

__ E __ __

5 | Holy Week

All during Lent we have been getting ready for Easter, the holiest day of the year. During the week before Easter, we make our final preparations. This week is called Holy Week. During Holy Week, we remember the events that led to Jesus' sacrifice on the Cross for our salvation.

Passion (Palm) Sunday

The last Sunday of Lent is called Passion Sunday and is sometimes also called Palm Sunday. We remember that the crowds waved palms and called Jesus king as he rode into Jerusalem. They shouted, "Hosanna to the Son of David" (Matthew 21:9).

Before Mass the priest blesses palm branches. We then walk in procession with them. We hear the Gospel story of Jesus' death on the Cross. After Mass, we take the palms home. Each time we look at a palm, it reminds us to love and praise Jesus every day. We can pray, "Praise and honor to you, Lord Jesus Christ, King of endless glory."

The Easter Triduum

During Holy Week, we celebrate the Easter Triduum. The word *Triduum* means "three days." We celebrate the Easter Triduum on three days as we remember the Paschal Mystery.

On Holy Thursday night, we remember Jesus' Last Supper. We remember how Jesus showed his love for his friends by washing their feet. We remember Jesus' gift of himself in the Eucharist. At church the priest washes the feet of twelve people to remind us that we are all to serve others as Jesus did. We honor the Blessed Sacrament in a procession.

On Good Friday, we remember that Jesus died for us. We listen to the Gospel of Jesus' passion and death. We venerate the Cross because it is the way to salvation.

On Holy Saturday evening, we remember that Jesus was buried in the tomb. We wait in hope for Easter, remembering all the great things God has done to save us. On this night we will celebrate the Easter Vigil, the high point of the Easter Triduum, which then ends on Easter Sunday.

The Stations of the Cross

Throughout the year, and especially during Lent and Holy Week, we pray the Stations of the Cross, also known as the Way of the Cross. The fourteen stations of the Stations of the Cross tell what happened on Good Friday, the day after Jesus' Last Supper. They tell the story of how Jesus suffered and died because he loved us so much. At each station, we think about the event shown and we say a prayer. We thank Jesus for his great love.

Recognize a Station

For each situation, write the number of the station from Jesus' "Way of the Cross" booklet that can tell you how to follow Jesus.

1. I'm with some friends who start looking at a book with bad pictures. I'm afraid to say that I don't want to see the pictures.

_____

2. No matter how hard I try, I make lots of spelling mistakes in my writing. I feel like giving up.

_____

3. My friend is really sick. I want to visit him in the hospital, but I am afraid it will make me sad.

_____

4. I practiced a lot and wanted to win the swim meet, but a friend won it instead.

_____

5. My friend is working really hard to do his math problems, but he still doesn't get the right answers. I'm pretty good at math.

_____

6 | Easter

What might have been the thoughts and feelings of the disciples of Jesus on that first Easter morning, when they discovered that his tomb was empty?

Imagine what it was like: Jesus, your friend, was arrested and sentenced to death. He was beaten and made to carry a cross. Then he was crucified. Sad and scared, some friends buried him in the tomb. The tomb was sealed with a large stone.

Now, three days later, some of your friends are reporting amazing experiences. Some have been to the tomb and found that the stone has been rolled away. Jesus' body is not inside. Not only that, Mary of Magdala says that she saw two angels in the tomb and that she met Jesus in the garden near the tomb. She said that she didn't recognize him at first; she thought he was the gardener. But then Jesus spoke to her, and she knew him at once.

adapted from John 20:1–18

What would you have thought? What would you have done?

The disciples of Jesus were sad, confused, and fearful on that first Easter day. They stayed together because they were afraid. But then things became clearer:

On the evening of that first day of the week, when the doors were locked, where the disciples were, for fear of the Jews, Jesus came and stood in their midst and said to them, "Peace be with you." When he had said this, he showed them his hands and his side. The disciples rejoiced when they saw the Lord. [Jesus] said to them again, "Peace be with you. As the Father has sent me, so I send you." And when he had said this, he breathed on them and said to them, "Receive the holy Spirit. Whose sins you forgive are forgiven them, and whose sins you retain are retained.

John 20:19–23

Easter and the Gift of Peace

When the Risen Lord appeared to his disciples, the first thing he said to them is "Peace be with you." He knew what his friends needed most. They needed to know that everything was now okay. They needed to see that the figure before them was really Jesus raised from the dead. They needed to know that Jesus forgave them. They needed courage and strength to face the days ahead. They needed to know that Jesus had not abandoned them and that he was going to be with them always in his gift of the Holy Spirit.

Jesus' greeting communicated all of these things to his disciples . . . and to us. Jesus says to us, "Peace be with you." Jesus knows that we need his peace, too.

Peace Prayer

Write a prayer to Jesus telling him what you most need his gift of peace to do for you. Use the letters in the word "peace" to start each line of your prayer.

P_____

E_____

A_____

C_____

E_____

Amen

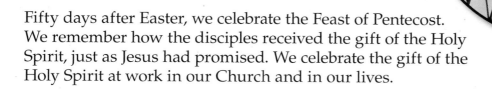

7 | Pentecost

Fifty days after Easter, we celebrate the Feast of Pentecost. We remember how the disciples received the gift of the Holy Spirit, just as Jesus had promised. We celebrate the gift of the Holy Spirit at work in our Church and in our lives.

The apostles had all gathered together in Jerusalem as Jesus had told them to do. While they waited for the Holy Spirit, they prayed. Suddenly there was the sound of a loud wind. Something like tongues of fire rested on the heads of those who were there. The Holy Spirit had come! The apostles began to speak in different languages to people who had arrived from different nations.

adapted from Acts of the Apostles 2:1–11

How is the appearance of the Holy Spirit described in this reading?

_____

What do the disciples do after receiving the gift of the Holy Spirit?

_____

We cannot see the Holy Spirit. However, we can see the effects of the Holy Spirit in our lives. Saint Paul wrote about this in a letter to early Christians:

. . . the fruit of the Spirit is love, joy, peace, patience, kindness, generosity, faithfulness, gentleness, self-control. . . . If we live in the Spirit, let us also follow the Spirit.

Galatians 5:22–23, 25

We call these the fruits of the Holy Spirit. In addition to the nine fruits of the Holy Spirit named by Saint Paul, the Church has identified three more: goodness, modesty, and chastity. When we see these qualities, we know the Holy Spirit is working in our lives.

Pentecost Prayer Service

Opening Song

First Reading from The Acts of the Apostles 2:1–11

Intercessions

> The response is: "Into our hearts, O Spirit, come!"

Leader: We thank you, heavenly Father, for giving us Jesus and for sending the Spirit in his name . . . ℟

We pray that the Spirit enlightens the minds and hearts of our Holy Father, all bishops, priests, deacons, and all of the faithful . . . ℟

We pray that our hearts be filled with the love of God, as the apostles' hearts were filled on the first Pentecost . . . ℟

We ask the Holy Spirit to come to each person's heart today and make all Christians living temples of God . . . ℟

We ask that the Holy Spirit will comfort the sick, the dying, and all those who suffer because of a lack of love . . . ℟

Second Reading from Romans 8:26–27

Response to the Second Reading: Song

Closing Prayer

All: Breathe in me, O Holy Spirit,
That my thoughts
May be all holy.
Act in me, O Holy Spirit,
That my work, too,
May be holy.
Draw my heart, O Holy Spirit,
That I love
Only what is holy.
Strengthen me, Holy Spirit,
That I may defend all that is holy.
Guard me then, O Holy Spirit,
That I always
May be holy.

What Catholics Should Know

(continued next page)

(continued from previous page)

Prayer and How We Pray

God is always with us. He wants us to talk to him and listen to him. In prayer we raise our hearts and minds to God. We are able to speak to and listen to God because through the Holy Spirit, God teaches us how to pray.

We Pray in Many Ways

Since prayer is so important, the Church teaches us to pray often and in many different ways. Sometimes we bless or adore God (prayer of blessing and adoration). Other times we ask God for something for ourselves (prayer of petition). Sometimes we pray for others (prayer of intercession). We also thank God in prayer (prayer of thanksgiving). Finally, we can also praise God (prayer of praise). We can pray alone or with others. We can pray silently or out loud.

We Meditate and Contemplate

One way to pray is to meditate. To meditate is to think about God. We try to keep our attention and focus on God. In meditation we may use Scripture, prayer books, or icons, which are religious images, to help us concentrate and spark our imagination.

Another way to pray is to contemplate. This means that we rest quietly in God's presence.

We Get Ready to Pray

We live in a busy, noisy, and fast-paced world. Because of this, we can have difficulty concentrating. In order to meditate or reflect, we need to prepare ourselves. We can get ready for meditation by moving our bodies into a comfortable position, sitting with our backs straight and both feet on the floor. We can close our eyes, fold our hands in front of us, take a deep breath, and then slowly let it out. We can establish a rhythm by slowly counting to three while breathing in and slowly counting to three while breathing out. Concentrating on our breathing helps us quiet our thoughts.

We Avoid Distractions

If we become distracted by thinking about something such as the day at school or a sporting event, we can just go back to thinking about our breathing. After a little practice, we will be able to avoid distractions, pray with our imagination, and spend time with God or Jesus in our hearts.

Prayers We Pray as Catholics

We can pray with any words that come to mind. Sometimes when we find that choosing our own words is difficult, we can use traditional prayers. Memorizing traditional prayers such as the following can be very helpful. When we memorize prayers, we take them to heart, meaning that we not only learn the words, but also try to understand and live them. See the inside front and back covers of your books for the most frequently used prayers.

Hail, Holy Queen

Hail, holy Queen, Mother of mercy,
hail, our life, our sweetness, and our hope.
To you we cry, the children of Eve;
to you we send up our sighs,
mourning and weeping in this land
    of exile.
Turn, then, most gracious advocate,
your eyes of mercy toward us;
lead us home at last
and show us the blessed fruit of
    your womb, Jesus:
O clement, O loving, O sweet
    Virgin Mary.

The Angelus

Verse. The angel of the Lord declared unto Mary.

Response. And she conceived of the Holy Spirit.
Hail Mary . . .

Verse. Behold the handmaid of the Lord.

Response. May it be done unto me according to your word.
Hail Mary . . .

Verse. And the Word was made flesh.

Response. And dwelt among us.
Hail Mary . . .

Verse. Pray for us, O holy Mother of God.

Response. That we may be made worthy of the promises of Christ.

Let us pray.
Lord,
fill our hearts with your grace:
once, through the message of an angel
you revealed to us the incarnation of
    your Son;
now, through his suffering and death
lead us to the glory of his resurrection.
We ask this through Christ our Lord.

Amen.

Nicene Creed

I believe in one God,
the Father almighty,
maker of heaven and earth,
of all things visible and invisible.

I believe in one Lord Jesus Christ,
the Only Begotten Son of God,
born of the Father before all ages.
God from God, Light from Light,
true God from true God,
begotten, not made, consubstantial with
    the Father;
through him all things were made.
For us men and for our salvation
he came down from heaven,
(bow your heads as you pray the next phrase)
and by the Holy Spirit was incarnate of the
    Virgin Mary,
and became man.

For our sake he was crucified under
    Pontius Pilate,

he suffered death and was buried,
and rose again on the third day
in accordance with the Scriptures.
He ascended into heaven
and is seated at the right hand of the Father.
He will come again in glory
to judge the living and the dead
and his kingdom will have no end.

I believe in the Holy Spirit, the Lord, the giver
    of life,
who proceeds from the Father and the Son,
who with the Father and the Son is adored
    and glorified,
who has spoken through the prophets.

I believe in one, holy, catholic and apostolic
    Church.
I confess one Baptism for the forgiveness of sins
and I look forward to the resurrection of
    the dead
and the life of the world to come. Amen.

Benedict XVI, Pope Emeritus

Benedict XVI, when he was pope, suggested that certain prayers that are shared by the universal Church could be learned in Latin and prayed as a sign of the universal nature of the Church. English versions of the following prayers appear on the inside front cover of this book.

Signum Crucis (Sign of the Cross)

In nomine Patris,
et Filii,
et Spiritus Sancti.
Amen.

Gloria Patri (Glory Be to the Father)

Gloria Patri,
et Filio,
et Spiritui Sancto.
Sicut erat in principio,
et nunc, et semper,
Et in saecula saeculorum.
Amen.

Pater Noster (Lord's Prayer)

Pater noster, qui es in caelis,
sanctificetur nomen tuum.
Adveniat regnum tuum.
Fiat voluntas tua,
sicut in caelo et in terra.
Panem nostrum quotidianum da nobis hodie,
et dimitte nobis debita nostra
sicut et nos dimittimus debitoribus nostris.
Et ne nos inducas in tentationem,
sed libera nos a malo.
Amen.

Ave Maria (Hail Mary)

Ave Maria, gratia plena,
Dominus tecum.
Benedicta tu in mulieribus,
et benedictus fructus ventris tui, Iesus.
Sancta Maria, Mater Dei, ora pro nobis peccatoribus,
nunc, et in hora mortis nostrae.
Amen.

Upon entering a church, a boy makes the Sign of the Cross after dipping his fingers in holy water. Catholics make the Sign of the Cross during Mass and at other times as well.

The Rosary

The Rosary helps us pray to Jesus through Mary. When we pray the Rosary, we think about the special events, or mysteries, in the lives of Jesus and Mary.

The Rosary is made up of a string of beads and a crucifix. We hold the crucifix in our hands as we pray the Sign of the Cross. Then we pray the Apostles' Creed. Next to the crucifix, there is a single bead, followed by a set of three beads and another single bead. We pray the Lord's Prayer as we hold the first single bead and a Hail Mary at each bead in the set of three that follows. Then we pray the Glory Be to the Father. On the next single bead we think about the first mystery and pray the Lord's Prayer.

There are five sets of 10 beads; each set is called a decade. We pray a Hail Mary on each bead of a decade as we reflect on a particular mystery in the lives of Jesus and Mary. The Glory Be to the Father is prayed at the end of each set. Between sets is a single bead on which we think about one of the mysteries and pray the Lord's Prayer. In some places people pray the Hail, Holy

Our Lady of the Rosary, stained glass, Correze, France.

Queen after the last decade. See page 186. We end by holding the crucifix in our hands as we pray the Sign of the Cross.

10. Think about the fourth mystery. Pray the Lord's Prayer.

9. Pray 10 Hail Marys and one Glory Be to the Father.

11. Pray 10 Hail Marys and one Glory Be to the Father.

8. Think about the third mystery. Pray the Lord's Prayer.

12. Think about the fifth mystery. Pray the Lord's Prayer.

7. Pray 10 Hail Marys and one Glory Be to the Father.

6. Think about the second mystery. Pray the Lord's Prayer.

5. Pray 10 Hail Marys and one Glory Be to the Father.

4. Think about the first mystery. Pray the Lord's Prayer.

13. Pray 10 Hail Marys and one Glory Be to the Father.

14. Pray the Hail, Holy Queen.

3. Pray three Hail Marys and one Glory Be to the Father.

2. Pray the Lord's Prayer.

15. Pray the Sign of the Cross.

1. Pray the Sign of the Cross and the Apostles' Creed.

Mysteries of the Rosary

The Church had three sets of mysteries for many centuries. In 2002 Pope John Paul II proposed a fourth set of mysteries—the Mysteries of Light, or the Luminous Mysteries. According to his suggestion, the four sets of mysteries might be prayed on the following days: the Joyful Mysteries on Monday and Saturday, the Sorrowful Mysteries on Tuesday and Friday, the Glorious Mysteries on Wednesday and Sunday, and the Luminous Mysteries on Thursday.

Pope John Paul II.

The Joyful Mysteries

1. *The Annunciation.* Mary learns she has been chosen to be the mother of Jesus.

2. *The Visitation.* Mary visits Elizabeth, who tells her that she will always be remembered.

3. *The Nativity.* Jesus is born in a stable in Bethlehem.

4. *The Presentation.* Mary and Joseph take the infant Jesus to the Temple to present him to God.

5. *The Finding of Jesus in the Temple.* Jesus is found in the Temple, discussing his faith with the teachers.

The Luminous Mysteries

1. *The Baptism of Jesus in the River Jordan.* God proclaims that Jesus is his beloved Son.

2. *The Wedding Feast at Cana.* At Mary's request, Jesus performs his first miracle.

3. *The Proclamation of the Kingdom of God.* Jesus calls all to conversion and service to the kingdom.

4. *The Transfiguration of Jesus.* Jesus is revealed in glory to Peter, James, and John.

5. *The Institution of the Eucharist.* Jesus gives us his Body and Blood at the Last Supper.

The Sorrowful Mysteries

1. *The Agony in the Garden.* Jesus prays in the garden of Gethsemane on the night before he dies.

2. *The Scourging at the Pillar.* Jesus is beaten with whips.

3. *The Crowning with Thorns.* Jesus is mocked and crowned with thorns.

4. *The Carrying of the Cross.* Jesus carries the cross on which he will be crucified.

5. *The Crucifixion.* Jesus is nailed to the cross and dies.

The Glorious Mysteries

1. *The Resurrection.* God the Father raises Jesus from the dead.

2. *The Ascension.* Jesus returns to his Father in heaven.

3. *The Coming of the Holy Spirit.* The Holy Spirit comes to bring new life to the disciples.

4. *The Assumption of Mary.* At the end of her life on earth, Mary is taken body and soul into heaven.

5. *The Coronation of Mary.* Mary is crowned as queen of heaven and earth.

Stations of the Cross

The 14 Stations of the Cross represent events from Jesus' passion and death. At each station, we use our senses and our imagination to reflect prayerfully on Jesus' suffering, death, and Resurrection.

1. Jesus Is Condemned to Death.
Pontius Pilate condemns Jesus to death.

2. Jesus Takes Up His Cross.
Jesus willingly accepts and patiently bears his cross.

3. Jesus Falls the First Time.
Weakened by torments and loss of blood, Jesus falls beneath his cross.

4. Jesus Meets His Sorrowful Mother.
Jesus meets his mother, Mary, who is filled with grief.

5. Simon of Cyrene Helps Jesus Carry the Cross.
Soldiers force Simon of Cyrene to carry the cross.

6. Veronica Wipes the Face of Jesus.
Veronica steps through the crowd to wipe the face of Jesus.

7. Jesus Falls a Second Time.
Jesus falls beneath the weight of the cross a second time.

8. Jesus Meets the Women of Jerusalem.
Jesus tells the women to weep not for him, but for themselves and for their children.

9. Jesus Falls the Third Time.
Weakened almost to the point of death, Jesus falls a third time.

10. Jesus Is Stripped of His Garments.
The soldiers strip Jesus of his garments, treating him as a common criminal.

11. Jesus Is Nailed to the Cross.
Jesus' hands and feet are nailed to the cross.

12. Jesus Dies on the Cross.
After suffering greatly on the cross, Jesus bows his head and dies.

13. Jesus Is Taken Down from the Cross.
The lifeless body of Jesus is tenderly placed in the arms of Mary, his mother.

14. Jesus Is Laid in the Tomb.
Jesus' disciples place his body in the tomb.

The closing prayer—sometimes included as a 15th station—reflects on the Resurrection of Jesus.

Celebrating and Living Our Catholic Faith

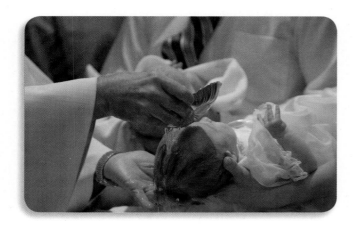

The Seven Sacraments

Jesus touches our lives through the sacraments. Our celebrations of the sacraments are signs of Jesus' presence in our lives and a means for receiving his grace. The Church celebrates seven sacraments, which are divided into three categories.

Sacraments of Initiation

These sacraments lay the foundation of every Christian life.

Baptism

In Baptism we receive new life in Christ. Baptism takes away original sin and gives us new birth in the Holy Spirit. Its sign is the pouring of water.

Confirmation

Confirmation seals our life of faith in Jesus. Its signs are the laying of hands on a person's head, most often by a bishop, and the anointing with oil. Like Baptism, Confirmation is received only once.

Eucharist

The Eucharist nourishes our life of faith. We receive the Body and Blood of Christ in the form of bread and wine.

Sacraments of Healing

These sacraments celebrate the healing power of Jesus.

Penance and Reconciliation

Through the sacrament we receive God's forgiveness. Forgiveness requires being sorry for our sins. We receive Jesus' healing grace through absolution by the priest. The signs of this sacrament are the confession of sins and the words of absolution.

Anointing of the Sick

This sacrament unites a sick person's suffering with that of Jesus and brings forgiveness of sins. Oil, a symbol of strength, is the sign of this sacrament. A person is anointed with oil and receives the laying on of hands from a priest.

Oil used during the Sacrament of Anointing of the Sick.

Sacraments at the Service of Communion

These sacraments help members serve the community.

Holy Orders

In Holy Orders men are ordained as priests, deacons, or bishops. Priests serve as leaders of their communities, and deacons serve to remind us of our baptismal call to help others. Bishops carry on the teachings of the apostles. The signs of this sacrament are the laying on of hands and anointing with chrism by a bishop.

Matrimony

In Matrimony a man and woman are united with each other as a sign of the unity between Jesus and his Church. Matrimony requires the consent of the couple as expressed in the marriage promises. The couple and their wedding rings are the signs of this sacrament.

Order of the Mass

Sunday is the day on which we celebrate the Resurrection of Jesus. Sunday is the Lord's Day. We gather for Mass, rest from work, and perform works of mercy.

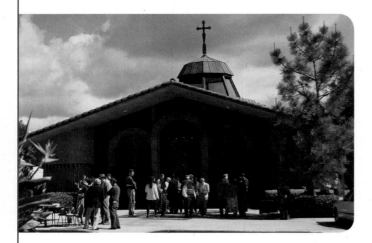

People all over the world gather at God's eucharistic table as brothers and sisters.

The Mass is the high point of the Christian life, and it follows a set order.

Introductory Rites—preparing to celebrate the Eucharist

- *Entrance Chant*—We gather as a community and praise God in song.
- *Greeting*—We pray the Sign of the Cross. The priest welcomes us.
- *Penitential Act*—We remember our sins and ask God for mercy.
- Gloria—We praise God in song.
- *Collect Prayer*—We ask God to hear our prayers.

Liturgy of the Word—hearing God's plan of salvation

- *First Reading*—We listen to God's Word, usually from the Old Testament.
- *Responsorial Psalm*—We respond to God's Word in song.
- *Second Reading*—We listen to God's Word from the New Testament.
- *Gospel Acclamation*—We sing "Alleluia!" (except during Lent) to praise God for the Good News.
- *Gospel Reading*—We stand and listen to the Gospel of the Lord.
- *Homily*—The priest or the deacon explains God's Word.
- *Profession of Faith*—We proclaim our faith through the Nicene Creed.
- *Prayer of the Faithful*—We pray for our needs and the needs of others.

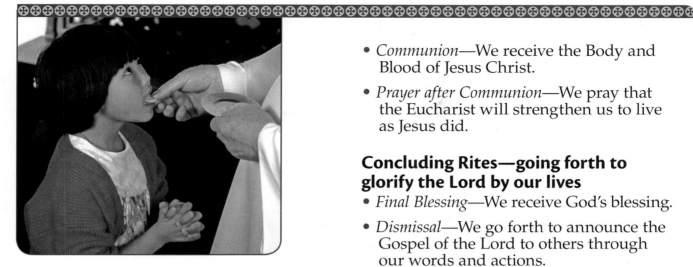

Liturgy of the Eucharist—celebrating Jesus' presence in the Eucharist

- *Presentation and Preparation of the Gifts*—We bring gifts of bread and wine to the altar.

- *Prayer over the Offerings*—The priest prays that God will accept our sacrifice.

- *Eucharistic Prayer*—This prayer of thanksgiving is the center and high point of the entire celebration.

- *Preface*—We give thanks and praise to God.

- *Holy, Holy, Holy*—We sing an acclamation of praise.

- *Consecration*—The bread and wine are consecrated and truly become the Body and Blood of Jesus Christ, our Risen Lord.

- *The Mystery of Faith*—We proclaim the mystery of our faith.

- *Amen*—We affirm the words and actions of the Eucharistic Prayer.

Communion Rite—preparing to receive the Body and Blood of Jesus Christ

- *Lord's Prayer*—We pray the Lord's Prayer.

- *Sign of Peace*—We offer one another Christ's peace.

- *Lamb of God*—We pray for forgiveness, mercy, and peace.

- *Communion*—We receive the Body and Blood of Jesus Christ.

- *Prayer after Communion*—We pray that the Eucharist will strengthen us to live as Jesus did.

Concluding Rites—going forth to glorify the Lord by our lives

- *Final Blessing*—We receive God's blessing.

- *Dismissal*—We go forth to announce the Gospel of the Lord to others through our words and actions.

Holy Days of Obligation

Holy Days of Obligation are the days other than Sundays on which we celebrate the great things God has done for us through Jesus and the saints. On Holy Days of Obligation, Catholics gather for Mass.

Six Holy Days of Obligation are celebrated in the United States.

January 1—Mary, Mother of God

40 days after Easter—Ascension (In many U.S. dioceses, it is the Seventh Sunday of Easter.)

August 15—Assumption of the Blessed Virgin Mary

November 1—All Saints

December 8—Immaculate Conception

December 25—Nativity of Our Lord Jesus Christ

Ascension.

Precepts of the Church

The Precepts of the Church describe the minimum effort we must make in prayer and in living a moral life. All Catholics are called to move beyond the minimum by growing in love of God and love of neighbor. The Precepts are as follows:

1. To keep holy the day of the Lord's Resurrection. To worship God by participating in Mass every Sunday and on Holy Days of Obligation. To avoid those activities (like needless work) that would hinder worship, joy, or relaxation.

2. To lead a sacramental life. To receive Holy Communion frequently and the Sacrament of Reconciliation regularly.

3. To confess one's sins once a year so as to prepare to receive the Eucharist and to continue a life of conversion.

4. To observe the marriage laws of the Church. To give religious training, by word and example, to one's children. To use parish schools and catechetical programs.

5. To strengthen and support the Church—one's own parish and parish priests, the worldwide Church, and the pope.

6. To do penance, including abstaining from meat and fasting from food on the appointed days.

Living Our Faith

The Ten Commandments

As believers in Jesus Christ, we are called to a new life and are asked to make moral choices that keep us unified with God. With the help and grace of the Holy Spirit, we can choose ways to act that keep us close to God, help other people, and be witnesses to Jesus in the world.

The Ten Commandments guide us in making choices that help us live as God wants us to live. The first three commandments tell us how to love God; the other seven tell us how to love our neighbor.

Moses with the Ten Commandments.

1. I am the Lord your God: you shall not have strange gods before me.
2. You shall not take the name of the Lord your God in vain.
3. Remember to keep holy the Lord's Day.
4. Honor your father and your mother.
5. You shall not kill.
6. You shall not commit adultery.
7. You shall not steal.
8. You shall not bear false witness against your neighbor.
9. You shall not covet your neighbor's wife.
10. You shall not covet your neighbor's goods.

The Great Commandment

The Ten Commandments are fulfilled in Jesus' Great Commandment: "You shall love God with all your heart, with all your soul, with all your mind, and with all your strength.

You shall love your neighbor as yourself." (adapted from Mark 12:30–31)

The New Commandment

Before his death on the cross, Jesus gave his disciples a new commandment: "Love one another. As I have loved you, so you also should love one another." (John 13:34)

The Church of the Beatitudes, overlooking the Sea of Galilee, Israel.

The Beatitudes

The Beatitudes are the teachings of Jesus in the Sermon on the Mount, described in Matthew 5:1–10. The Beatitudes fulfill God's promises made to Abraham and to his descendants and describe the rewards that will be ours as loyal followers of Christ.

Blessed are the poor in spirit,
for theirs is the kingdom of heaven.

Blessed are they who mourn,
for they will be comforted.

Blessed are the meek,
for they will inherit the land.

Blessed are they who hunger and thirst
for righteousness,
for they will be satisfied.

Blessed are the merciful,
for they will be shown mercy.

Blessed are the clean of heart,
for they will see God.

Blessed are the peacemakers,
for they will be called children of God.

Blessed are they who are persecuted
for the sake of righteousness,
for theirs is the kingdom of heaven.

Making Good Choices

Our conscience is the inner voice that helps us know the law God has placed in our hearts. Our conscience helps us to judge the moral qualities of our own actions. It guides us to do good and avoid evil.

The Holy Spirit can help us form a good conscience. We form our conscience by studying the teachings of the Church and following the guidance of our parents and pastoral leaders.

God has given every human being freedom of choice. This does not mean that we have the right to do whatever we please. We can live in true freedom with the Holy Spirit, who gives us the virtue of prudence. This virtue helps us recognize what is good in every situation and to make correct choices. The Holy Spirit gives us the gifts of wisdom and understanding to help us make the right choices in life in relationship to God and others. The gift of counsel helps us reflect on making correct choices in life.

The Ten Commandments help us make

moral choices that are pleasing to God. We have the grace of the sacraments, the teachings of the Church, and the good example of saints and fellow Christians to help us make good choices.

Making moral choices involves the following steps:

1. Ask the Holy Spirit for help.

2. Think about God's law and the teachings of the Church.

3. Think about what will happen as a result of your choice.

4. Seek advice from someone you respect, and remember that Jesus is with you.

5. Ask yourself how your choice will affect your relationships with God and others.

Making moral choices takes into consideration the object of the choice, our intention in making the choice, and the circumstances in which the choice is made. It is never right to make an evil choice in the hope of gaining something good.

An Examination of Conscience

An examination of conscience is the act of reflecting on how we have hurt our relationships with God and others. The questions below help us in our examination of conscience.

My Relationship with God
What steps am I taking to help me grow closer to God and to others?

Do I participate at Mass with attention and devotion on Sundays and holy days?

Do I pray often and read the Bible?

Do I use God's name and the names of Jesus, Mary, and the saints with love and reverence?

My Relationships with Family, Friends, and Neighbors

Have I set a bad example by my words or actions? Have I treated others fairly? Have I spread stories that hurt other people?

Am I loving toward those in my family? Am I respectful of my neighbors, my friends, and those in authority?

Do I show respect for my body and for the bodies of others? Do I keep away from forms of entertainment that do not respect God's gift of sexuality?

Have I taken or damaged anything that did not belong to me? Have I cheated, copied homework, or lied?

Do I quarrel with others just so I can get my own way? Do I insult others to try to make them think they are less than I am? Do I hold grudges and try to hurt people who I think have hurt me?

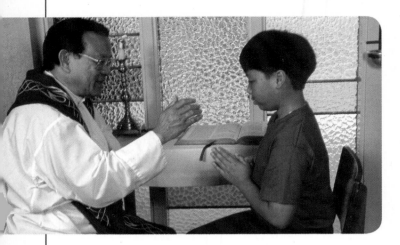

How to Make a Good Confession

An examination of conscience is an important part of preparing for the Sacrament of Reconciliation. The Sacrament of Reconciliation includes the following steps:

- The priest greets us, and we pray the Sign of the Cross. He invites us to trust in God. He may read God's Word with us.

- We confess our sins. The priest may help and counsel us.

- The priest gives us a penance to perform. Penance is an act of kindness or prayers to pray, or both.

- The priest asks us to express our sorrow, usually by reciting the Act of Contrition.

- We receive absolution. The priest says, "I absolve you from your sins in the name of the Father, and of the Son, and of the Holy Spirit." We respond, "Amen."

- The priest dismisses us by saying, "Go in peace." We go forth to perform the act of penance he has given us.

Virtues

Virtues are gifts from God that lead us to live in a close relationship with him. Virtues are like habits. They need to be practiced; they can be lost if they are neglected. The three most important virtues are called the *theological virtues* because they come from God and lead to God. The *cardinal virtues* are human virtues acquired by education and good actions. *Cardinal* comes from *cardo*, the Latin word for *hinge*, meaning "that on which other things depend."

Theological Virtues
faith   hope   charity

Cardinal Virtues
prudence   fortitude
justice   temperance

Gifts of the Holy Spirit

The Holy Spirit makes it possible for us to do what God asks by giving us these gifts.

wisdom   understanding
counsel   fortitude
knowledge   fear of the Lord
piety

Fruits of the Holy Spirit
The Fruits of the Holy Spirit are signs of the Holy Spirit's action in our lives.

love   joy   peace
patience   kindness   generosity
goodness   chastity   faithfulness
gentleness   self-control modesty

Works of Mercy

The Corporal and Spiritual Works of Mercy are actions we can perform that extend God's compassion and mercy to those in need.

Corporal Works of Mercy

The Corporal Works of Mercy are the kind acts by which we help our neighbors with their material and physical needs:

Feed the hungry.

Give drink to the thirsty.

Clothe the naked.

Shelter the homeless.

Visit the sick.

Visit the imprisoned.

Bury the dead.

Spiritual Works of Mercy

The Spiritual Works of Mercy are acts of compassion by which we help our neighbors with their emotional and spiritual needs:

Counsel the doubtful.

Instruct the ignorant.

Admonish sinners.

Comfort the afflicted.

Forgive offenses.

Bear wrongs patiently.

Pray for the living and the dead.

The Bible and You

God speaks to us in many ways. One way that God speaks to us is through the Bible. The Bible is the most important book in Christian life because it is God's message, or revelation. The Bible is the story of God's promise to care for us, especially through his Son, Jesus. At Mass we hear stories from the Bible. We can also read the Bible on our own.

The Bible is not just one book; it is a collection of many books. The writings in the Bible were inspired by the Holy Spirit and written by different authors using different styles.

The Bible is made up of two parts. The Old Testament contains 46 books that tell stories about the Jewish people and their faith in God before Jesus was born. It also contains the Ten Commandments, which guide us to live as God wants us to live.

The New Testament contains 27 books that tell the story of Jesus' life, death, and Resurrection, and the experience of the early Christians. For Christians the most important books of the New Testament are the four Gospels—Matthew, Mark, Luke, and John. Many of the 27 books are letters written by Saint Paul.

How Do You Find a Passage in the Bible?

Bible passages are identified by book, chapter, and verse—for example, Gn 1:28. The name of the book comes first. It is often abbreviated. Your Bible's table of contents will help you find out what the abbreviation means. In our example, *Gn* stands for the *Book of Genesis.* After the name of the book, there are two or more numbers. The first number identifies the chapter, which in our example is chapter 1. The chapter number is followed by a colon. The second number or numbers identify the verses. Our example shows verse 28.

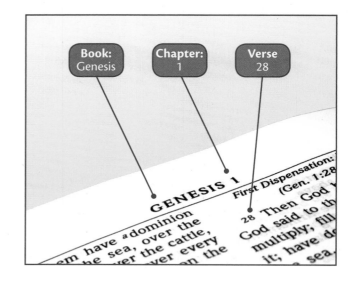

Showing Our Love for the World

Through the themes of Catholic Social Teaching, the Church encourages us to participate in the following areas of social action.

Life and Dignity of the Human Person

All human life is sacred, and all people must be respected and valued over material goods. We are called to ask whether our actions as a society respect or threaten the life and dignity of the human person.

Call to Family, Community, and Participation

Families must be supported so that people can participate in society, build a community spirit, and promote the well-being of all, especially the poor and vulnerable.

Rights and Responsibilities

Every person has a right to life as well as a right to those things required for human decency. As Catholics, we have a responsibility to protect these basic human rights in order to achieve a healthy society.

Option for the Poor and Vulnerable

In our world many people are rich, while others are extremely poor. As Catholics, we are called to pay special attention to the needs of the poor by defending and promoting their dignity and by meeting their immediate material needs.

The Dignity of Work and the Rights of Workers

The basic rights of workers must be respected: the right to productive work, fair wages, and private property; and the right to organize, join unions, and pursue economic opportunity. Catholics believe that the economy is meant to serve people and that work is not merely a way to make a living, but is an important way in which we participate in God's creation.

Solidarity

Because God is our Father, we are all brothers and sisters with the responsibility to care for one another. Solidarity is the attitude that leads Christians to share spiritual and material goods. Solidarity unites rich and poor, weak and strong, and helps create a society that recognizes that we depend on one another.

Care for God's Creation

God is the creator of all people and all things, and he wants us to enjoy his creation. The responsibility to care for all that God has made is a requirement of our faith.

Glossary

A

Abba an informal word for *Father* in the language Jesus spoke. Jesus called God the Father "Abba."

absolution the forgiveness God offers us in the Sacrament of Penance and Reconciliation. After we say that we are sorry for our sins, we receive God's absolution from the priest.

adore to worship God above all else because he is our creator. The First Commandment tells us to adore God.

adultery being unfaithful to one's marriage partner. A person who commits adultery breaks his or her. marriage promises.

altar the table in the church on which the priest celebrates Mass, during which the sacrifice of Christ on the cross is made present in the Sacrament of the Eucharist. The altar represents two aspects of the mystery of the Eucharist. First, it is where Jesus Christ offers himself for our sins. Second, it is where he gives us himself as our food for eternal life.

ambo a raised stand from which a person reads the Word of God during Mass

angel a spiritual creature who brings a message from God

Angelus a prayer honoring the Incarnation of Jesus. The Angelus is prayed in the morning, at noon, and in the evening.

Annunciation the announcement to Mary by the angel Gabriel that God had chosen her to be the mother of Jesus

apostle one of twelve special men who accompanied Jesus in his ministry and were witnesses to the Resurrection

Apostles' Creed a statement of Christian belief. The Apostles' Creed, developed out of a creed used in Baptism in Rome, lists simple statements of belief in God the Father,

Stained glass image of the **Annunciation.**

Jesus Christ the Son, and the Holy Spirit. The profession of faith used in Baptism today is based on the Apostles' Creed.

Ascension the return of Jesus to heaven. In the Acts of the Apostles, it is written that Jesus, after his Resurrection, spent 40 days on earth, instructing his followers. He then returned to his Father in heaven.

Assumption Mary's being taken to heaven, body and soul, by God at the end of her life. The feast of the Assumption is celebrated on August 15.

B

Baptism the first of the three sacraments by which we become members of the Church. Baptism frees us from original sin and gives us new life in Jesus Christ through the Holy Spirit.

Beatitudes the eight ways we can behave to live a blessed life. Jesus teaches us that if we live according to the Beatitudes, we will live a happy Christian life.

benediction a prayer service in which we honor Jesus in the Blessed Sacrament and receive his blessing

Bible a collection of books that tell the history of God's promise to care for us and his call for us to be faithful to him. God asked that people be faithful first through the beliefs of the Jewish people and then through belief in the life, death, and Resurrection of Jesus Christ.

bishop a man who has received the fullness of Holy Orders. He has inherited his duties from the original apostles. He cares for the Church today and is a principal teacher in the Church.

Blessed Sacrament the Body of Christ. It is kept in the tabernacle to adore and to be taken to the sick.

blessing a prayer that calls for God's power and care upon some person, place, thing, or special activity

Body and Blood of Christ the bread and wine that has been consecrated at Mass by the priest. It still looks like bread and wine, but it is truly the Body and Blood of Jesus Christ.

C

catholic one of the four Marks of the Church. The Church is catholic because Jesus is fully present in it and because Jesus has given the Church to the whole world.

charity a virtue given to us by God. Charity helps us love God above all things and our neighbor as ourselves.

Christ a title that means "anointed with oil." It is from a Greek word that means the same thing as the Hebrew word *Messiah,* or "anointed." It is the name given to Jesus after the Resurrection.

Christian the name given to all those who have been anointed through the gift of the Holy Spirit in Baptism and have become followers of Jesus Christ

Christmas the day on which we celebrate the birth of Jesus (December 25)

Church the name given to all the followers of Christ throughout the world. It is also the name of the building where we gather to pray to God and the name of our community as we gather to praise God.

commandment a standard, or rule, for living as God wants us to live. Jesus summarized all the commandments into two: love God and love your neighbor.

Communion of Saints the union of all who have been saved in Jesus Christ, both those who are alive and those who have died

confession the act of telling our sins to a priest in the Sacrament of Penance and Reconciliation. The sacrament itself is sometimes referred to as "confession."

Confirmation the sacrament that completes the grace we receive in Baptism. Confirmation seals, or confirms, this grace through the seven Gifts of the Holy Spirit that we receive as part of Confirmation. This sacrament also unites us more closely in Jesus Christ.

conscience the inner voice that helps each of us know the law that God has placed in our hearts. It guides us to do good and avoid evil.

contrition the sorrow we feel when we know that we have sinned, followed by the decision not to sin again. Contrition is the most important part of our celebration of the Sacrament of Penance and Reconciliation.

Corporal Works of Mercy kind acts by which we help our neighbors with their everyday, material needs. Corporal Works of Mercy include feeding the hungry, giving drink to the thirsty, clothing the naked, sheltering the homeless, visiting the sick and the imprisoned, and burying the dead.

covenant a solemn agreement between people or between people and God. God made covenants with humanity through agreements with Noah, Abraham, and Moses. These covenants offered salvation. God's new and final covenant was established through Jesus' life, death, and Resurrection.

Creation God's act of making everything that exists outside himself. Creation is everything that exists. God said that all creation is good.

Creator God, who made everything that is and whom we can come to know through everything he created

creed a brief summary of what people believe. The Apostles' Creed is a summary of Christian beliefs.

D

deacon a man ordained through the Sacrament of Holy Orders to help the bishop and priests in the work of the Church

devil a spirit created good by God who became evil because of disobedience. The devil tempted Jesus in the desert.

disciple a person who has accepted Jesus' message and tries to live as he did

E

Easter the celebration of the bodily raising of Jesus Christ from the dead. Easter is the most important Christian feast.

Emmanuel a name from the Old Testament that means "God with us." Because Jesus is always with us, we often call him by the name *Emmanuel*.

epistle a letter written by Saint Paul or another leader to a group of Christians in the early Church. Twenty-one of the 27 books of the New Testament are epistles.

Celebrating the **Eucharist** at Mass.

Eucharist the sacrament in which we give thanks to God for giving us the Body and Blood of Jesus Christ. This sacrament brings us into union with Jesus Christ and his saving Death and Resurrection.

examination of conscience the act of prayerfully thinking about what we have said or done that may have hurt our relationship with God or others. An examination of conscience is an important part of preparing to celebrate the Sacrament of Penance and Reconciliation.

F

faith a gift of God that helps us believe in him and live as he wants us to live. We express our faith in the words of the Apostles' Creed.

fasting limiting the amount we eat for a period of time, to express sorrow for sin and to make ourselves more aware of God's action in our lives

free will our ability to choose to do good because God has made us like him

A sculpture of the **Holy Family.**

G

Gospel the good news of God's mercy and love. We experience this news in the story of Jesus' life, death, and Resurrection. The story is presented to us in four books in the New Testament: the Gospels of Matthew, Mark, Luke, and John.

grace the gift of God given to us without our deserving it. Sanctifying grace fills us with his life and enables us to always be his friends. Grace also helps us live as God wants us to.

Great Commandment Jesus' essential teaching that we are to love God and to love our neighbor as we love ourselves

H

heaven the life with God that is full of happiness and never ends

Hebrews the descendants of Abraham, Isaac, and Jacob, who were enslaved in Egypt. God helped Moses lead the Hebrew people out of slavery.

holy one of the four Marks of the Church. It is the kind of life we live when we share in the life of God, who is all holiness. The Church is holy because of its union with Jesus Christ.

Holy Communion the reception of the Body and Blood of Jesus Christ. It brings us into union with Jesus Christ and his saving Death and Resurrection.

Holy Family the family made up of Jesus; his mother, Mary; and his foster father, Joseph

Holy Spirit the third Person of the Trinity, who is sent to us as our helper and, through Baptism and Confirmation, fills us with God's life.

homily an explanation of God's Word. A homily explains the words of God that we hear in the Bible readings at church.

hope the trust that God will always be with us. We also trust that he will make us happy now and help us live in a way that keeps us with him forever.

I

Incarnation the Son of God, Jesus, being born as a full human being in order to save us. The Incarnation is one of the main mysteries of our faith.

inspired influenced by the Holy Spirit. The human authors of Scripture were influenced by the Holy Spirit. The creative inspiration of the Holy Spirit makes sure that the Scripture is taught according to the truth God wants us to know for our salvation.

Israelites the descendants of Abraham, Isaac, and Jacob. God changed Jacob's name to "Israel," and Jacob's 12 sons and their children became the leaders of the 12 tribes of Israel. (*See* Hebrews.)

J

Jesus the Son of God, who was born of the Virgin Mary and who died and was raised from the dead so that we can live with God forever. His name means "God saves."

Joseph the foster father of Jesus, who was engaged to Mary when the angel announced that Mary would have a child through the power of the Holy Spirit

justice the strong, firm desire to give to God and others what is due them. Justice is one of the four central human virtues, called the cardinal virtues, by which we guide our Christian life.

K

Kingdom of God God's rule over us. We experience the Kingdom of God in part now, and we will experience it fully in heaven. The Kingdom of God was announced in the Gospel and is present in the Eucharist.

L

Last Supper the last meal Jesus ate with his disciples on the night before he died. At the Last Supper, Jesus took bread and wine, blessed them, and said that they were his Body and Blood. Every Mass is a remembrance of this last meal.

Lectionary for Mass the book that contains all the Bible stories we read at Mass

Liturgy of the Eucharist the second half of the Mass, in which the bread and wine are consecrated and truly become the Body and Blood of Jesus Christ, our Risen Lord. We then receive the Body and Blood of Jesus Christ in Holy Communion.

Liturgy of the Word the first half of the Mass, in which we listen to God's Word from the Bible and consider what it means for us today

Lord the name for God that was used in place of the name he revealed to Moses, *Yahweh*, which was considered too sacred to pronounce. The New Testament also uses the title Lord for Jesus, recognizing him as God himself.

(At right) Stained glass image of the **Last Supper**, Abbey Notre Dame, Beaugency, France.

Lord's Day Sunday is the day Christians set aside for special worship of God. Each Sunday Mass commemorates the Resurrection of Jesus on Easter Sunday. Besides telling us to offer God worship we all owe him, the Third Commandment says Sunday is a day for relaxation of mind and body and to perform works of mercy.

M

martyrs those who have given their lives for the faith. It comes from the Greek word for "witness." A martyr is the supreme witness to the truth of the faith and to Christ to whom he or she is united. The seventh chapter of the Acts of the Apostles recounts the death of the first martyr, the deacon Stephen.

Mary the mother of Jesus. She is called blessed and "full of grace" because God chose her to be the mother of the Son of God.

Mass the most important sacramental celebration of the Church. The celebration of the Mass was established by Jesus at the Last Supper as a remembrance of his death and Resurrection. At Mass we listen to God's Word from the Bible and receive the Body and Blood of Christ.

Messiah a title that means "anointed with oil." It is from a Hebrew word that means the same as the Greek word *Christ,* the name given to Jesus after the Resurrection.

miracle act of wonder that cannot be explained by natural causes but is a work of God. In the Gospels, Jesus works miracles as a sign that the Kingdom of God is present in his ministry.

mission the work of Jesus Christ that is continued in the Church through the Holy Spirit. The mission of the Church is to proclaim salvation through Jesus' life, death, and Resurrection.

moral choice a choice to do what is right. We make moral choices because they are what we believe God wants. We can make them because we have the freedom to choose what is right and avoid what is wrong.

moral law a rule for living that has been established by God and people in authority who are concerned about the good of all people. Moral laws are based on God's direction to us to do what is right and to avoid what is wrong.

mortal sin a serious decision to turn away from God by doing something that we know is wrong and so cuts us off from God's life

mystery a truth revealed by God that we cannot completely understand. The truth that the Son of God became man is a mystery of our faith.

N

New Testament the 27 books of the second part of the Bible, which tell of the teaching, ministry, and saving events of the life of Jesus. The four Gospels present Jesus' life, death, and Resurrection. The Acts of the Apostles tells the story of the message of salvation as it spreads through the growth of the Church. Various letters instruct us on how to live as followers of Jesus Christ. The Book of Revelation offers encouragement to Christians living through persecution.

O

obedience the act of willingly following what God asks us to do for our salvation. The Fourth Commandment requires children to obey their parents, and all people are required to obey civil authority when it acts for the good of all.

Old Testament the first 46 books of the Bible, which tell of God's covenant with the people of Israel and his plan for the salvation of all people. The first five books are known as the Torah. The Old Testament is fulfilled in the New Testament, but God's covenant presented in the Old Testament has permanent value and has never been revoked, or set aside.

Ordinary Time the part of the liturgical year outside of the seasons of feasts and the preparation for them. Ordinary means not common, but counted time, as in ordinal numbers. It is devoted to growth in understanding the mystery of Christ in its fullness. The color of Ordinary Time is green to symbolize growth.

❮ The Bible contains both the **Old Testament** and the **New Testament.**

Painting of **Pentecost,** St. Maron's Church, Minneapolis, Minnesota.

original sin the result of the sin by which the first human beings disobeyed God and chose to follow their own will rather than God's will. Because of this act, all human beings lost the original blessing that God intended, and they became subject to sin and death. In Baptism we are restored to life with God through Jesus Christ.

P

parable one of the simple stories that Jesus told to show us what the Kingdom of God is like. Parables present images, or scenes, drawn from everyday life. These images show us the radical, or serious, choice we make when we respond to the invitation to enter the Kingdom of God.

parish a community of believers in Jesus Christ who meet regularly in a specific area to worship God under the leadership of a pastor

Paschal Mystery the work of salvation accomplished by Jesus Christ through his passion, death, Resurrection, and Ascension. The Paschal Mystery is celebrated in the liturgy of the Church. Its saving effects are experienced by us in the sacraments.

Passover the Jewish festival that commemorates the delivery of the Hebrew people from slavery in Egypt. In the Eucharist we celebrate our passover from death to life through Jesus' death and Resurrection.

penance the turning away from sin because we want to live as God wants us to live (*See* Sacrament of Penance and Reconciliation.)

Pentecost the 50th day after Jesus was raised from the dead. On this day the Holy Spirit was sent from heaven, and the Church was born.

personal sin a sin we choose to commit, whether serious (mortal) or less serious (venial). Although the result of original sin is to leave us with a tendency to sin, God's grace, especially through the sacraments, helps us choose good over sin.

pope the Bishop of Rome, successor of Saint Peter, and leader of the Roman Catholic Church. Because he has the authority to act in the name of Christ, the pope is called the Vicar of Christ. The pope and all the bishops together make up the living, teaching office of the Church.

prayer the raising of our hearts and minds to God. We are able to speak to and listen to God in prayer because he teaches us how to do so.

John the Baptist was a **prophet.**

prayer of petition a request of God asking him to fulfill a need. When we share in God's saving love, we understand that every need is one that we can ask God to help us with through petition.

Precepts of the Church those positive requirements that the pastoral authority of the Church has determined as necessary. These requirements describe the minimum effort we must make in prayer and the moral life. The Precepts of the Church ensure that all Catholics move beyond the minimum by growing in love of God and love of neighbor.

priest a man who has accepted God's special call to serve the Church by guiding it and building it up through the celebration of the sacraments

prophet a person called by God to speak to the people for him. John the Baptist was a great prophet.

psalm a prayer in the form of a poem. Psalms were written to be sung in public worship. Each psalm expresses an aspect, or feature, of the depth of human prayer. Over several centuries 150 psalms were gathered to form the Book of Psalms, used in worship in Old Testament times.

purgatory a state of final cleansing after death of all our human imperfections to prepare us to enter into the joy of God's presence in heaven

R

reconciliation the renewal of friendship after that friendship has been broken by some action or lack of action. In the Sacrament of Penance and Reconciliation, through God's mercy and forgiveness, we are reconciled with God, the Church, and others.

Redeemer Jesus Christ, whose life, death on the cross, and Resurrection from the dead set us free from sin and bring us redemption.

Resurrection the bodily raising of Jesus Christ from the dead on the third day after his death on the cross. The Resurrection is the crowning truth of our faith.

Revelation God's communication of himself to us through the words and deeds he has used throughout history. Revelation shows us the mystery of his plan for our salvation in his Son, Jesus Christ.

Rosary a prayer in honor of the Blessed Virgin Mary. When we pray the Rosary, we meditate on the mysteries of Jesus Christ's life while praying the Hail Mary on five sets of 10 beads and the Lord's Prayer on the beads in between.

S

Sabbath the seventh day, when God rested after finishing the work of creation. The Third Commandment requires us to keep the Sabbath holy. For Christians Sunday became the Sabbath because it was the day Jesus rose from the dead and the new creation in Jesus Christ began.

sacrament one of seven ways through which God's life enters our lives through the work of the Holy Spirit. Jesus gave us three sacraments that bring us into the Church: Baptism, Confirmation, and the Eucharist. He gave us two sacraments that bring us healing: Penance and Anointing of the Sick. He also gave us two sacraments that help members serve the community: Matrimony and Holy Orders.

Sacrament of Penance and Reconciliation the sacrament in which we celebrate God's forgiveness of our sins and our reconciliation with God and the Church. Reconciliation includes sorrow for the sins we have committed, confession of sins, absolution by the priest, and doing the penance that shows our sorrow.

sacramental an object, a prayer, or a blessing given by the Church to help us grow in our spiritual life

sacrifice a gift given to God to give him thanks. Jesus' sacrifice on the cross was the greatest sacrifice.

Sacrifice of the Mass the sacrifice of Jesus on the cross, which is remembered and made present in the Eucharist

saint a holy person who has died and is united with God. The Church has said that this person is now with God forever in heaven.

salvation the gift of forgiveness of sin and the restoration of friendship with God. God alone can give us salvation.

Satan the leader of the evil spirits. His name means "adversary." God allows Satan to tempt us.

Savior Jesus, the Son of God, who became human to forgive our sins and restore our friendship with God. *Jesus* means "God saves."

Scripture the holy writings of Jews and Christians collected in the Old and New Testaments of the Bible

Sermon on the Mount the words of Jesus, written in chapters 5 through 7 of the Gospel of Matthew, in which Jesus reveals how he has fulfilled God's law given to Moses. The Sermon on the Mount begins with the eight Beatitudes and includes the Lord's Prayer.

sin a choice we make on purpose that offends God and hurts our relationships with other people. Some sin is mortal and needs to be confessed in the Sacrament of Penance and Reconciliation. Other sin is venial, or less serious.

Son of God the title revealed by Jesus that indicates his unique relationship to God the Father

soul the part of us that makes us human and an image of God. Body and soul together form one unique human nature. The soul is responsible for our consciousness and our freedom.

Spiritual Works of Mercy the kind acts through which we help our neighbors meet the needs that are more than material. The Spiritual Works of Mercy include counseling the doubtful, instructing the ignorant, admonishing sinners, comforting the afflicted, forgiving offenses, bearing wrongs patiently, and praying for the living and the dead.

synagogue the Jewish place of assembly for prayer, instruction, and study of the Law. Jesus attended the synagogue regularly to pray and to teach.

(At right) Baptism is a **sacrament.**

T

tabernacle a container in which the Blessed Sacrament is kept so that Holy Communion can be taken to the sick and the dying.

Temple the center of Jewish worship in Jerusalem where sacrifices were offered to God

temptation an attraction, from outside us or from inside us, that can lead us to not follow God's commands

Ten Commandments the 10 rules that God gave to Moses on Mount Sinai that sum up God's law and show us what is required to love God and our neighbor

Trinity the mystery of one God existing in three Persons: the Father, the Son, and the Holy Spirit.

V

venial sin a choice we make that weakens our relationship with God or other people. It wounds and diminishes the divine life in us.

W

witness the passing on to others, by our words and actions, the faith that we have been given. Every Christian has the duty to give witness to the good news about Jesus Christ that he or she has come to know.

worship the adoration and honor given to God in public prayer

Y

Yahweh the name of God in Hebrew, which God told Moses from the burning bush. *Yahweh* means "I am who am." Out of respect for God's name, Jews never say this name but replace it with other names.

Index

Scripture Index

Art Credits

When there is more than one picture on a page, credits are supplied in sequence, left to right, top to bottom. Page positions are abbreviated as follows: (t) top, (c) center, (b) bottom, (l) left, (r) right.

FRONT MATTER:
iii(br) © The Crosiers/Gene Plaisted OSC
iv(c) Kathryn Seckman Kirsch

UNIT 1:
3(t) © The Crosiers/Gene Plaisted OSC
5 © The Crosiers/Gene Plaisted OSC
6(t) © The Crosiers/Gene Plaisted OSC
7(b) Kathryn Seckman Kirsch
8 (puzzle) Robert Voigts
9(t) © The Crosiers/Gene Plaisted OSC
10 Dick Mlodock
11(t) Dick Mlodock
12(b) © The Crosiers/Gene Plaisted OSC
15(b) Gary Yeowell/The Image Bank/Getty Images
16(r) © mediacolor's/Alamy
16(tl) © The Crosiers/Gene Plaisted OSC
16(bl) W. P. Wittman Limited
17(t) © The Crosiers/Gene Plaisted OSC
18(t) Andreas Solaro/AFP/Getty Images
19 © The Crosiers/Gene Plaisted OSC
20 Phil Martin Photography
21(b) © The Crosiers/Gene Plaisted OSC
26a(b) © The Crosiers/Gene Plaisted OSC
26b(t) © The Crosiers/Gene Plaisted OSC
26d(cb) © Dennis MacDonald/Alamy

UNIT 2:
29(b) © The Crosiers/Gene Plaisted OSC
30 William Gorman
31 William Gorman
35(b) William Gorman
36(b) © The Crosiers/Gene Plaisted OSC
36(c) Kathryn Seckman Kirsch
37 Phil Martin Photography
38(t) © The Crosiers/Gene Plaisted OSC
41(b) W. P. Wittman Limited
41(t) W. P. Wittman Limited
42 Kathryn Seckman Kirsch
44 (crossword) Proof Positive/Farrowlyne Assoc., Inc.
46 © Kapoor Baldev/Sygma/CORBIS
47(t) © The Crosiers/Gene Plaisted OSC
49 Dick Mlodock
50(b) © The Crosiers/Gene Plaisted OSC
50(t) © The Crosiers/Gene Plaisted OSC
52(t) Kathryn Seckman Kirsch
53(t) © The Crosiers/Gene Plaisted OSC
53(b) Douglas Klauba
54 © The Crosiers/Gene Plaisted OSC
55(t) Erich Lessing/Art Resource, NY
55(b) Kathryn Seckman Kirsch
56 (t) Robert Voigts

57(c) Phil Martin Photography
60 Kathryn Seckman Kirsch
60a Kathryn Seckman Kirsch
60a(b) Len Ebert/PC&F Inc.
60c Kathryn Seckman Kirsch
60d(b) Kathryn Seckman Kirsch and Donna Antkowiak

UNIT 3:
66(c) © The Crosiers/Gene Plaisted OSC
66(t) © The Crosiers/Gene Plaisted OSC
66(b) © The Crosiers/Gene Plaisted OSC
67(bl) W. P. Wittman Limited
67(tr) W. P. Wittman Limited
69(b) © The Crosiers/Gene Plaisted OSC
71 Robert Korta
72(t) Robert Korta
73 Kathryn Seckman Kirsch
75(t) W. P. Wittman Limited
75(b) © The Crosiers/Gene Plaisted OSC
77(t) © The Crosiers/Gene Plaisted OSC
78(t) © The Crosiers/Gene Plaisted OSC
78(b) © The Crosiers/Gene Plaisted OSC
79 Kathryn Seckman Kirsch
81(b) Robert Korta
84 Karen Kouf
88 Kathryn Seckman Kirsch
88b Mia Basile and Kevin Peschke
88c Per Magnus Persson/Veer

UNIT 4:
91(t) © The Crosiers/Gene Plaisted OSC
92(t) Kathryn Seckman Kirsch and Robert Voigts
92(b) © The Crosiers/Gene Plaisted OSC
93 Robert Korta
94(b) Kathryn Seckman Kirsch
97(t) W. P. Wittman Limited
99(t) Dick Mlodock
99(b) Kathryn Seckman Kirsch
100(b) Dick Mlodock
103(b) © The Crosiers/Gene Plaisted OSC
104(t) © The Crosiers/Gene Plaisted OSC
104(c) Robert Voigts and Kathryn Seckman Kirsch
104(b) W. P. Wittman Limited
107 © Getty/Stone/Stuart O'Sullivan
109(t) © The Crosiers/Gene Plaisted OSC
112(t) Hulton Archive/Getty Images
114 Kathryn Seckman Kirsch
115(t) © The Crosiers/Gene Plaisted OSC
116(t) © The Crosiers/Gene Plaisted OSC
118(c) Mary O'Connor
118(b) © The Crosiers/Gene Plaisted OSC
119 The Barron Prize
120 Kathryn Seckman Kirsch
121(b) W. P. Wittman Limited
122 Robert Korta
123(t) Dick Mlodock

123(b) Robert Voigts
125 Lois Axeman
127(b) © The Crosiers/Gene Plaisted OSC
128 Robert Voigts and Kathryn Seckman Kirsch
132 Phil Martin Photography
132b(c) © The Crosiers/Gene Plaisted OSC
132d(bl) © The Crosiers/Gene Plaisted OSC

UNIT 5:
135(b) Dick Mlodock
136(tl) © The Crosiers/Gene Plaisted OSC
136(cl) Jeff Greenberg/PhotoEdit
136(bl) W. P. Wittman Limited
136(r) W. P. Wittman Limited
137 William Gorman
138 © The Crosiers/Gene Plaisted OSC
141(t) © The Crosiers/Gene Plaisted OSC
141(b) © The Crosiers/Gene Plaisted OSC
142(t) Dick Mlodock
143(b) © The Crosiers/Gene Plaisted OSC
144 © The Crosiers/Gene Plaisted OSC
145 Kathryn Seckman Kirsch
147(t) © The Crosiers/Gene Plaisted OSC
147(b) © The Crosiers/Gene Plaisted OSC
148 William Gorman
149(l) Mary Wilshire
150 Dick Mlodock
151(t) © The Crosiers/Gene Plaisted OSC
151(c) © The Crosiers/Gene Plaisted OSC
151(b) © The Crosiers/Gene Plaisted OSC
152 © The Crosiers/Gene Plaisted OSC
153(t) © The Crosiers/Gene Plaisted OSC
154(l) © The Crosiers/Gene Plaisted OSC
154(r) Robert Voigts
155(t) W. P. Wittman Limited
155(b) © The Crosiers/Gene Plaisted OSC
157 Robert Voigts
158 © The Crosiers/Gene Plaisted OSC
159(c) © The Crosiers/Gene Plaisted OSC
159(cb) Robert Voigts
161 Proof Positive/Farrowlyne Assoc., Inc.
166a(t) Yoshikazu Tsuno/AFP/Getty Images
166b(t) Kathryn Seckman Kirsch and George Hamblin/Steve
Edsey & Sons
166d Kathryn Seckman Kirsch

SPECIAL SEASONS AND LESSONS:
167(c) © The Crosiers/Gene Plaisted OSC
168 Julie Lonneman/www.thespiritsource.com
169 © The Crosiers/Gene Plaisted OSC
170 © The Crosiers/Gene Plaisted OSC
171(l) Kathryn Seckman Kirsch

171(r) Kathryn Seckman Kirsch
173 © The Crosiers/Gene Plaisted OSC
175 Kathryn Seckman Kirsch
177(b) © The Crosiers/Gene Plaisted OSC
179(t) © The Crosiers/Gene Plaisted OSC
180(t) W. P. Wittman Limited
181(t) © The Crosiers/Gene Plaisted OSC

WHAT CATHOLICS SHOULD KNOW:
184(b) Myrleen Ferguson Cate/PhotoEdit
185(b) Lon C. Diehl/PhotoEdit
188(t) vario images GmbH & Co.KG/Alamy
188(b) Myrleen Ferguson Cate/PhotoEdit
189(t) © The Crosiers/Gene Plaisted OSC
190 Greg Kuepfer
191(t) CSI Productions/Alamy
192 From Fourteen Mosaic Stations of the Cross © Our Lady of the
Angels Monastery Inc., Hanceville Alabama. All Rights Reserved
193(b) Greg Kuepfer
195(t) Myrleen Ferguson Cate/PhotoEdit
195(b) © The Crosiers/Gene Plaisted OSC
196(cr) Myrleen Ferguson Cate/PhotoEdit
197 Stock Montage, Inc./Alamy
198(t) © Richard T. Nowitz/Corbis
198(b) © The Crosiers/Gene Plaisted OSC
200 Myrleen Ferguson Cate/PhotoEdit
201(b) Myrleen Ferguson Cate/PhotoEdit
203 Jeff Greenberg/PhotoEdit

GLOSSARY:
205 © The Crosiers/Gene Plaisted OSC
209 © The Crosiers/Gene Plaisted OSC
211 © The Crosiers/Gene Plaisted OSC
212 © The Crosiers/Gene Plaisted OSC

LESSON CUTOUTS AND PULLOUTS:
221(t) Kathryn Seckman Kirsch
221(c) © The Crosiers/Gene Plaisted OSC
221(b) Kathryn Seckman Kirsch
Advent Wreath: Robert Korta
Way of the Cross Booklet (cover): Kathryn Seckman Kirsch
Way of the Cross Booklet (stations): Nan Brooks
Reconciliation Booklet (3): © The Crosiers/Gene Plaisted OSC
Reconciliation Booklet (cover): © The Crosiers/Gene Plaisted OSC
Walking with Jesus Booklet (cover): © The Crosiers/Gene Plaisted OSC
Walking with Jesus Booklet (12 t): Kathryn Seckman Kirsch
Walking with Jesus Booklet (10–flower): Kathryn Seckman Kirsch
Walking with Jesus Booklet (9): Kathryn Seckman Kirsch
Walking with Jesus Booklet (8): Kathryn Seckman Kirsch
Along the Way of Holiness: Kathryn Seckman Kirsch
Advent Calendar: Kathryn Seckman Kirsch

Lesson Cutouts and Pullouts

- Act of Faith Card

- Jesus Card

- VIP Shield

- Christ Candle

- My Way of the Cross Booklet

- I Celebrate the Sacrament of Reconciliation Booklet

- Walking with Jesus Booklet

- Along the Way of Holiness

- Advent Calendar

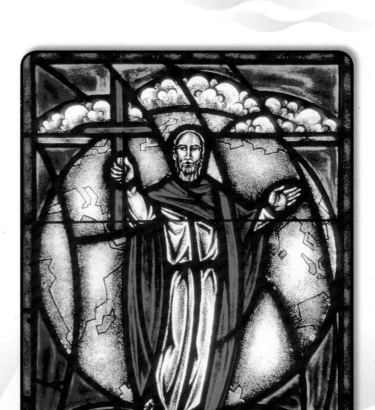

Act of Faith

O my God, I firmly believe that you are one God in three divine Persons, Father, Son, and Holy Spirit. I believe that your divine Son became man and died for our sins, and that he will come to judge the living and the dead. I believe these and all the truths which the holy Catholic Church teaches, because you have revealed them, who can neither deceive nor be deceived. Amen.

Chapter 1

Fold back.

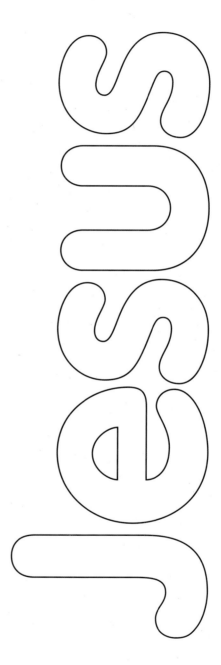

Chapter 11

Cut.

Chapter 13

Cut along candle to fold line.

Fold back.   **Fold back.**

Christmas

Jesus Rises from the Dead

Jesus is our Savior. His death destroyed the power of sin and death. His Resurrection gave us new life— a never-ending life of glory with God.

Think. Do my words and actions tell others that I am a child of God?

Pray. Heavenly Father, help me to do everything to bring others to you. Let me grow each day in the new life Jesus offers me.

16

My Way of the Cross Booklet

God, our Father, you sent Jesus, your Son, to bring us to eternal life with you. Jesus loves you, and he loves me so much that he was willing to suffer and die. Help me to love you and all people as Jesus does, and to follow him on the Way of the Cross. Amen.

This booklet belongs to

Thirteenth Station

Jesus Is Taken Down from the Cross

Friends of Jesus gently took his lifeless body from the cross. They laid it in the arms of Mary, his Mother.

Think. Do I respect the bodies of others as temples of God?

Pray. Dear Jesus, show me how to be kind and gentle. Teach me how to care for others.

14

Second Station

Jesus Is Made to Carry His Cross

Jesus did not complain when the heavy cross was laid upon his shoulders.

Think. Do I love God and others enough to do what is good, even when I do not feel like doing it?

Pray. I want to follow you, Jesus. Help me to carry my cross.

3

First Station

Jesus Is Condemned to Death

Jesus had done nothing wrong but was condemned to death. Pilate knew that Jesus was innocent, but he thought the crowds would turn against him if he set Jesus free.

Think. When others do wrong, do I join them?

Pray. Help me, Jesus, to be fair and to do what is right.

Fourteenth Station

Jesus Is Placed in the Tomb

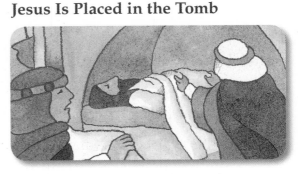

A friend of Jesus' offered to bury his body in the tomb prepared for his own death.

Think. What am I willing to share with others today?

Pray. Dear Jesus, help me to follow you faithfully, even when I am frightened and lonely.

Third Station

Jesus Falls the First Time

Jesus was weak and tired. The cross was heavy, and he fell. Soldiers shouted at him to get up, but no one came to help him.

Think. Who needs my help in carrying a cross today?

Pray. Dear Jesus, help me to be kind to those in need.

Twelfth Station

Jesus Dies on the Cross

Jesus suffered for three long hours on the cross. He forgave those who hurt him, and he gave us his Mother to care for us.

Think. Am I willing to forgive others, even those who have hurt me?

Pray. I adore you, O Christ, and I bless you, because by your holy cross, you have redeemed the world.

Eleventh Station

Jesus Is Nailed to the Cross

Jesus' hands and feet were nailed to the cross. How greatly he suffered to free us from sin! But he did not cry out in pain.

Think. Do I control myself when I am angry?

Pray. Dear Jesus, help me when I am treated unfairly.

12

Fourth Station

Jesus Meets His Mother

It was hard for Mary to see her Son suffering, but she followed Jesus all the way to Calvary. She was willing to suffer with him.

Think. How can I help my parents today?

Pray. Mary, Mother of Sorrows, pray for my family. Help us to love Jesus more each day.

5

Ninth Station

Jesus Falls the Third Time

A third time Jesus fell beneath the heavy cross. He was worn out, but he struggled back to his feet to free us from the power of sin.

Think. Does my example help others to do the right thing?

Pray. Dear Jesus, give everyone who is tired and discouraged the strength to follow you.

10

Sixth Station

Veronica Wipes the Face of Jesus

The holy woman Veronica wanted to help Jesus. She pushed her way past the soldiers to wipe the face of Jesus.

Think. Who might need my kindness today?

Pray. Dear Jesus, help me choose to help others, even when I must stand alone.

7

Fifth Station

Simon Helps Jesus Carry His Cross

Simon of Cyrene was forced to help Jesus carry his cross. When Simon took up the cross, Jesus' pain was a little less.

Think. How can I help someone today?

Pray. Jesus, I could not help you carry your cross, but whatever I do to others I do to you. Help me to be kind and helpful.

6

Tenth Station

Jesus Is Stripped of His Clothes

The soldiers roughly tore the clothes from Jesus' body. They did not care how they made Jesus feel.

Think. Do I treat people with respect?

Pray. Dear Jesus, help me to be respectful to others in all I think, do, and say.

11

Seventh Station

Jesus Falls the Second Time

Jesus fell a second time under his heavy cross, but he did not give up. Again he lifted the cross and continued on his way.

Think. When something is difficult, do I just give up?

Pray. Dear Jesus, help me when I am discouraged and feel weak. I want to follow you in everything I do.

8

Eighth Station

Jesus Meets the Women of Jerusalem

Some women wept when they saw Jesus suffering as he carried his cross. Jesus looked at the women kindly and asked them not to cry for him. Even in his suffering, Jesus thought of others.

Think. How can I help people when they are sad?

Pray. Dear Jesus, help me comfort those who are sad. Teach me what to say.

9

How Much Have I Loved Others?

- Have I obeyed my parents and others who take their place? How have I shown them my love by my words and actions?

- How have I cared for the gifts of life? Have I been kind to everyone in my family? to others? Have I hurt anyone by something I have said or done?

- Have I shown respect for my body and those of others? Have my thoughts, words, and actions been pure?

- How well have I cared for all that God has given me? Have I been careful with or damaged the things of others?

- Have I been honest? Have I returned what I borrowed? Have I taken something that was not mine?

- Have I spoken the truth? Have I kept private information of others to myself? Have I kept all my promises?

Jesus and the Sinful Woman

One day Jesus was invited out for a meal. While Jesus and the other guests were eating, a sinful woman came to tell Jesus she was sorry.

The sinful woman went to Jesus and wept. Her tears fell on his feet, and she wiped them away with her long hair. Jesus looked at her with love. He knew how sorry she was and how much she loved him.

5. Confess Your Sins to the Priest

- Greet the priest when he welcomes you.
- Make the Sign of the Cross.
- The priest may read God's Word with you.
- Listen while the priest asks God to help you make a good confession.
- Confess your sins. You may begin by saying how long it has been since your last confession.
- Listen to the penance the priest gives you. Pray an Act of Contrition.
- Say "Amen" after the priest prays the words of absolution.

6. Thank God for His Forgiving Love

Priest: Give thanks to the Lord, for he is good.

You: His mercy endures forever.

Do the penance you were given as soon as you can.

I Celebrate the Sacrament of Reconciliation

This booklet belongs to

Jesus said, "Her many sins have been forgiven, so she has shown great love."

Then Jesus spoke to the woman and said, "Your sins are forgiven. Your faith has saved you. Go in peace."

adapted from Luke 7:47–50

The woman's heart was filled with peace and joy.

If we confess our sins, then God, who is faithful and just, will forgive them. He will cleanse us from every wrongdoing.

adapted from 1 John 1:9

4

3. Examine Your Conscience

We examine our consciences to find out how we have loved God and others. We ask ourselves how we have kept God's commandments.

How Much Have I Loved God?

- Have I remembered to speak to God in prayer each morning and evening? How well have I prayed?
- Have I always used God's name with love and respect?
- Have I celebrated the Eucharist on Sunday (or Saturday evening) and holy days? How well have I prayed and sung during Mass? Have I been on time?
- Have I thanked God for his goodness?
- Have I told God I was sorry when I have sinned?
- Have I often asked God to help me?

5

God loves us even when we fail to love him and others. God forgives our sins and calls us back to his love. This booklet will help you prepare to celebrate the Sacrament of Reconciliation.

1. Pray to the Holy Spirit

Holy Spirit, show me how good God is. Show me how I can love God and others as Jesus did. Show me how I have failed. Help me to be sorry for my sins.

Come, Holy Spirit, fill the hearts
of your faithful
And kindle in them the fire of
your love.

2. Think of God's Forgiving Love

Read from the Bible or think about how Jesus showed us God's forgiving love.

2

4. Pray an Act of Contrition

We tell God that we are sorry for our sins when we pray an Act of Contrition.

My God,
I am sorry for my sins with all my heart.
In choosing to do wrong
and failing to do good,
I have sinned against you
whom I should love above all things.
I firmly intend, with your help,
to do penance,
to sin no more,
and to avoid whatever leads me to sin.
Our Savior Jesus Christ
suffered and died for us.
In his name, my God, have mercy.

Amen.

Ask God to help you think of some way to show that you are really sorry.

7

Chapter 14

A Final Scripture Story

The collectors of the temple tax came to Peter and said, "Doesn't Jesus pay the temple tax?"

"Yes," Peter said.

When Peter came into the house, before he had time to speak, Jesus asked him: "What is your opinion? From whom do the kings take taxes? From their subjects or from foreigners?"

Peter said, "From foreigners."

Jesus said, "Then the subjects need not pay. But so that we may not offend them, go to the sea, drop in a hook, and take the first fish that comes up. Open its mouth and you will find a coin worth twice the temple tax. Give that to them for me and for you."

adapted from Matthew 17:24-27

What does this story tell us about Jesus? What does it tell us about Peter?

Did Jesus have to pay the temple tax? Why did he pay it? Why do you think Jesus sent Peter to fish for the tax?

Talk to Jesus about obeying your parents and others who care for you.

12

Walking with Jesus

A Scripture Prayer Booklet

This book belongs to

Chapter 25

Blessed are the peacemakers, for they will be called children of God.

Matthew 5:9

Read. Let us then pursue what leads to peace and to building up one another. (Romans 14:19)

Think. St. Paul tells us to pursue, or "go after," what leads to peace. What will lead to peace when somebody calls me a name? when a bully tries to pick a fight with me? when my brother or sister and I argue about doing some chore?

Pray. Jesus, King of Peace, fill me with your peace. Help me to be at peace and to spread your peace to others. [Add your own words. Speak to Jesus.]

Act. How can I be a peacemaker at school? at home? in my neighborhood?

Your turn! Would you like to present another beatitude as these two have been? Try it!

11

you are invited

At Baptism, you received a special invitation to heaven. But how do you get there? Saint Thomas asked that question at the Last Supper: "How can we know the way?" Jesus' answer was also meant for us.

I am the way and the truth and the life. No one comes to the Father except through me.

John 14:6

Who is our way to the Father? _____

Through Scripture activities in this booklet, you will learn how to walk with Jesus.

Fill in the missing words in this poem-prayer:

Dear Jesus,

If you walk with me,

Happy will I _____!

I'll try to be like you

In everything I _____.

Love, _____

2

Along the Beatitude Way

Read the "footprints" and follow the directions. Each time you do what you decided on, color a flower petal.

Blessed are the poor in spirit, for theirs is the kingdom of heaven.

Matthew 5:3

PEACE

Read. We are treated as . . . poor yet enriching many; as having nothing and yet possessing all things. (2 Corinthians 6:8–10)

Think. How can we be poor yet make others richer? What does it mean to have nothing yet possess all?

Pray. Jesus, make me poor in spirit, that I may want heavenly instead of earthly things. [Add your own words. Talk to Jesus.]

Act. What can I give someone today that won't cost me anything but will enrich that person? [A smile?]

Along the Way of God's Word

Let the word of Christ dwell in you richly . . .

Colossians 3:16

Choose a verse here and let it dwell in you. Think about it, pray about it, and learn it by heart. Then color the heart near that verse.

♡ Your love for me is great . . .
Psalm 86:13

♡ Envy and anger shorten one's life . . .
Sirach 30:24

♡ Happy those . . . who seek the LORD with all their heart.
Psalm 119:2

♡ You are the salt of the earth.
Matthew 5:13

♡ This I command you: love one another.
John 15:17

♡ For the wages of sin is death, but the gift of God is eternal life in Christ Jesus our Lord.
Romans 6:23

♡ Cast all your worries upon him because he cares for you.
1 Peter 5:7

♡ Do not be conquered by evil but conquer evil with good.
Romans 12:21

♡ Rejoice in the Lord always.
Philippians 4:4

♡ Do you not realize that Jesus Christ is in you?
2 Corinthians 13:5

IV	V	VI IX	VIII	VII X

Read. "The second is like it: You shall love your neighbor as yourself." (Matthew 22:39)

Think. The second greatest commandment includes the fourth through tenth commandments. Finish the summaries of these commandments:

Fourth: O _____, love, and respect your parents.

Fifth: Respect l _____, your own and that of others.

Sixth and Ninth: Be faithful and p _____ in thought, word, and action; respect your b _____ and others'.

Eighth: Be t _____ in what you say and do; respect the t _____.

Seventh and Tenth: Be fair and h _____ in dealing with others; respect your p _____ and theirs.

What word appears in every summary?

Pray. Dear Lord, thank you for making me and giving me so many gifts. [Name some.] Thank you for my family and friends, and all of their gifts. Help me to respect myself and others. [Add your own words. Talk to Jesus.]

Act. What do I need to do to show more respect for myself? How can I show more respect for my family? What can I do to show more respect for friends, classmates, and others (maybe someone I have not treated kindly)?

(9)

Along the Way of Forgiveness

"What woman having ten coins and losing one would not light a lamp and sweep the house, searching carefully until she finds it? And when she does find it, she calls together her friends and neighbors and says to them, 'Rejoice with me because I have found the coin that I lost.' In just the same way, I tell you, there will be rejoicing among the angels of God over one sinner who repents."

Luke 15:8–10

God looks for sinners the way the woman looked for her lost coin.

Did you ever lose something? How did you feel?

How do you think Jesus feels when a person he loves, and even died for, turns away from him?

Talk to God about his love for sinners like you. Ask for the grace to forgive sinners as God forgives them.

Plan to celebrate the Sacrament of Reconciliation soon.

(4)

Along the Way of the Commandments

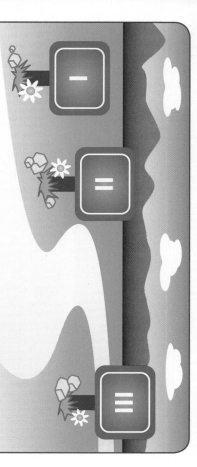

Read. You shall love the Lord, your God, with all your heart, with all your soul, and with all your mind. This is the greatest and the first commandment.

Matthew 22:37–38

Think. The first and greatest commandment Jesus tells us about combines the first three of the Ten Commandments. Do you recall what these are? This little verse will help you.

> *First:* I must honor God;
> *Second:* honor his name;
> *Third:* keep the Lord's Day holy—
> That will be my aim!

Pray. Loving Jesus, help me to show my love for you, your Father, and the Holy Spirit by honoring you and God's name and by worshiping and praying to you. [Add your own words. Speak to Jesus.]

Act. Decide on a special way to show your love for God—in prayer, by honoring God's name, and through worship.

Chapter 13

Along the Way of the Eucharist

… the Lord Jesus, on the night he was handed over, took bread, and after he had given thanks, broke it and said, "This is my body that is for you. Do this in remembrance of me."

1 Corinthians 11:23–24

Think about the wonderful gift of the Eucharist. God feeds us at Mass with his Word and with himself.

Pay close attention to the readings for two Sundays. Then answer these questions.

Sunday 1

What was one important idea in the readings?

What was one good thought you heard in the readings?

Sunday 2

What message in the readings did you hear?

What new idea did you hear in the homily?

Try to form the habit of reading Scripture at least five minutes every Sunday to celebrate the Lord's Day!

Chapter 12

Along the Way of Holiness

Use this calendar for a month to help you live out the Word of God. Ask someone to help you find the passage for the day. When you have read it and have done what is suggested, put a star in the circle.

Sunday	Monday	Tuesday	Wednesday	Thursday	Friday	Saturday
Try to remember one good thought from the readings at Sunday Mass.	*Eph 1:1–2* Be kind to everyone you meet today.	*Col 3:15* Thank your parents or teacher for something.	*Mt 5:44* Forgive someone who has hurt you. Say a prayer for that person.	*Sir 6:14* Tell your best friend what makes him or her special.	*Phil 4:4* Smile at everyone you meet.	*1 Thes 5:18* List things that happened to you lately and thank God for them.
Tell someone about the readings or the homily from the Sunday Mass.	*Jas 2:15–17* Give your allowance to a group that helps those who are needy.	*Eph 4:25* Decide always to tell the truth. Ask God to help you.	*Ps 139:13–14* Thank God for the gift of life.	*Col 3:17* Do your homework extra well for the Lord.	*Phil 4:6* Pray about something that is worrying you.	*Pro 15:1* Answer politely your parents and others who care for you.
Discuss the homily with someone.	*Jn 3:16* Memorize this verse and thank God for his love.	*Mt 5:16* Help with dinner, set the table, or wash the dishes.	*Ps 98:1* Sing a song for the Lord or write your own psalm.	*Ti 3:1* Obey all the rules, even the little ones.	*Heb 13:2* Invite someone to your home or to do something with you.	*Mt 6:6* Spend an extra five minutes in quiet prayer in your room.
Memorize a verse or two from the Sunday readings.	*Mt 25:40* Help a friend—with a chore or homework, perhaps.	*Col 3:12* Say nice things about other people.	*Ps 136:1* List good things that God has given you. Thank God.	*Rom 12:17* Ask God to help you love as God loves us.	*1 Thes 5:11* Put a thank-you note to a family member where he or she will find it.	*Lk 6:38* Make a bookmark with God is good on it and give it to someone.

Advent Calendar

First Week of Advent

Prayer: *To you, my God, I lift my soul. I trust in you.*

Monday	Tuesday	Wednesday	Thursday	Friday	Saturday
Mary and Joseph lived happily in Nazareth, doing their daily work with joy.	Joseph received the order from the Roman ruler to go to Bethlehem and register.	Mary and Joseph got their house ready and packed what they would need for the trip.	Mary and Joseph traveled by donkey.	Mary and Joseph ate the same food that the poor people ate on their journey.	After traveling all day, Mary and Joseph shared a meal and found a place to rest.
I will do my daily work well today, and with joy—for God.	*I will respect my parents, teachers, and others in authority.*	*I will not complain today, even if I must do things I do not like.*	*I will be satisfied with the things I have and not ask for things that I do not need.*	*I will eat healthful foods today rather than those that are not good for me. I will thank God for the food I have and pray for those who are hungry.*	*I will do something special to bring joy to my parents and family today.*

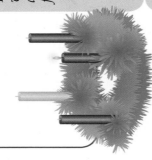

Second Week of Advent

Prayer: *Come, Lord Jesus, and save all the nations.*

Monday	Tuesday	Wednesday	Thursday	Friday	Saturday
Mary and Joseph traveled with many different people on their way to Bethlehem.	Mary and Joseph were very tired at the end of the day because travel was uncomfortable and hard.	When Mary and Joseph reached Bethlehem, they were pushed and pressed by the crowd. They tried to stay calm.	Joseph and Mary looked for a clean, comfortable place to stay.	Joseph and Mary went from door to door, but in every place they heard "No room!"	Mary and Joseph tried not to be discouraged when told there was no room. Many people would have liked to help.
I will be kind to all I meet today—and in a special way to someone I do not like.	*I will help my parents with some chores to give them time to relax after a long day's work.*	*I will keep calm and not lose my temper when I am pushed or treated rudely.*	*I will honor Mary in a special way today by being cheerful. I will pray the Joyful Mysteries of the Rosary.*	*I will make room in my heart for others and will try to show special love for someone who seems lonely or unhappy.*	*I will ask Mary to help me make room for Jesus in my heart by doing what he wants me to do.*

O Come, Jesus

Third Week of Advent

Prayer: *I will be happy, O Lord, for you are near!*

Monday	Mary and Joseph were offered only a stable to stay in. They accepted gratefully.	I will show gratitude for the kindness shown to me today.
Tuesday	The animals helped to warm the stable by being there.	I will share the warmth of my friendship with others, especially with someone I do not like.
Wednesday	Joseph cleaned the stable for Mary and for Jesus, who would soon be born.	I will keep my heart pure today by thinking, doing, and speaking only kind things.
Thursday	Joseph and Mary put fresh straw in the manger to make a bed for the Christ Child.	I will brighten the day for others by smiling and showing how happy I am that Jesus is coming.
Friday	Joseph and Mary tried to make the stable a comfortable place for the night.	I will secretly do a kind act for someone who is not very friendly toward me.
Saturday	Mary unpacked the swaddling clothes that would keep the baby Jesus warm.	I will warm my heart with love for Jesus by doing a kind act for everyone in my family.

Fourth Week of Advent

Prayer: *Come, Emmanuel; come, O ransom captive Israel!*

Monday	Mary and Joseph waited patiently for the coming of Jesus.	I will try to be patient today, especially when others keep me waiting or do things that bother me.
Tuesday	Mary and Joseph thanked God for a safe trip and the stable to stay in.	I will thank God for all he gives me. I will show my parents I am grateful for all they do for me.
Wednesday	Mary and Joseph were at peace because they trusted God to care for them.	I will trust God to help me today to be a peacemaker in school and at home.
Thursday	A beautiful, very bright star shone in the night sky over the stable.	I will bring the brightness of joy to everyone I meet today.
Friday/Saturday	Mary and Joseph prepared for the coming of Jesus.	I will be helpful at home on these last days before Jesus' birthday.
Christmas Day	Mary and Joseph welcomed Jesus with great love!	I will welcome Jesus with great love also, and offer him all my good acts and prayers during the weeks of Advent.